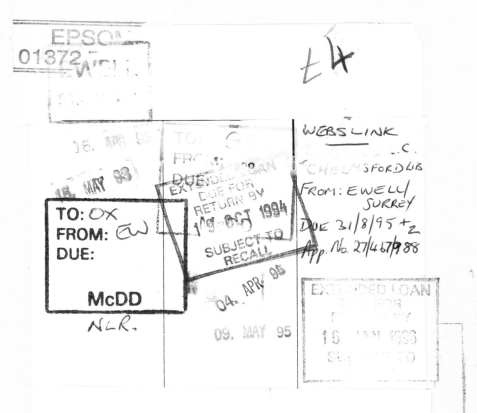

THE LADY LEVER ART GALLERY

# Catalogue
## of
# Embroideries

Detail from *The Drowning of the Pharaoh in the Red Sea* (LL5229, p. 59)

THE LADY LEVER ART GALLERY

# *Catalogue of Embroideries*

XANTHE BROOKE

ALAN SUTTON

NATIONAL MUSEUMS & GALLERIES
ON MERSEYSIDE

First published in the United Kingdom in 1992
Alan Sutton Publishing Ltd · Phoenix Mill · Far Thrupp · Stroud · Gloucestershire
in association with
Trustees of the National Museums and Galleries on Merseyside

First published in the United States of America in 1992
Alan Sutton Publishing Inc · Wolfeboro Falls · NH 03896–0848

British Library Cataloguing in Publication Data

Brooke, Xanthe
  Lady Lever Embroidery Catalogue
  I. Title
  746.44

ISBN 0 7509 0149 7 (hbk)
ISBN 0 7509 0242 6 (pbk)


Library of Congress Cataloging in Publication Data applied for

Typeset in 10/12 Bembo.
Typesetting and origination by
Alan Sutton Publishing Limited.
Colour separation by Yeo Valley Reprographics Ltd.
Printed in Great Britain by
The Bath Press, Bath, Avon.

# Contents

# List of Colour Plates

# Foreword

Embroideries are among the most popular museum exhibits, arousing some of the most enthusiastic responses from our visitors, yet paradoxically they are also often the least accessible. As the museum artefacts are most prone to damage from light many embroideries invariably have to be kept in store and displayed only from time to time. We are therefore particularly delighted to see the publication of this catalogue of the Lady Lever's embroidery collection, one of the richest collections of pictorial embroideries in Britain. The catalogue's full illustrations and detailed commentary will make the whole collection visually and intellectually accessible to both the public and scholarly communities, so providing a powerful impetus to NMGM's aim of promoting through scholarship the understanding and enjoyment of its collections. Our thanks go to Xanthe Brooke, Curator of European Paintings, who has incorporated much fascinating and entertaining information in the catalogue's introductory essays and entries. We hope that through this publication our audience and future visitors will have their understanding and appreciation of the Lady Lever Art Gallery's collection increased, sentiments which we are sure the founder of the gallery, the 1st Lord Leverhulme, would have happily endorsed.

Richard Foster,
Director, National Museums &
Galleries on Merseyside

Julian Treuherz,
Keeper of Art Galleries

# Preface

Wherever and whenever embroideries are exhibited they always stimulate curiosity about their makers, their design and the skills displayed in their creation by the many now anonymous embroiderers. Who were they and how did they gain their skills? From where did they get their inspiration? Who decided the subject matter to be embroidered or created their designs? In the past, and even today, embroidered pictures of the Stuart and Georgian periods have often been rather patronizingly 'admired' for their 'naïve charm', if for nothing else. When compared with the norms of painting, these pictures, in which figures are surrounded by outsize flowers, beasts and birds, are easily dismissed for their lack of pictorial perspective, thereby missing the ingenuity and skill with which different shades of coloured silks are juxtaposed, intricate stitches worked and materials of differing texture – floss silks, gold thread, lace and spangles – are combined to create fine examples of the embroiderer's art. Embroidery historians themselves have often preferred to concentrate on the professional work produced in the sixteenth century or the flowered designs stitched on eighteenth-century costume, but these seemingly naïve pictures, often stitched by young girls, have other significant stories to tell. Their flowering landscapes may ignore the dramatic history of events in seventeenth- and eighteenth-century England or Europe (with a notable exception in the Lady Lever collection (LL5292)), yet they actually reveal much about the activities and expectations of the female population and attitudes towards female education, and occasionally they throw light on developments in the national political, religious, cultural and aesthetic life of English society at grass-roots level. In addition they provide us with a good impression of people's decorative surroundings, particularly those of the middle classes and the gentry whose numbers, wealth and power expanded during the three centuries covered by this catalogue.

The introductory essay and catalogue entries unveil the hidden and intriguing significance of many of the stories depicted, and show how such needlework pictures can tell us about teenage girls' education, socialization and relationships, within changing family life and their links to religious and political values of the period.

Many pictorial embroideries still survive, though often in poor condition – a number of museums in Britain and the United States have collections, most British country houses still have one or more examples and they often provide the mainstay of textile auctions. Most of them are the products, not of professional workshops, but of individual girls wishing to show off their prowess with a needle, and for this reason they have often been kept and passed down from generation to generation. Several pictures now in collections, including the Lady Lever Art Gallery, have had explanatory labels attached by later family members stating who had worked them or to whom they had belonged.

As only a small selection from the gallery's holdings of embroidery can be displayed at any one time, this illustrated catalogue offers the opportunity to discover the whole collection acquired by William Hesketh Lever as examples of a domestic art which he greatly appreciated and wished others to admire as well.

# Acknowledgements

I should like to express my thanks to the many people who have helped my researches over several years. In particular I owe a deep debt of gratitude to Tina Levey for enthusiastically undertaking the massive task of checking my typescript and for her practical support and advice on the publication of this catalogue. I am also especially grateful to Margaret Swain who has never failed to offer cheerful encouragement and much helpful information. Over the years many colleagues and fellow embroidery enthusiasts have been generous in sharing their knowledge with me. In particular I should like to thank Valerie Hector for sharing with me her research on beadwork, Charlotte Mayhew (now Dugdale) for allowing me to consult her thesis and Mr Jack Richardson for offering his practical knowledge. Among colleagues in the museum world I am especially grateful to Linda Parry, Clare Brown and Paul Harrison of the Victoria and Albert Museum; Carole Humphrey of the Fitzwilliam Museum; Ann French of the Burrell Collection; and Lynn Szygenda of the Embroiderer's Guild Collections, all of whom gave their time, information and help in my researches. My thanks also go to my colleagues in the National Museums and Galleries on Merseyside and in particular to Lucy Wood at the Lady Lever Art Gallery and Edward Morris at the Walker Art Gallery for their willingness to offer support and assistance and a special thanks to Janet Bennett for her work in compiling the Appendix. Finally I should like to thank those who have supported the publication of this catalogue with grants: the Pasold Research Fund and the Marc Fitch Fund.

# Notes on the Catalogue

Each catalogue entry provides the present accession number prefixed by the letters LL as well as, in brackets, previous inventory numbers allotted in Lever's lifetime, either as a running number system (WHL, or X for new acquisitions after May 1914) or according to which of his houses they were kept in (H for The Hill, Hampstead, or TM for Thornton Manor, Wirral). Also provided, where appropriate, is the catalogue number from the previous needlework catalogue by Theresa Macquoid, *The Lady Lever Art Gallery Collections Part III: Furniture, Tapestries and Needlework*, published in 1928. This catalogue is referred to in the text as either the Macquoid or the 1928 catalogue. The introductions to the various catalogue sections provide a history of the development of pictorial needleworks and other embroidered textiles in Britain as represented by the Lady Lever collection; they thus stress the development of the seventeenth-, eighteenth- and early nineteenth-century embroideries in which the collection is richest. The technical descriptions which head each entry were produced without unframing the item. The Appendix lists all the embroidered pieces sold from Lever's collection after his death (he was then Lord Leverhulme) in a series of auctions held in the UK and New York in 1925 and 1926. If the whereabouts of a sold item is known it is stated. This catalogue does not include the substantial number of fine embroideries found on pieces of furniture in the Lady Lever Collection. It is hoped that in the future a combined catalogue of furniture and embroidery will be produced. Further information on Lever's embroidery collecting, comparing him with other contemporaries may be found in the 1992 volume of the *Journal of the History of Collections*.

Photograph of one of the rooms in Lever's house The Hill, Hampstead, as it was sometime between 1906 and 1910

# William Hesketh Lever and his Embroidery Collection

The nature of the embroidery collection at the Lady Lever Art Gallery reflects very closely several of William Hesketh Lever's concerns as a self-made soap-manufacturing magnate, employer and art patron. Throughout his life he was concerned to preserve and display art of the highest quality and skill, especially British art, in order to inspire the ordinary working man and, more particularly, the predominantly female workforce of his Port Sunlight soap factory, which lay at the opposite end of Port Sunlight village from the purpose-built art gallery. In embroidery, and especially the pictorial needlework Lever specialized in collecting, he found an art-form which demonstrated the high level of skill that ordinary women had attained in the past and might once again be inspired to do.

Lever's collection of needlework appears to have been specifically his own and not that of his wife, after whom the gallery was named as a memorial. His earliest interest in Stuart embroidery emerged in the last few years of the nineteenth century and coincided with the creation of Lever's first museum, the Hall i' th' Wood Folk Museum, which he donated to his native town of Bolton in 1900. This essentially social-history collection was established in a sixteenth- and seventeenth-century half-timbered manor-house, for which Lever acquired suitable furniture including seventeenth-century stumpwork embroidery. About a year later he began to build himself a bungalow near Bolton, overlooking Rivington Pike. According to his son it was the furnishing of this house that stimulated Lever into collecting old English needlework pictures. By 1907 one whole room in his Hampstead home, The Hill, was devoted to mainly seventeenth-century embroidered pictures, caskets, mirror frames and screens and christened the 'Stuart Room'. So from the very start Lever's collecting of needlework stemmed from the desire to buy for didactic public display, first for Hall i' th' Wood and after 1923 for the Lady Lever Art Gallery, and in order to decorate his private residences in London, Cheshire, Lancashire and Scotland.

The beginning of the twentieth century saw a growing interest in embroidery among collectors, especially raised-work items, which newly-established art publications such as the *Connoisseur* began to promote. Lever, therefore, was part of a small group of collectors in Britain and America, such as Percy Griffiths, Sir Frederick Richmond, Lady Wolseley, Irwin Untermyer, Mrs Lilla Hailstone and Theresa Macquoid (the author of the first catalogue of the Lever embroidery collection), who showed an interest in embroideries. These collectors often knew each other and bought from each other's collections. Lever acquired pieces from both Percy Griffiths (LL5231, LL5299, LL5417–18, pp. 34, 32, 252, 265) and Lady Wolseley (LL5397–8, LL5410, LL5420–21, pp. 257–9, 269, 271) and in turn, the American judge, Irwin Untermyer, purchased seven items from the auctions held in New York after Lever's death. Lever's collection was particularly distinguished for its focus on pictorial needleworks and for the extent of its collection of Stuart, Georgian and Regency pieces. The greatest testimony to the popularity of collecting Stuart embroidery, particularly raised-work, in the first decade of the century, was the number of fakes created to satisfy the market. Lever was such a major purchaser that, not surprisingly, a number of counterfeit items, such as LL5284 (p. 86), also got into his collection.

Collectors' interest in Stuart embroidery also had the effect of raising its price at auction. On occasions when Lever felt that a piece had been bought too expensively, (as with LL5265, p. 70), he would complain to his embroidery dealers, even if, as was the case with *Paris and Pallas (Athene) with the Four Continents* (LL5260, p. 66), it was of good quality and condition. It was mainly the seventeenth-century Stuart and early eighteenth-century Queen Anne embroideries which appealed most to Edwardian collectors and interior decorators. Late Georgian and Regency pieces of the last decades of the eighteenth and the first third of the nineteenth century fetched much lower prices. That factor alone might have encouraged Lever, an astute businessman, to buy, but he never bought solely on grounds of price and high quality; the delicacy of the skills shown and the appealing subjects in many late Georgian and Regency pictures also attracted him. Most of his fairly small collection of nineteenth-century embroideries consisted of the painted silk pictures popular during the Regency period, but a few had been worked by his or his wife's family and were probably kept for sentimental reasons.

Lever's somewhat unusual interest in eighteenth-century needlework reflected an already pronounced enthusiasm for eighteenth-century fine and decorative arts, particularly paintings and furniture. Many of his embroideries of the period, sold to him as 'pictures', had in fact been removed from pieces of furniture – chairs, sofas, screens – and framed up for sale by dealers. Lever indeed occasionally used a furniture dealer, Frank Partridge, rather than his embroidery dealers (almost exclusively D.L. Isaacs of New Oxford Street and his successor M. Harris and Sons) when purchasing eighteenth-century items and the odd Elizabethan piece of bed furniture (LL5228, p. 205). A few other notable needlework collectors, such as Lady Wolseley, who had encouraged Lever's early enthusiasm, also developed their interest from one in furniture. Lever's attraction to embroidery of the early eighteenth century also reflects the general taste – first evoked in Thackeray's novels of the 1850s and 1860s – for the 'Queen Anne' period and especially anything that could be considered quaint and naïvely charming.

Lever's regard for embroidery might also have been stimulated by late Victorian attempts to revive domestic crafts and the activities of groups and individuals within the Arts and Crafts movement. They aimed to re-create ancient embroidery techniques and re-introduce imaginative design and fine workmanship to needlework after what they saw as the decline brought on by Berlin woolwork. In fact Lever showed little interest in collecting contemporary embroidery, and there is only one Arts and Crafts piece in the entire collection (a coverlet, LL5443, p. 223). But the movement's belief in the refining influence of beauty – that beautiful objects, if made widely available to the public, would raise the tone of society – chimed well with Lever's intentions, which he stated at the opening of the Lady Lever Art Gallery, where he hoped 'Art' would be an inspiration to everyone: 'within the reach of all of us, however humble we may be', displaying 'Art of the home, not of the palace'.

Lever's concentration on British pictorial needlework meant that his collection had fewer items of other sorts of embroidery popular among Edwardian collectors, such as samplers and costume accessories. Samplers as we know them now, with alphabets, numerals and verses surrounded by stylized figures and flowers, had been one of the most frequently preserved types of needlework throughout the centuries. Even the most pedestrian or ineptly worked piece was more likely to have survived than any other type of embroidery as family sentiment turned it into an heirloom. Indeed one of Lever's selection of samplers was just such a piece (LL5322, p. 236). The few examples owned by him of the seventeenth-century type of sampler, sewn in bands with practice stitches and patterns, were sold off after his death (see Appendix).

The richly decorated gloves and shoes of the first half of the seventeenth century proved particularly attractive to Edwardian collectors. Indeed one of the most significant glove collections, put together at the beginning of the twentieth century by Robert Spence and now at the Museum of Costume, Bath, was the subject of two illustrated articles in the art press of 1919–20, which may well have attracted Lever's attention and encouraged him to collect further in this field. Some of Lever's earliest known purchases, from the 1906 sale of Viscountess Wolseley's collection of Stuart needlework, were of small dress accessories such as purses and shoes (LL5397–8, LL5420–1, pp. 257–9, 269, 271). He also bought from another significant collector of costume accessories, Jeffrey Whitehead. His sale in 1915 provided the bulk of Lever's small collection of English and French purses (LL5400–6, LL5408, pp. 260–5, 267–8).

Considering Lever's particular liking for Stuart and Georgian embroidery, a major omission from the present collection is any example of crewel-work, apart from the cannibalized motifs from a hanging which went to form three pelmets (LL5439–41, p. 211). In the last decade of the seventeenth and into the next century this type of embroidery was worked predominantly in deep blue, green and yellow wools with touches of red on a linen/cotton mixture called fustian, with a favourite design (derived from far-eastern chintz) of multi-branched trees and exotic flowers growing from hillocks. Different forms of crewel-work with monochrome or multi-coloured designs had been produced from at least the sixteenth century onwards and are consequently to be found in many present-day collections, but not that of the Lady Lever.

Another type sparsely represented in the collection is continental pictorial embroidery of the seventeenth and eighteenth centuries. The few examples that remain in the collection are often unusual and display a high quality of work

(LL5248–9, pp. 49–51). However, on the whole, Lever's predominant interest lay with what he considered to be the indigenous craftsmanship of the English and their national style. Although the bias towards British material of the present-day collection is in part due to the fact that much of his collection of foreign embroidery, which included a selection of Chinese items, was sold in 1925 and 1926 (see Appendix). Some of the continental pieces which remain, particularly the Flemish and the French items, may have been mistakenly acquired as British, for seventeenth-century Flemish work was closely allied in style and subject-matter to British, while eighteenth-century French embroidered furnishings were copied internationally. The couple of Central European and Swiss pieces, however, have their own distinctive style and religious themes (LL5101, LL5286, pp. 84, 220). One particularly unusual picture, *St Paschal Baylon's Vision of the Host* (LL5246, p. 134), might have attracted Lever's attention because of its similarity in technique to a series of pictures owned by an older northern collector, Mrs Lilla Hailstone of Horton Hall. Her private collection (started 'of late') of 'Ancient Framed Needlework Pictures' was published in an illustrated catalogue in 1897, at about the time that Lever first began to collect embroidery seriously.

For most of his collecting life Lever lived surrounded by his embroidery collection. It formed the decorative background to several of his many residences. At The Hill, Hampstead, his favoured London home, the dining-room was hung entirely with Stuart pictorial embroideries and mirrors, and other rooms displayed upholstered furniture and needlework caskets. Other pieces were transferred to his mansion on the Wirral at Thornton Hough. Originally a good part of his collection was displayed in the corridors and inglenooks of his Bungalow, situated in landscaped gardens overlooking the Rivington reservoir near his home-town of Bolton. The Bungalow collection was the second of its type to be kept there, for in July 1913 a Lancashire suffragette, Edith Rigby, angered by the Liberal government's stance on votes for women and the treatment of imprisoned suffragettes, decided to attack the 'superfluous' property of a prominent local Liberal and set fire to Lever's Rivington Bungalow. The Bungalow was entirely destroyed along with his collection of needlework pictures. The irony was that Lever fully supported the women's suffrage cause. The only parts of his first collection to survive were those he kept at other homes. From 1914 he rebuilt both The Bungalow and his needlework collection and from then on, perhaps as a precautionary measure, The Bungalow predominantly stored the less valuable Georgian and Regency pieces and more pieces were kept at The Hill and Thornton Manor. The second collection was itself depleted after his death when about half of it was sold, mainly in America (see Appendix). It was the remaining half that was partially and rather hastily catalogued by Theresa Macquoid, herself a pictorial needlework collector on a minor scale, for publication in 1928. The collection that is now housed in the Lady Lever Art Gallery is, therefore, only a small part of what Lever originally acquired to admire for himself, to inspire his workforce and to delight future visitors to the gallery.

# THE PICTORIAL EMBROIDERIES

Detail from *Man Rowing a Boat with Dolphins and other Animal Motifs* (LL5285, see p. 81)

# Jacobean and Stuart Period

## 1. Techniques and Use

Elizabethan and Stuart England saw an extraordinary flowering of the embroiderer's art, both in the quantity created and in the great number of techniques used. Domestic embroidery, intended for the house, flourished particularly, whether produced by the amateur at home or the professional in a workshop. Throughout the period the embroiderer's skill was absolutely essential to the creation of a comfortable home for all from the middle classes upwards. At a time when virtually all furniture was made of unupholstered wood, embroidered curtains, cushions, wall-hangings and valances were all essential furnishings to ensure comfort and privacy in bed, on bench, chair, stool, window-seat or in church pew. As the number and power of the middle ranks of society grew at this time, more could afford to, and wanted to, show off their wealth in displays of richly woven and embroidered textiles.

The most common embroidery technique in use at the beginning of the seventeenth century was tent-stitch work in silks and wools on linen canvas. It was eminently suitable for use on furnishing fabrics, as it was hard-wearing and simple to produce, yet versatile enough to produce effects of great delicacy in design and execution. The pair of valances in the collection (LL5226–7, pp. 203–4), for example, are worked entirely in tent stitch with only a few other stitches and knots used to highlight buttons and jewellery. The stitch also imitated the visual effect of the more expensive woven tapestries, which only the richest in society could afford. Tent stitch (from the French *tenter*, to stretch, because the canvas was stretched on a needlework frame or tent, to be worked) has remained popular for furnishing covers along with related stitches such as Irish or Florentine stitch. Indeed its twentieth-century name of 'tapestry-stitch' has led to the present-day confusion between hand-stitched embroidery on a woven fabric and woven tapestry. The embroideries also had motifs in common with Elizabethan tapestries and table carpets. Thus the hound chasing a hare across a landscape filled with trees and the well-stocked ponds with a multi-turreted palace on the skyline, has many parallels with the borders found on sixteenth- and seventeenth-century woven tapestry panels and cushions produced by the Sheldon workshops in Bordesley, Worcestershire and Barcheston, Warwickshire. Other recurring features – the flower-covered arbours, sculpted fountains and curtained pavilions with domed tops – also have parallels in Elizabethan embroidery.

In the seventeenth century, canvas-work was not only embroidered as a practical hard-wearing furnishing-fabric, but was also used to create decorative pictures and to cover a wide variety of objects from prayer-books to mirror frames and work-caskets or trinket boxes. Canvas-work panels intended purely as decorative pictures came into vogue during the second quarter of the century, to be followed shortly afterwards by the other most common needlework technique of the period, silk-work embroidery, in which pictures and other items were worked in fine silks and small amounts of gold and silver thread, metal purl, seed pearls, spangles and other materials, on a cream, silk-satin ground, which normally had green stripes woven into the selvedge. A wide variety of straight stitches was used, the most common ones being long and short, and satin stitch, in vivid shades of colours, to render subjects in a form of 'needle-painting'. The satin's smooth but delicate background made it harder to work on than canvas, but easier for the design to be drawn in pen and ink. This type of embroidery also gave greater scope for showing off a wider and more demanding range of needleworking skills and stitches on the pre-drawn pictures. In the most accomplished hands, however, both canvas-work and silk-work could reproduce designs very accurately and finely.

The ability simply to reproduce a drawn design in stitches was certainly not the attraction of the third and final needlework technique popular in the seventeenth-century, raised- or 'embossed' work, as it was referred to by contemporaries, or 'stumpwork' as it was called from the Victorian period onwards. A craze for this type of embroidery lasted for about three decades from about the late 1650s onwards. It became fashionable to acquire such pieces at the beginning of the twentieth century when collectors such as Lever were charmed by the technique's vitality and seeming spontaneity. Indeed an article appearing in the the first volume of the *Connoisseur* (1901) stated that it was only within the last two or three years that needlework pictures had received the attention they merited. Raised-work was technically a dramatically different sort of needlework, involving the creation, and application on to a satin ground, of three-dimensional figures, plants and buildings, usually stuffed with wool, sometimes leather and parchment, or raised with the aid of small wooden moulds covered by silk, on which details were embroidered or drawn. Fine wire bent into shape and covered with a variety of lace and buttonhole stitches was used to make leaves, petals, butterfly and birds' wings which stood proud of the surface and so dramatically emphasized certain features. To complete the figures a variety of trimmings was used – bows and ribbons of plaited silks, collars of lace, and a scattering of seed pearls and glass beads. Most raised-work pictures incorporated other techniques as well: flat straight stitches used beside raised lace stitch (perhaps in an attempt to provide a form of pictorial perspective), and single motifs, called slips, of fruits or flowers worked on canvas, sometimes stiffened with card and applied to the smooth ground. All of this, together with the use of metal thread, knitted fabric, purl, spangles, seed pearls, beads, pieces of mica and lace, created glittering, richly patterned embroidery, practical only as a decorative picture, a panel on a casket, or a frame of a mirror, which by the end of the century was a common 'luxury' item in middle-class households. The decorative border extended the size of the typically small, precious mirrors and the use of silver or gold thread emphasized its reflectiveness and also enhanced its luxuriousness (LL5218, p. 192). When used with care, thought and ingenuity the raised-work technique could create designs full of contrasting textures and subtly shaded colours as delicate silks were juxtaposed with gleaming metal thread. In a related technique, pictures, wire baskets and occasionally boxes were entirely covered in coloured, striped, clear and opaque glass beads, which were threaded together and secured to each other, and previous rows, by looped stitches. Despite their intricacy, in the right hands, and with virtuoso techniques, beads could produce effects replicating the weight and texture of the clothes and fabrics depicted. Thus the heavy 'velvet' of the king's cloak in Anne Sawell's raised beadwork picture of a *King and Queen* (LL5257, p. 88) is worked with beads on a heavy linen canvas ground and padded and draped to give the effect of weight, while the queen's mantle, presumably intended to be silk, is reproduced in strings of beads hung together in a light gauzy pattern with no backing. Unlike the silk threads, which have now faded through time, the beads have retained their colour and may give some idea of the original bright colours favoured by the embroiderers.

The mass of differing materials and threads used on raised-work pictures reflect in their own way the conspicuous spending which greeted Charles II's accession to the throne in 1660, as the population sought release from Cromwellian strictures against purchasing vanities. The often rather ungainly three-dimensional figures who populate the pictures were merely a young person's expression of the sculptural solidity and exuberance of seventeenth-century visual arts as a whole. Although there was some slight precedent for the development of raised-work in the lightly embossed figures embroidered by professional work-shops in England in the sixteenth century on ecclesiastical vestments, ceremonial clothing and highly ornate costume accessories, such as gloves (see LL5415, p. 250), stylistically it was more akin to seventeenth-century embossed and painted plaster decoration. On walls and ceilings of buildings such as Hardwick Hall and Culross Palace, Scotland, figures from biblical scenes are surrounded by plants and vegetation in a similar manner to those in raised-work embroideries. Raised-work pictures produced by youngsters at home were also a peculiarly British phenomenon. On the continent, in the Netherlands and central Europe, raised-work went down a different path altogether (see LL5101, p. 84). It was sometimes produced in the form of metal thread embroidery and often associated with ecclesiastical workshops rather than domestic work for the home.

The craze for raised-work did not last the century. By the reign of William and Mary (1688–1701) it seems to have disappeared. Indeed the change in fashion may have been stimulated by the taste of the queen, herself a noted needlewoman, for chairs, stools, hangings and screens covered in the more practical canvas-work.

## 2. The Embroiderers

Whatever the technique or combination of styles used to produce the pictorial needleworks, we know that many of them were embroidered at home by young or adolescent girls to furnish the home, educate the child in a practical and decorative skill, and provide a vehicle for her to show off her talent. It is significant that in 1688 Randle Holme in his *Academy of Armory*, a late seventeenth-century form of encyclopaedia, regarded raised-work and various kinds of tent-stitch work and silk embroidery on canvas and satin to be the domain of the schoolmistress and her youthful scholars, rather than of the professional adult seamstress. When Hannah Woolley, gentlewoman and former schoolmistress published *The Gentlewoman's Companion* in 1675, the list of her accomplishments as a school mistress was headed by 'Needlework of very different sorts' and 'Bugle-work' (beadwork). Professionals were more likely to work on the large-scale hangings, of complex design and craftsmanship, which from about the mid-century began to go out of fashion as wooden panelling came into favour as a wall-covering. As almost all the pictorial embroideries were worked by youthful amateurs the quality varies; from those who obviously had no aptitude and therefore no enjoyment, to those who enthusiastically enjoyed showing off their prowess with the needle. Just as important in creating pictorial needleworks, was an eye for colour combinations and an ability to choose and place silks in groups which shade gently from one colour to the next, and so create effects that still delight.

Many pictorial panels were intended to cover the caskets in which the young girls kept mirrors, writing materials and needlework equipment or perhaps perfume and jewellery. Evidence that the casket was considered the culmination of a young girl's needlework education comes from the few documented pieces, such as Hannah Smith's casket, completed when aged eleven (or 'almost 12 years of age' as she put it herself) in 1656 (Whitworth Art Gallery, Manchester), or Martha Edlin's collection of embroidered items (Victoria & Albert Museum, T.432–1990), which ranges from a simple alphabet sampler worked when she was eight to her casket, containing miniature embroidered gloves and toys, which she embroidered in 1671 at the same age as Hannah Smith. The long memorandum enclosed in Hannah Smith's casket, and written by her to certify ('sartifi') that it was her work, shows the personal significance to the young embroideresses of their projects. The frequent initialling or stitching of their names in silks or seed pearls confirms this impression. The memorandum also explains the division of labour involved in creating a casket. All the embroidered pieces meant to cover the top, sides, drawer-fronts, and inner and outer doors, were sent to a joiner to be mounted on a specially constructed box, trimmed with silver-thread braid or gold bobbin-lace and standing on silver ball-feet (see LL5256, p. 179). In Hannah's case they were taken from Oxford to London to be 'made up'. Inventories of local cabinet makers also show them making frames for embroidered mirrors. Working the pieces for a casket, some of which could be quite large (see LL5262, 39 × 52 cm, p. 184), took a long time and if the young seamstress was not skilled enough and grew bored they might be left unfinished or never applied to the casket (LL5252, p. 25). Several of the embroideries, now seen framed up as 'pictures' in Lever's collection, in fact originated as panels from such caskets (LL5297, p. 30). In the late nineteenth century they were sometimes dismantled to provide furniture and antique dealers with material to frame up and sell as individual pictures to the growing collectors' market.

The identity of most embroiderers remains elusive, despite those few pieces which have come down to us with explanatory matter from the girls themselves, and little is known about them and their social background. The information gained is usually restricted to a name and occasionally, as in the case of Hannah Smith, the year and circumstances under which the piece was made. But most pieces are not properly documented, their histories and provenance usually known only as far back as the immediately previous owner. That is why Damaris Pearse's spirited portrayal of *The Drowning of the Pharaoh in the Red Sea* (LL5229, p. 59) with its associated information on the social, religious and economic value which she attached to her needleworks and to the subject of this piece in particular, is so important. It does much to flesh out, not just one particular case, but suggests the context in which other pictures may have been created. Damaris was the daughter of a dissenting minister in the 1670s. Her raised-work picture reflects interestingly on, for example, the continuation of the Puritan and Cromwellian ethos well into the second half of the seventeenth century. Puritan dissenters had equated the Old Testament story of the pharaoh's death with the righteous regicide of Charles I and Cromwell had seen himself as a Moses leading his Israelites to the Promised Land. The Israelites' release from their bondage in Egypt and their safe arrival in Canaan was one of Damaris's favourite episodes from the Old Testament and one she chose to relate from her sickbed. Her speeches were published after her death in 1679, by her father as *A Present for Youth and Example for the Aged: or the Remains of Damaris Pearse*, to provide a role model for Christians, young and old. The book forms a commentary on her brief life of twenty years including references to the personal and economic importance to Damaris of her activities as an embroideress.

## 3. Design Sources and Popular Themes

Even when we know by whom a piece was embroidered, we still know little about how and by whom compositions were created and who chose them. Some documentary evidence, in the form of household accounts and letters, shows that rural homes often relied on travelling upholsterers or embroiderers to draw out designs, and that in grander households governesses were occasionally employed to perform such duties. But the quality of draughtmanship on those pieces where the original drawing can still be seen because not all of the composition was embroidered over (e.g. LL5271, *Judith and Holofernes*, p. 70) indicates strongly that designs were drawn by professional draughtsmen. The fact that a number of themes or stories were depicted repeatedly with minor, if any, variations in composition, for example *Abraham Sacrificing Isaac* (LL5256, p. 179), supports the assumption that certain designs were almost mass produced, in the form of designs drawn in ink on the canvas or satin for embroidery at home. The textile historian Nancy Graves Cabot discovered at least thirteen examples of *Abraham Expelling Hagar* embroidered from the same design, now in American collections and the Victoria and Albert Museum, and this list did not include the two Lady Lever versions (LL5241, LL5243, pp. 42, 43). The evidence for the sale of this type of kit form can be seen on those needleworks where stitches have worn away or dyes have rotted the silks to reveal the original drawn pattern. This was provided for the embroiderer's detailed guidance but she could interpret the design in her own way and with her own choice of materials and colours, in raised or flat-work, and occasionally, as worn embroideries reveal, she also chose to ignore the original design (as in LL5394, p. 115).

The kits must have been produced by those who had access to the engraved prints and etchings sold by London printsellers, such as Peter Stent and his successor John Overton, whose shops were active between the 1640s and 1708. Both men had their premises in the area around St Paul's, close to the traditional haberdashery and millinery area of Cheapside and London Bridge, where we know from advertisements that 'pattern drawers' also offered their services. Both publicized themselves as providing individual prints and books of prints for the use of embroiderers, governesses and gentlewomen. In 1671 Overton advertised a book of animals, birds and flowers as providing: 'Lively coloured [prints] for all sorts of Gentlewomen and School-Mistresses Works'. There was such a large market for these that two years later he produced an expanded version advertising that 'he is doing more as fast as time will permit'. Another St Paul's publisher and competitor to Stent, Robert Walton, specifically advertised himself in 1677 as providing 'maps and pictures . . . useful for divers callings, as Painters, Embroid-erers . . .'. Overton ran a form of mail order company for 'any Booksellers or others in the Countrey' who wished to buy from his stock. He also capitalized on the educational value for children of his books of flora and fauna. One was subtitled *A New Book of all Sorts of Beasts: or a Pleasant Way to Teach Yeoung Children to Reade almost as soon as Speake*. Its crude drawings were obviously intended as an early picture book for children and hence their continual reappearance on children's embroidered pictures.

The exile of the Court after the Civil War and the unadorned worship of the Church during the Commonwealth period (1649–60) also helped provide another source of pattern designers for domestic needlewomen. Some members of the Broderers' Company in London, such as the Nelham family, appear to have moved into supplying materials and producing designs during the period when their previous primary sources of employment, the Church and Court, had disappeared. The professional embroiderer, John Nelham, may have sold mat-erials and drawn out designs for pictorial needleworks during the latter part of the Commonwealth as suggested by a signed and addressed panel at Blair Atholl Castle datable to between 1654 and 1666. In 1653 John's father, Roger, had left him 'halfe of my books and prints and patterns which I do use for the drawing of workes'. The embroideress therefore did not work directly from the prints, as the motifs were often much too intricate or small to be stitched on the same scale. Instead they were probably enlarged or adapted for the textile grounds by professional draughtsmen. This adaptation ensured that the special characteristics of the flora and fauna depicted were not lost sight of once they were stitched. It also partly explains that aspect of Stuart embroidered pictures which is most often labelled 'quaint' – the disregard for scale and perspective, as flowers tower over people and snails the size of a head float by.

Businessmen, such as Stent, Overton and Walton, made a successful living out of catering for the burgeoning and wealthier middle classes. For though the Civil War and the early Commonwealth period discouraged expenditure on conspicuous luxury furnishings, the second half of the 1650s saw the development of more elaborate embroidery techniques, as evidenced by Hannah Smith's casket, and the return of the monarchy in 1660 released a desire to furnish house and family even more extravagantly than before. London was the main centre for fashionable shopping, but those with access to country towns could rely on regular markets and fairs to distribute needlework accessories, and travelling pattern-drawers, embroiderers, upholsterers and chapmen carrying small goods could service the needs of needlewomen throughout the country.

The Protestant sects of the period placed great emphasis on the study of Scripture and on laypeople being able to read the Bible, and the vast majority of illustrated Bibles published in the sixteenth and seventeenth centuries concentrated their illustrations on the Old Testament. It is not surprising, therefore, that some parts of Stent and Overton's stocks were made up of engravings illustrating the Bible, and particularly the Old Testament. Stent, for example, advertised for sale prints of *Abraham offering Isaac for Sacrifice*, *The Story of Susannah* and the *Pharao* [sic] *Drowned in the Red Sea* as well as a series of forty plates relating the *History of Genesis*. Several of these stories were favoured by embroiderers and can be identified even though the figures wear seventeenth-century dress. The predominance of Old Testament themes among seventeenth-century embroiderers was underlined by a recent survey of 525 pieces. This showed that whereas 294 depicted Old Testament stories, only 13 related to the New Testament. New Testament scenes, of course, could be and often were, labelled 'popish' in the early part of the century and were still a sensitive subject after Cromwell's Commonwealth, remaining so throughout a century charged with religious tension. Old Testament scenes, considered as historic events, were exempt from Puritan strictures. A few New Testament scenes, however, do recur in embroidered form. Mary Magdalene's meeting with the risen Christ dressed as a gardener (LL5365, p. 106) probably owed its popularity to the fact that the scene was used as the Christian frontispiece to the first of Stent's series of floral and animal illustrations (*A Book of Flowers, Fruicts* [sic], *Beasts, Birds and Flies*, undated). The appeal of another New Testament favourite, *Christ and the Samarian Woman at the Well* (LL5254, p. 104), may have rested on the fact that the story it depicted told of the important role played by a woman in spreading Christ's message.

The prints were mostly pirated from the Flemish, Dutch and German illustrated volumes of Old Testament history which flooded the country after the Reformation. One of these, which appears to have provided rich pickings for designers throughout Europe was the *Thesaurus Sacrarum Historiarum Veteris Testamenti* (*Dictionary of Sacred Stories from the Old Testament*) of Gerard de Jode (1531–91), which was published, in single sheet and book form, in 1585 (see LL5229, LL5241, LL5243, LL5247, LL5256, LL5258, LL5270, LL5271, pp. 59, 42, 43, 44, 179, 182, 57, 70). Some forty-two needlework pictures were identified by Nancy Graves Cabot as coming from this one book; more than thirteen embroideries still existing in major British and American collections derived from one design alone, *Abraham Expelling Hagar* (LL5241, LL5243, pp. 42–3), published by de Jode. Several Flemish artists made drawings specifically for reproduction as engravings. At least five hundred drawings were produced by Marten de Vos for book illustrations and prints, and his work was particularly used by the *Thesaurus* and indeed reissued in C.J. Visscher's *Theatrum Biblicum*, almost a century later, in 1674 (see LL5258, p. 182). Like various other biblical and narrative print series published in the later part of the sixteenth century, the *Thesaurus* was continually plundered for images, re-used, varied and adapted throughout the next century by a wide range of craftsmen – from silversmiths and glass engravers to potters and tapestry designers, as well as embroiderers.

One of the main reasons why the *Thesaurus* continued to provide so many designs almost a century after its first publication was that it was the main source of illustrations for the enormous output of Bibles and religious narrative series published, with captions in different languages, in the mid-seventeenth century, by the Visscher family of Amsterdam. The large printing and publishing concerns in Germany and the North and South Netherlands, such as the Visschers, dominated the European trade in prints and illustrated Bibles and were the source for much of the British trade.

The great majority of the sales advertised by Stent and Overton, however, consisted of print after print of flower, bird and animal motifs of the type which so often populate every inch of seventeenth-century pictorial embroideries. Many of the Stuart embroiderer's favourite bird motifs, such as the kingfisher, the parrot (see, for example, LL5221, and fig. 33, p. 194) and the peculiar hybrid of a bullfinch and parrot, which appears on the mirror frame LL5217 (p. 191), ultimately derive from Stent and Overton's prints, as also may the mythical beasts, such as the griffin, and the popular perfumed garden flowers of the time – the roses, carnation, honeysuckle and pansies and the newly imported plants, such as tulips. The prominence given to flowers and animals is a manifestation not only of children's interest but also that of contemporary society in nature, the seasons and the legendary wonders of the world. The encyclopaedic book compiled by Randle Holme, *The Academy of Armory*, devotes whole pages to illustrations of sea monsters and mermaids similar to those which recur on embroidered pictures (such as LL5285, LL5229, pp. 81, 59). The animals often placed in the corners of embroidered mirror frames – the ubiquitous lion, leopard, stag and unicorn – were those most familiar as supporters on the royal coat of arms, though in general one cannot go further and state that these motifs had a specific royalist meaning. Presumably when such animals appear accompanying a biblical figure embroidered with the features of Charles I, as occurs in LL5230 or LL5263 (pp. 22, 83), one is on safer ground in assuming so. It is, however, almost impossible to identify the precise source of these motifs. Both Stent and Overton reused engravings first published at the beginning of the century or even the middle of the previous one, often in carefully drawn Natural Histories and Herbals. With each adaptation, the bird, flower or insect was more crudely drawn, moving further away from its source, until it became the rather generalized outline which awaited the skilled embroiderer's needle and thread to revive it.

Books were also published in the first half of the seventeenth century which claimed to provide patterns and advice for the embroiderer. Though the stated intention of Richard Shorleyker's *A Schole-House for the Needle* (1624, republished in 1632) and James Boler's *The Needle's Excellency* (1631), was to provide patterns for needleworks, very few, if any, of the designs reproduced in these pattern books were the direct source for raised or tent-stitch pictorial embroideries. However, the introductory verses written for Boler's book by the poet John Taylor, charmingly catalogue the popular motifs of the day:

> Flowers, plants and fishes, beasts, birds, flies and bees
> Hils, dales, plaines, pastures, skies, seas, rivers, trees,
> There's nothing near at hand or farthest sought
> But with the needle may be shaped and wrought

But most of Shorleyker's designs appear to have been of more use as patterns for drawn-thread work and for professional lace makers than for domestic embroideresses. This suggests that most of the young embroideresses were more interested in the visually exciting products coming from the commercial establishments of Stent and others, than in redrawing, for their own use at home, the more mundane patterns provided by the embroidery literature. However, the publication of these two books in the 1620s and 1630s indicates that there was a strong interest in embroidery at the time.

As we have seen with Damaris Pearse, sometimes the theme chosen for embroidery had personal significance. The use of a satirical, political print, such as the anti-Catholic engraving *The Double Deliverance* (first published in 1622 and still being re-issued by Overton in 1666–7), as the basis for a needlework picture (LL5292, p. 18) is so unusual and rare that it too must be presumed to have had a personal significance. But of equal importance are the run-of-the-mill designs whose popularity among young embroideresses and their families provides an insight into female education and attitudes of the seventeenth century.

As there is both implicit and explicit evidence, either in the form of unfinished or badly worked pictures or in comments on samplers, that at least some girls did not enjoy their education in needlework, one must assume that the preferred scenes were chosen perhaps by the schoolmistress to entertain or with the agreement of the children concerned. It perhaps should not surprise us to find that many of the favoured themes represent biblical heroines. As previously mentioned, the few New Testament stories chosen for embroidery were mainly ones in which women played a prominent or crucial role, and the same occurs with the Old Testament scenes. The most popular Old Testament subjects were Sheba and Solomon (LL5230, p. 22), Esther and Ahasuerus (LL5280, p. 53), David and Bathsheba (LL5270, p. 57), Rebecca and Eliezer (LL5256, p. 179), David and Abigail, Ruth and Naomi, Judith and Holofernes (LL5271, p. 70), Jephthah's daughter (LL5261, p. 68), Abraham, Hagar and Sarah (LL5241, LL5243, pp. 42–3) and the sacrifice of Isaac (LL5256, p. 179). All but the last show women playing an influential, even a heroic, role in life. The women who are found in sixteenth- and seventeenth-century print series and books of famous, exemplary or valorous women – for example, Esther, Sheba, Sarah, Rebecca, Bathsheba and Judith – all appear repeatedly in embroideries. By the end of the seventeenth century such biblical heroines were being held up as an inspiration to contemporary women by women writers, such as Bathsua Makin in her *Essay to Revive the Ancient Education of Gentlewomen*, published in 1693. In some cases the tale may have been considered appropriate for a growing girl, such as the courtship of Isaac and Rebecca. The story of Abraham, Hagar and Sarah, which relates how Sarah the wife of Abraham forced her husband to evict his mistress, Hagar, and their illegitimate child, Ishmael, from the household showed a woman's power within marriage. Its great popularity (the Lady Lever has two versions of it and many others are to be found in collections around the country) may be due as much to the sympathy elicited in the story for Hagar and the abandoned child Ishmael. In other stories the key figures and their exploits, rather than providing role models, may be seen as seventeenth-century 'wonderwomen' – the female equivalents of David battling Goliath. They included the brave Judith saving her people by beheading Holofernes (LL5271, p. 70); Esther successfully interceding with her husband the Persian king Ahasuerus on behalf of her people, the Jews; and Queen Thomyrus holding the head of her enemy the tyrant Cyrus. There was also room for subjects who might be categorized as the intriguingly infamous – seductresses to a woman – whose downfall or lack of success might nevertheless be considered morally edifying, such as Jezebel (Holburne Museum, Bath), Bathsheba (LL5270, p. 57) and Potiphar's wife (LL5234, LL5269, pp. 20–21). David's affair with Bathsheba, and Potiphar's wife's attempted seduction of Joseph could also have been meant to represent, respectively, the seventh and tenth Commandments (against adultery and coveting a neighbour's manservant), as they did in a series of prints after the work of the sixteenth-century artist Heemskerk. The story of Joseph and Potiphar's wife, with its emphasis on the importance of chastity, is known to have been illustrated on other everyday domestic items of furniture. In the Netherlands, for example, the scene was often used to decorate linen chests.

Other popular themes may have proved attractive because they appealed to a double market. They told moving stories which related specifically to children and reinforced parental authority, even if in a rather gruesome way, in stories such as the *Judgement of Solomon* (LL5232, LL5266, pp. 35, 26), *Jephthah and his Daughter* (LL5261, p. 68) and *Abraham's Sacrifice of Isaac* (LL5243, p. 43). It is also the case that the first and last of these stories were frequently illustrated by painters and print-makers, particularly in the Netherlands, as was *Abraham, Hagar and Ishmael*, which was favoured by Rembrandt and his circle. The frequent use of these stories as design sources for embroidery must, to some extent, have depended on their availability as prints. But the tale of Jephthah's rash vow to sacrifice to God the first one he met on his return from victory was rarely engraved and even more rarely painted. The reason for its transformation into pictorial needlework by predominantly teenage girls must lie instead in the fact that Jephthah's vow resulted in the sacrifice of his daughter. It is equally notable that although prints existed relating the story of David and Goliath (one is pasted to the interior of a Lady Lever casket (LL5256, p. 179)) embroidered versions of it are very rare, the girls preferring David's female equivalent, Judith, and her triumph over Holofernes (LL5271, p. 70).

On the whole the classical legends were chosen less often than the Bible as subjects for embroidery. The Lady Lever's *Diana and Actaeon* (LL5231, p. 34) is unusual in depicting a narrative scene. When a classical theme was chosen it was more likely to represent a pair of gods, such as *Venus and Juno* (LL5235, p. 38). Other favourites, particularly set around mirror frames or on caskets, were allegorical groups such as the Virtues (LL5221, LL5223, pp. 194, 198), the Seasons (LL5222, p. 197), the Senses (LL5262, p. 184), the Elements (LL5273, p. 200) and the Four Continents (LL5219, p. 193). Many scenes, however, were so generalized or strayed so far from the original print that they are difficult to identify as a narrative or as allegorical groups, such as the one which may represent either *Venus and Ceres* or *Peace and Abundance* (LL5272, p. 73). In some cases they were probably never meant to illustrate a story. A vast number of seventeenth-century pictorial needleworks simply show a lady and a gentleman standing in a landscape formed of flowers, fountains and palatial houses. Sometimes they hold out to each other a flower and a book, probably representing the Bible. In such cases the pictures may well have been created to celebrate an engagement or as a wedding gift.

In the past the figures in such pictures have been misidentified. It was common for nineteenth- and twentieth-century dealers to identify all kings and queens as either Charles I and Henrietta Maria or Charles II and Catherine of Braganza depending on which half of the century they were dated to, and to suggest that most such pieces were worked at court or even to proclaim royalist sympathies during the Civil War. Such traditions also, of course, helped raise the prices, and for the most part can be dismissed as fanciful. Sometimes one of the male royal figures in a biblical scene such as *Esther and Ahasuerus*, *The Judgement of Solomon* or *Sheba and Solomon* can be recognized as a royal portrait (LL5230, p. 22), and the popularity of these themes may have depended on them providing an opportunity to honour reigning kings. But on the whole, embroidered royal portraits are rarer than one might expect and difficult to date, though there is evidence that prints of King Charles I and his family (LL5263, p. 83) were used once his son had returned to the throne. After his execution, when his propagandizing self-justification, *Eikon Basilike*, was published with illustrations and became an immediate best-seller, Charles I's portrait was considered suitable for domestic embroidery. The frontispiece of the *Eikon*, showing the king taking up the crown of thorns, was reproduced in an embroidered form (Victoria and Albert Museum, T.175–1961). Another portrait of the king (in a private collection) was possibly worked by his professional embroiderer at court, Edmund Harrison, though he was mainly employed on embroidering court liveries, masque costumes and lavish needlework pictures of Bible scenes, rather than royal portraits. Once the monarchy was restored in 1660 Charles II's own adventures during the Civil War became a suitable topic for illustration in thread (Holburne Museum, Bath, F236). Some embroidered pictures in country-house collections are known to have been worked by ladies of royalist households, but as Damaris Pearse's picture (LL5229) shows, other pictorial embroideries are just as likely to have come from households who had no affiliation to the monarchy.

# Canvas-work Pictures

LL5292 (WHL4144)

## The Defeat of the Armada and the Gunpowder Plot

After 1621

*Linen worked with silk in tent stitch.*

33 × 46.5 cm

LL5292 is a rare example of an embroidery with a political or satirical theme. The design is very closely based on an engraving entitled *The Double Deliverance*, devised by a zealous Puritan preacher, Samuel Ward of Ipswich, and published in Amsterdam in 1621 (fig. 1). The print was inscribed with verses and legends in Latin and English and some in Dutch. The embroiderer has faithfully copied, wherever possible, the English translations retaining only the Latin phrase '*In Foveam Quam Foderint*' ('How they dug themselves into a pit'), which is untranslated in the print, under the scene of the Papal Council. In place of the three

Provenance: Miss A.H. Little, Ladbroke Rd, London; sold Christie's, London, 2 March 1920, lot 55; purchased through M. Harris and Sons £325.10s.

Exhibited: National Maritime Museum, Greenwich, *Armada, 1588–1988*, 20 April – 4 September 1988, Cat. no. 16.32.

Literature: J.L. Nevinson, 'English Domestic Embroidery Patterns of the Sixteenth and Seventeenth Centuries', *Walpole Society*, 1939–40, vol. 28, pp. 9–10. Therle Hughes, 'Stuart Needlework', *Discovering Antiques*, BBC, 1970, illus. Alexander Globe, *Peter Stent, London Printseller*, University of British Columbia Press, 1985, p. 21 no. 515. Xanthe Brooke, 'Tales in Thread', *Antique Collector*, November 1990, pp. 118–121.

References: 1 Samuel Ward was imprisoned after complaints laid by the Spanish Ambassador for having the print published. John Blatchly, 'Samuel Ward's "Double Deliveraunce" and Thomas Scott's Vox Populi: an Anti-Spanish Partnership in Ipswich' in *Studies in Ipswich History* to be published. 2 It was still being sold by John Overton in 1667. Globe, as above, p. 136. 3 Blatchly, as above, lists various prints and items which made use of the Ward design including a brass plate in Somerset, for which see Philip Whittemore, 'A Brass Plate commemorating the Defeat of the Gunpowder Plot', *Transactions of the Monumental Brass Society*, vol. XIII part VI, 1985, pp. 549–51. The embroidery, of a similar size to LL5292, is now in a private collection in Cardiff. 4 Sir E. Harrison, *History of Ightham Church*, 1932, pp. 16–18; Lady Selby embroidered other designs, including a Garden of Paradise, which is also represented on her monument and an Acts of Jonah, which is shown in the portrait of her at Ightham Mote. For these and other embroideries worked by her see Katharine Esdaile, 'Gunpowder Plot in Needlework: Dame Dorothy Selby, "Whose Arte Disclos'd that Plot"', *Country Life*, June 1943, pp. 1094–6. 5 PROB 11/182/f5 Prerogative Court of Canterbury. Kindly brought to my attention by Bernard and Lily

Figure 1 *The Double Deliverance* engraved after a design by Puritan preacher Samuel Ward, published in Amsterdam in 1621. (*Courtesy of the British Museum*)

LL5292 (see also colour plate 1)

Carcase. James Carcase was a Kentish man and probably a dealer in 'Turkey Work' carpets, which were mainly produced in East Anglia. Both regions had close links to the printed and embroidered version of this anti-papist theme and it could be, therefore, that LL5292 also originated from south-eastern England.

1928 Catalogue no. 63.

verses along the bottom of the print (which describe the Armada and the Gunpowder Plot) the embroiderer has substituted the opening verses from Psalm 103, 'MY SOULE PRAISE THOU THE LORD AND ALL THAT IS WITH IN ME PRAISE HIS HOLY NAME MY SOUL PRAISE THOU THE LORD AND FORGET NOT ALL HIS BENEFITS', and she has omitted the all-seeing eye of God from the beam of light over Guy Fawkes. In addition she has not been able to resist inserting in the foreground some of the favourite animals of seventeenth-century embroiderers, a lolloping lion, a hare and a lamb.

The anti-Catholic print may originally have been intended as a warning against any political or marital alliance between England and Spain.[1] Its anti-Catholic sentiment proved popular and it was still being sold in the print shops in the late 1660s.[2] The print was also used by other craftsmen and embroiderers. For example Dame Dorothy Selby (1572–1641) of Ightham Mote, Kent, a renowned needlewoman, produced an embroidered version, which includes both the Latin and English phrases and follows the print more faithfully than LL5292.[3] To further celebrate her prowess with the needle, and her version of the *Double Deliverance* print in particular, Lady Selby had the design incised on a stone slab behind the bust which forms part of her tomb monument in Ightham Church, the inscription below which refers both to her skill with the needle and to the Gunpowder Plot embroidery.[4] The same 1621 print was almost certainly the design used for the 'longe pillowe of tentworke wherein is the Story of 88 and the Powther plott of the fiefte of November' which is described in the will of James Carcase dated 1637.[5] Stylistically LL5292 could also have been worked in the 1630s or '40s, possibly intended as a cover for a cushion on which an ardent Protestant might rest her Bible or prayer-book.

## LL5234 (WHL3215)

## Joseph and Potiphar's Wife

Second quarter of the seventeenth century

*Canvas worked with silk in tent stitch with a silver-thread braid border.*

Joseph is shown fleeing from the amorous attentions of the wife of his employer Potiphar. The scene follows the Bible description closely: 'And she caught him by his garment,

25 × 36 cm

Provenance: purchased through F. Partridge, 5 July 1917, £40 and displayed at The Hill, Hampstead.

References: **1** Simon Schama, *The Embarrassment of Riches*, 1987, p. 101, n. 87. **2** Kerrich, *Catalogue of Marten van*

LL5234

*Heemskerk*, 1829. **3** Gerard de Jode, *Thesaurus Sacrarum Historiarum Veteris Testamenti*, 1585, illustration to Genesis 39; Bernard Salomon, *Quadrins Historiques de la Bible*, 1555. **4** Background scene in Brussels tapestry sold Christie's, 8 December 1988, lot 221; French tent-stitch panel Sir Frederick Richmond's collection sold Christie's, 23 June 1987, lot 23. **5** The design basis for all these prints may have been the School of Raphael fresco in the Vatican loggia. **6** Burrell Collection 29/54, 29/55.

1928 Catalogue no. 10.

saying, Lie with me: and he left his garment in her hand, and fled, and got out of the house' (Genesis 39:12). The spurning of Potiphar's wife by Joseph was a stock theme in Dutch art, appearing in paintings and a Rembrandt etching. As an example of devotion to God's law and the triumph of innocence over lust the scene featured prominently both in the text and as an engraved frontispiece,[1] in Jacob Cats' extremely popular advice to the Christian housewife (*Christelijke Self-Strijt*) published in 1655, and it was often found decorating household linen chests. The scene was also used by the sixteenth-century Dutch artist Marten van Heemskerk to illustrate the tenth commandment against coveting a neighbour's manservant.[2] As such the scene provided a suitable moralizing and decorative theme for the teenage embroideress.

This manifestly indoor scene is provided with a landscape setting, as is the other embroidered version in the collection (LL5269), despite the fact that most engraved sources, such as de Jode's and Bernard Salomon's[3] give it an interior setting and many tapestries and embroideries of the period follow this lead.[4] Neither of the Lady Lever embroideries follow the de Jode print nor any other engravings used in sixteenth-century illustrated Bible series by Bernard Salomon or Virgil Solis.[5] The composition is identical to two tent-stitch pictures in the Burrell Collection, even down to the domed tester of the bed, the positioning of the pond, the rabbit on the hillock and the frog in the rushes.[6] LL5234 may have come from a casket, with the braiding acting as a border to the edge.

LL5269 (WHL4268)

## Joseph and Potiphar's Wife

Second quarter of the seventeenth century

*Canvas worked with silk in tent, stem, and satin stitches, with coiled silk pile, purl and French knots and small amounts of detached buttonhole stitch and metal thread with applied seed pearls and a border of silver strips and silver lace.*

A more sedate version of the same story shown on LL5234. The scene is set in a similar landscape, but the composition is otherwise differently treated with an additional figure running in on the left. The additional figure is also found on a tent-stitch picture in the Burrell Collection.[1] The finely worked tent-stitch panel is bordered by a thin strip of braiding attached to a wider silk border with silver lace fringe of the type often found decorating the edges on embroidered casket tops, which suggests that LL5269 may originally have been mounted on a box.

30.5 × 36.5 cm

Provenance: Arthur Hardy Wood, Duddleswell Manor, Uckfield; sold Christie's, 20 July 1920, lot 105, £48.6.0.; bought through M. Harris and Sons, 24 July 1920.

References: **1** Burrell Collection 29/53. The Burrell design is similar, as is the size, though Joseph's actions are much less sedate and the quality of work is clumsier.

1928 Catalogue no. 94.

LL5269

LL5230 (WHL525)

## The Reception of the Queen of Sheba by King Solomon

Mid-seventeenth century

*Fine canvas worked with silk in very fine tent stitch.*

37.5 × 49.5 cm

LL5230 is one of a group of embroideries in the collection which depict the same scene (see LL5247, and LL5274, pp. 44, 74). The subject of a queen accompanied by her entourage offering gifts to a king shown seated or standing beneath a canopy, is one of the most common themes in seventeenth-century pictorial embroidery. The scene is sometimes

Provenance: acquired sometime between July 1906 and June 1907 and kept at The Hill, Hampstead. It seems to appear in G.M. Ellwood, *English Furniture and Decoration 1680–1800*, Batsford, c. 1906–10, p. 22, but in a different frame.[4]

References: **1** The Esther and Ahasuerus theme usually follows Esther 4:5 by showing King Ahasuerus holding out his sceptre to his kneeling consort in acceptance of her intercession, thus

LL5230

saving her life and that of her people. But for another possible depiction, in which the king holds an uncrowned lady's hand, see LL5280 (p. 53). **2** See LL5247, 5274. A print after a painting by Marten van Heemskerk depicts Sheba presenting a flower to the king with her left hand while a vase full of money stands upon the step of his throne. Kerrich, *Catalogue of Marten van Heemskerk*, 1829, pp. 26–7. **3** V&A No. T.237–1978, dated to the third quarter of the seventeenth century in which the figures are definitely part of the story of Esther and a panel piece formerly in Sir Frederick Richmond's collection sold Christie's, 23 June 1987, lot 142, dated mid-seventeenth century, which may be wrongly identified. The V&A also have a tent-stitch *Sheba and Solomon* which bears slight similarities to LL5230, No. T.125–1926 **4** It was displayed originally in a gilt frame in the 'Stuart Room' at The Hill and thus escaped the disastrous Rivington Bungalow fire of 1913 which destroyed much of Leverhulme's first embroidery collection. The present tortoiseshell frame was purchased from Frank Partridge in October 1920.

1928 Catalogue no. 27.

misidentified as Esther and Ahasuerus, as was LL5230 when it was catalogued in 1928.[1] The flower held out by the Queen of Sheba is probably meant as an equivalent to the pots and urns usually borne by the Queen and her servants in painted and other embroidered versions of the scene.[2] However, two other embroideries which bear a close similarity in format to LL5230, including a gift of flowers, are both entitled *Esther and Ahasuerus*.[3] The confusion over identifying the two scenes is exacerbated by the fact that the usual embroidered format for the *Reception of Sheba by Solomon* bears very little relationship to the various possible print sources. For example, Gerard de Jode's print of the subject has a prominently displayed pile of gifts, a courtier in Roman military dress and a beardless king, although the relative positions of monarchs, maids and parasol do coincide to some extent (fig. 2). The common misidentification of the scene underlines the frequent use of stock characters, such as the luxuriantly bearded courtier and the maid with a parasol, in different embroidery designs and the inter-relationship of the two scenes, both representing foreign queens or consorts visiting or appealing to male monarchs. Bearing in mind the nature of Sheba's visit; to ask questions of wisdom of the wisest of potentates (1 Kings 10:1–13), it is interesting to note that compared to LL5247 and LL5274 Solomon bears a portrait-like resemblance to Charles I. A deliberate identification of Solomon with Charles I is made more plausible by the four royal beasts, the unicorn, stag, leopard and lion, in the corners. The picture's size and shape would suggest it was originally a casket top. It is finely worked, in good condition and its silks retain a freshness of colour.

Figure 2    Gerard de Jode's print of the Reception of Sheba by Solomon. (*Courtesy of the British Museum*)

LL5250 (WHL4050)

## King, Queen and Trainbearer

Mid-seventeenth century

*Canvas worked with silk in long and short stitch, stem stitch and French knots with couched metal thread and attached purl and seed pearls.*

13.3 × 22.5 cm

LL5250

Provenance: Miss E.E. Worth, 3 Greenford Park Villas, Southall; sold Christie's, 31 July 1919, as part of lot 130[1], £26.5.0; bought through M. Harris and Sons, 5 August 1919, £3.11.9 and kept at The Hill, Hampstead.

References: **1** Its pair, a 'Charles II embroidery worked with figures, birds, etc. in coloured silks on satin and enriched with seed pearls', 8 x 8¾ in framed, is no longer in the collection.

1928 Catalogue no. 39.

15.5 × 25.5 cm

Provenance: Ria Ponsonby;[2] purchased through M. Harris and Sons, 6 November 1919, £55; displayed originally at The Hill, Hampstead.

References: **1** V&A, T.125–1937 whose hanging scene is very closely related to LL5252; Sotheby's, New York, 19 November 1988, lot 184. **2** A printed book-plate on the back with Ria Ponsonby's name shows a three-gabled half-timbered house and garden within an oval medallion and floral garland. There appears to be no support for the statement in gallery files that the house is Great Tangley Manor [sic], Surrey, and linking a Miss Maria Ponsonby to the house.

1928 Catalogue no. 12.

The two panels which make up LL5250 were probably intended for the outside or inside of the doors to an embroidered work casket. The panels appear never to have been used for this purpose and were left partly unfinished on the canvas. The figures shown are most likely to represent Solomon and Sheba or possibly King Ahasuerus and Queen Esther, who are frequently depicted in this way, for example in LL5230, LL5247, LL5274 and LL5280 (pp. 22, 44, 74, 53).

LL5252 (WHL4089)

## The Hanging of Haman

Second quarter to mid-seventeenth century

*Canvas worked with silk in tent and rococo stitches with couched thread and cord. The figures outlined in running stitches.*

A thin rectangular panel such as LL5252 probably originally ran along the front or sides of an embroidered casket. The casket presumably depicted the rest of the story of Esther revealing the treacherous Haman's plot against the Jews to her husband, King Ahasuerus (Esther 7:1–10). An example of another scene from the story can be seen in LL5280. The downfall of Chancellor Haman and his subsequent fate, on the gallows he had prepared for Esther's Jewish kinsman, Mordecai, featured prominently in embroidered versions of the theme.[1] The bare canvas border of about 1 cm wide running along the top and bottom of the panel has been used by the embroiderer to try out patterns of stitches and to finish off threads.

LL5252

LL5266 (WHL3521)

## The Judgement of Solomon

Early to mid-seventeenth century[1]

*Canvas worked with silk in tent stitch and a few cross stitches with applied tassels and silver thread chain.*

As is usual with embroidered versions of the story, the court in which Solomon gives judgement is set in a landscape or, as here, among a variety of flowers, animals and insects, including strawberry plants, vines, roses, pinks, carnations and a frog. None of the plants or animals appear to have a symbolic significance. The story itself, in which Solomon gave judgement between two mothers claiming the same living child (1 Kings 3:16–28), besides symbolizing justice in the general sense, was always considered flattering to the contemporary monarch, either James I or Charles I, emphasizing his wisdom and right to rule. It has also been suggested that the story of the struggle between two factions, whose claims

24 × 33 cm

Provenance: purchased through Cyril Andrade, Duke Street, 10 May 1918, £40; displayed at The Hill, Hampstead.

References: **1** When purchased it was described as a James I *petit-point* picture. **2** Mayhew, thesis, University St Andrews, 1988, p. 29. **3** *The Illustrated Bartsch*, vol. 20, pt. 1, p. 275.

1928 Catalogue no. 35.

LL5266

threaten to destroy the child, may have had contemporary allusions to the struggle between Monarch and State.[2]

Despite the fact that all the known painted and printed depictions set the court scene indoors surrounded by courtiers, LL5266 does bear close resemblance to Jost Amman's woodcut of the scene in his *Biblia*[3] (fig. 3). The embroidery appears to correspond with the print in various ways, not only in its flight of steps leading to the 'lion' throne; the bearded king with arms out wide and the kneeling disputing women, but even to the child lying on a tasselled cushion.

29 × 37 cm

Provenance: purchased through D.L. Isaacs, 1 January 1917, £30; first displayed at The Hill, Hampstead.

1928 Catalogue no. 90.

LL5290 (WHL3137)

## *Oak Tree Surrounded by Floral and Animal Motifs*

Second half of the seventeenth century

*Linen worked with silk in tent, running, rococo, and basket filling stitch. The linen ground is very threadbare in places.*

The central oval cartouche of oak trees in a landscape is surrounded by motifs which include (clockwise from bottom left) an oak tree with acorns, a pink, a small vase of flowers, an eglantine rose, a squirrel in a nut tree and a peacock. In the late sixteenth century this type of composition, with a central motif of a tree or flower surrounded by a trailing floral border, was popular, but the size of the motifs in LL5290 and the variety of stitches are more like those worked from the 1640s onwards.

LL5290

LL5255 (WHL4390)

## *Agricultural and Rural Pursuits*

Mid-seventeenth century

*Linen canvas worked with silk and wool in fine tent stitch.*

This unusual and finely embroidered panel may represent a seventeenth-century form of the Arcadian landscape more typical of the eighteenth century, in which shepherdesses guard their flocks in a landscape peopled with the stock embroidered motifs of huntsmen, fishermen and wildfowlers. Such motifs were also popular in the sixteenth and seventeenth centuries,[1] and the dating of 1650 given by the 1928 catalogue was presumably based on the costume details of the central figures. When purchased the embroidery was described as a 'Queen Anne' needlework picture and similar subjects were embroidered in the first quarter of the eighteenth century, including the needlework screen that

24 × 32.5 cm

Provenance: purchased through M. Harris and Sons, 1 November 1922, £75, for the Lady Lever Art Gallery.

Exhibited: *The Subversive Stitch: Embroidery in women's lives 1300–1900*, Whitworth Art Gallery, Manchester, 27 May– 29 August 1988, no. 64.

References: **1** A.J.B. Wace, 'Embroidery in the collection of Sir Frederick Richmond Bart', pt. II, *Apollo*, vol. XVIII, 1933, fig. VII; Christie's, South Kensington, 23 June 1987, lot 106 illus. pl. 8. **2** George Wingfield Digby, 'Lady Julia Claverley Embroideress', *Connoisseur*, vol. 145, 1960. **3** Y. Hackenbroch, *English Needleworks in the Irwin Untermyer Collection*, fig. 136, pl. 98; Leverhulme collection sale, *see* Appendix AG1, lot 197.

1928 Catalogue no. 103.

LL5255 (see also colour plate 2)

Lady Julia Claverley finished in 1727, based on Francis Cleyn's illustrations to Virgil's *Eclogues* and *Georgics* published by John Ogilvy in 1654.[2] One of the screen's images of a man ploughing a field, illustrating a verse from the *Georgics*, is very closely related to the same image on the Lady Lever embroidery. Other analogous scenes of country life, thought to have been embroidered in the first quarter of the eighteenth century, include the farmyard scene in the Untermyer Collection, Metropolitan Museum of Art, New York, which was originally in Lever's collection.[3] None of these partially naturalistic views of country pursuits and agricultural activities depict the anecdotal central scene of a peg-legged boy doffing his hat to a well-dressed gentry couple.

LL5295 (WHL3061)

## Cavalier Doffing his Hat to a Lady

Initialled 'MH' and dated 1678

*Canvas worked with silk in tent stitch.*

This scene is one of the most commonly embroidered non-biblical or narrative themes in the seventeenth century.[1] Engraved betrothal or marriage portraits of the 1640s to '60s sometimes show the gentleman doffing his hat while the lady holds a Bible and offers her hand.[2] Embroideries which show these gestures, particularly if accompanied by the figures of Faith and Hope,[3] may be a young relative's marriage or betrothal present.

LL5295's frame is not original and was fitted to the embroidery after it was sold to Lever.

18 × 28.5 cm

Provenance: purchased through D.L. Isaacs, 17 November 1916, £22.

References: **1** For some further examples in raised-work as well as canvas-work see LL5341 beadwork (p. 90); M.B. Huish, *Sampler and Tapestry Embroideries*, 1900, pl. XLVII, dated 1657; Whitworth Art Gallery New Acquisitions, May–September 1985; Sotheby's, New York, 19 November 1988, lot 179. **2** Alexander Globe, *Peter Stent London printseller c. 1642–1665*, 1985, cat. 24a pl. 29, 30. **3** Sotheby's, 22 April 1966, lot 42.

1928 Catalogue no. 7.

LL5295

LL5297 (WHL3422)

## Family Group of Gentleman, Lady and Child

Third quarter of the seventeenth century

*Linen worked with laid silk in satin, running and chain stitch.*

12.5 × 21 cm

The picture was originally intended as a panel for the outside of a casket or small box. The peculiarly shaped 'cloud' above the child's head is in fact an embroidered key-plate meant to fit around a key-hole suggesting that the panel was to be fitted to the front of a casket. The fact that the key-hole has been embroidered over suggests that either the panel was never fitted or that the amateur embroideress misunderstood the design drawn on the canvas. The most interesting thing about LL5297 is one of the labels on the back in an eighteenth-century hand, which probably refers to a previous owner or the embroideress herself.[1] She is described as the 'niece of Bishop Juxton', who may be identified as William Juxon (1582–1663) Bishop of London, Archbishop of Canterbury and companion of Charles I at his execution. Juxon's descendants in later centuries owned Charles I's personal Bible, given to Juxon before the king's death and other memorabilia, including a curious set of a miniature portrait with interchangeable scenes.[2] Another label describes LL5297

Provenance: the Miss Macknights(?), Maldon(?) Lodge, Wallington, Surrey, Mr J.Y. Macknight; P.D. Griffiths sold Christie's, 22 January 1918, lot 115, along with a needlework bag, £17.17, bought by the dealer Withens; purchased by Lever through M. Harris and Sons, 1 March 1918, £24, first displayed at The Hill, Hampstead.

Exhibited: Manchester, Platt Hall, 21/6/1955 – 7/11/1955.

References: **1** The label reads:

Memoranda of Mr. Kings[?]
at Bakewell in Derbyshire
My Grandmother young was born
she[?] was a neice [sic] to Bishop
Juxton
Jas:[James] Dick[?] 1233 [or 1733] Golds . . .[?]

**2** Revd W. Hennessy Marah, *Memoirs of Archbishop Juxon*, 1869, pp. 86–7, 89–90. The interchangeable scenes were probably painted on mica. **3** M.B. Huish, *Samplers and Tapestry Embroideries*, 1900, pl. XLVIII; G.S. Seligman and T. Hughes,

LL5297

*Domestic Embroidery*, 1926, pls. 87a, b. The casket was previously owned successively by Theresa Macquoid, the author of the first Lady Lever embroidery catalogue, and Percival Griffiths, the important embroidery collector.

1928 Catalogue no. 44.

as portraying Charles I, Henrietta Maria and the Princess of Wales(?). As none of the figures hold symbols of royalty this seems unlikely unless the embroidery was worked during the Commonwealth period when any portrayal of the monarchs might show them incognito. Another embroidery using exactly the same design of a family holding a book (Bible?), bird and flower and flanked by exactly the same flowers, a tulip and carnation, does date from this period. It was used on the back of a tent-stitch casket dated 1657.[3]

LL5298 (WHL3425)

## Bust Portrait of a Lady in an Oval Cartouche with Floral and Animal Motifs

Late seventeenth century or early eighteenth century, initialled 'DL'

*Canvas motifs worked with silk in tent stitch on what appears to be a knitted(?) ground fabric.*

The lady's coiffure and dress are of the William and Mary period. She is shown against a feigned marble background and the cartouche is placed on a yellow ground.

21.5 × 24 cm

Provenance: purchased through M. Harris and Sons, 1 March 1918, £27.10.0.

1928 Catalogue no. 86.

LL5298

LL5299 (WHL3438)

## *Joseph Brought before the Pharaoh*

Late seventeenth or eighteenth century[1]

*Canvas worked with silk and wool in tent stitch, with some surface and raised satin stitch, and highlights on beards and the Pharaoh's crown in long and short stitch. The threads on some of the faces have worn away.*

Joseph is shown being taken from prison to interpret the Pharaoh's dreams (Genesis 41:14). LL5299 appears to be an embroidered copy of a woven tapestry cushion of the type produced by the Sheldon works at Barcheston and Bordesley (Warwickshire and Worcestershire) between about 1561 and the early seventeenth century.[1] The deep blue border of flowering plants along with the shape and size of LL5299 are all characteristic of Sheldon cushions.[2]

48 × 50 cm

Provenance: Percival Griffiths; sold Christie's, 12 March 1918, lot 269; purchased through Harris and Sons, 15 March 1918 for £35.14.0. and first displayed at The Hill, Hampstead.

References: **1** However, the earliest gallery inventory dates it to *c.* 1800. **2** For another embroidered copy of a Sheldon tapestry cushion see LL5225 *The Sacrifice of Isaac* (p. 101), which may have been worked early in the eighteenth century. **3** There are no examples of the Joseph story among known Sheldon tapestry pieces; E.A.B. Barnard and A.J.B. Wace, 'The Sheldon Tapestry Weavers and their work', *Archaeologia*, vol. LXXVII, 1928, pp. 283–314; Wace, 'Sheldon Tapestry cushions in the collection of Sir William Burrell', *Old Furniture*, vol. V, 1928, pp. 78–81; G.W. Digby and W. Hefford, *Victoria and Albert Museum: The Tapestry Collection Medieval and Renaissance*, 1980.

1928 Catalogue no. 91.

LL5299

# Silk-work Pictures

LL5287 (WHL3132)

*Lady holding Flower and Book*

Mid–seventeenth century

LL5287

*Satin worked with silk, metal thread, glass beads and spangles in satin and long and short stitches with couched metal thread, purl, knots, with braided silk and detached buttonhole stitch and a small amount of padding. Some of the stitching on the stag's antlers has been lost and the watercolour shading of the lion's mane is visible.*

Embroideries showing a lady holding a book (possibly a Bible) and a flower and surrounded by floral and animal motifs were fairly common in the middle of the seventeenth century.[1] LL5287 may have been owned by Mrs Rachel Head, a collector of needleworks at the beginning of the twentieth century.[2] The advice she provided on the collection and display of historical embroideries in the various articles she wrote for the *Connoisseur* and the *Burlington Magazine* may have influenced Lever's own collecting.

21 × 27.5 cm

Provenance: the collection of Mrs Rachel Head by 1901; purchased through D.L. Isaacs as a pair with LL5296 (*Vase of Flowers*), 12 January 1917, for £35 and first displayed at The Hill, Hampstead.

Literature: Mrs Head, 'A Collection of Needlework Pictures', *Connoisseur*, 1901, vol. 1 Sept.–Dec., p. 155, illus. vii.

Exhibited: Platt Hall, Manchester, 21/6/1955 – 7/11/1955.

References: **1** For an example in tent stitch on satin, Sotheby's, London, 4 July 1986, Rous Lench Collection Sale, lot 608 and a related piece in tent stitch on canvas in the Cooper-Hewitt Museum, New York, 1959–170-2. **2** See *Connoisseur*, 1901, article by Mrs Head where LL5287 is illustrated, but its owner is not identified. For other seventeenth-century works in her collection, *Connoisseur*, March 1905, p. 177.

1928 Catalogue no. 6.

## LL5231 (WHL2689)

## *Diana and Actaeon*

Mid-seventeenth century

*Satin worked with silk and purl in long and short, satin, fine stem and chain stitches with a variety of padded, detached buttonhole and fine lace filling stitches, applied mica and couched metal thread and coiled silk pile.*

A rare subject for the period derived from classical mythology rather than the more usual Old Testament scene. There is, however, another depiction of the story in tent stitch at Hardwick Hall, Derbyshire. The latter was embroidered by Bess of Hardwick and her ladies some fifty years or more before LL5231 and appears, unlike the Lady Lever picture, to derive its design from almost contemporary woodcuts by Bernard Solomon.[1] In LL5231 Actaeon can be seen on the right in the process of being turned into a stag by the goddess Diana while in the background, now fully a stag, he is attacked by the huntsman's hounds. The whole composition is placed within a cord frame. LL5231 was probably originally the lid to a casket. The quality of materials and stitching is very fine and compositional details, such as the nymphs' calves visible through the water, are very well executed. In her catalogue Theresa Macquoid romantically suggested that Diana and the nymphs' hair was composed of human hair. In reality it appears to be a combination of carefully curled silks and painted metal purl.

32.5 × 40 cm

Provenance: purchased through D.L. Isaacs, 17 December 1915, £40 and subsequently displayed in The Bungalow, Rivington.

References: **1** John Nevinson, 'Embroideries at Hardwick Hall', *Country Life*, vol. CLIV, November 1973, p. 1760. Another *Diana and Actaeon* was in the collection of Percival Griffiths, who formed a collection of seventeenth- and eighteenth-century embroideries almost contemporaneously with Lever. Griffiths' piece also seems to be related to a Solomon print. Eugenie Gibson, 'The Percival D. Griffiths Collection of Old English Needlework', *Connoisseur*, vol. LXII, 1922, p. 18–19. There is also a mid-seventeenth century picture with a theme from classical mythology, *Alpheus Pursuing the Nymph Arethusa*, in the V&A, T.50–1924.

1928 Catalogue no. 50.

LL5231

LL5232 (WHL2694)

## The Judgement of Solomon

Second half of the seventeenth century

*Satin worked with silk and metal thread in satin stitch, long and short, back stitch, and other raised straight stitches in lattice and brick pattern with French knots and couched thread and cord with cut silk pile and applied mica. Three green stripes of the selvedge are visible at the left-hand edge.*

The crudely generalized figures of LL5232 make it difficult to judge whether it derives from a specific print, though the soldier swinging his scimitar over the dangling child comes

27 × 37 cm

Provenance: Fitz Henry collection(?);[2] purchased through D.L. Isaacs, 17 December 1915, £14 along with another small seventeenth-century panel showing a queen appearing from a tent, subsequently sold. See Appendix AG1, lot 73. Kept at Thornton Manor.

References: **1** *Illustrated Bartsch*, vol. 20, pt. 1, p. 275 (see LL5266, p. 26). **2** The previous two pieces on the Isaacs invoice

LL5232

are specifically stated to have come from the 'Fitz Henry' collection. The list is ambiguous as to whether LL5232 also derived from that collection.

1928 Catalogue no. 38.

closest to his equivalent in Jost Amman's woodcut for his illustrated *Biblia* (1 Kings 3:16–28).[1] Neither is it similar to the other *Judgement of Solomon* in the collection, LL5266. The picture's disparities in scale are such that a large bird perched on a twig to the left comes perilously close to looking like an angel's wings or the mother's drapery. Although many of the features, like the bird, have been crudely worked, some areas around the rose and tulip in the lower corners show a variety of well-worked stitches. LL5232's selvedge shows the three green stripes commonly found on the silk satin ground fabric used in the seventeenth century.

## LL5233 (WHL3072)

### *Jacob, Rachel, Leah and Laban*

Third quarter of the seventeenth century

*Satin worked with silk and metal thread, and in long and short, running, satin and split stitches with applied canvas slips, couched cord, French knots, purl, other raised stitches and padded, cut silk pile.*

The central scene placed within an oval cartouche does not depict any precise part of the story of Jacob and Rachel (Genesis 29:9–30 and 30:28–43) in which Jacob falls in love with Laban's younger daughter Rachel but is tricked by him into first marrying the elder daughter Leah. The scene does, however, show various elements within the story: the well at which Jacob first meets Rachel and the speckled sheep given to Jacob from Laban's flock. This compilation of images is not the usual way in which the story was illustrated in the seventeenth century. (Another equally unusual depiction of the theme is found on LL5268, p. 69.)

39.5 × 50.5 cm

Provenance: purchased through D.L. Isaacs, 30 November 1916, £48; and displayed at The Hill, Hampstead.

References: **1** M. Swain and J. Nevinson, 'John Nelham's Needlework Panel', *Bulletin of the Needle and Bobbin Club*, 1982, pp. 3–14.

1928 Catalogue no. 88.

LL5233 (see also colour plate 3)

Both the narrative scene and the spot motifs of flowers, birds and animals are very finely worked, even the features of the faces have been embroidered in fine silks. The large flowers in the corners appear to be from the peony family while those embroidered on to the satin include a honeysuckle, a campanula(?) and a strawberry plant. Although the previous catalogue dated LL5233 to *c.* 1700 there is no reason why it should not have an earlier date. Indeed the use of canvas slips and the oval scrolled frame to the central scenes, which is similar to one at Blair Castle datable to about 1654–60, would suggest an earlier dating for LL5233.[1] The contemporary lacquer frame was probably 'married' up to the embroidery once the latter was removed from its casket.

LL5235 (WHL3369)

## Sacred and Worldly Love (Venus and Juno(?))

Second half of the seventeenth century

*Satin worked with silk in long and short stitch, stem, running, chain, satin, cross and speckling stitches with silk threads couched in a variety of lattice patterns.*

In Macquoid's catalogue LL5235 was referred to as *Sacred and Profane Love* and it could well show the crowning by cupid of religious ardour or charity at the expense of worldly or secular power. It could also represent the choice between the two goddesses – Juno, wielding her sceptre, and Venus, whose Renaissance symbol was a flaming heart, as was that of Charity.[1] The subject may be derived from Hercules's choice between Vice and Virtue, which was a popular allegory in Renaissance and Baroque art and featured in an adapted form in at least two seventeenth-century embroideries.[2] One formerly in Mrs Hailstone's collection showed close affinities with LL5235, and depicted a helmeted military man standing

31.5 × 44.5 cm

Provenance: purchased through M. Harris and Sons, 13 November 1917, £30.

References: **1** A mid-seventeenth-century embroidered depiction of Charity holding a flaming heart is in the Holburne Museum, Bath, F.233. **2** *Illustrated Catalogue of Ancient Framed Needlework Pictures in the Possession of Mrs S.H. Lilla Hailstone*, 1897, no. 85, pl. II, referred to as 'Cavalier with two women'; Sir Frederick Richmond's Collection sale, Christie's, 23 June 1987, lot 87. **3** Sir Frederick Richmond's panel shows a man between Venus, holding a flaming heart and Diana with a bow.

1928 Catalogue no. 92.

LL5235

between two women, holding respectively a flaming heart and a sceptre, with castles placed behind each of them.[3]

## LL5238 (WHL3464)

## *Venus, Adonis and Cupid*

Mid-seventeenth century

26 × 26 cm

*Satin worked with silk in long and short, satin, running and stem stitches with purl and small amounts of cut and coiled silk pile and some detached lace and buttonhole stitches.*

Provenance: purchased as a pair with LL5237 (p. 63) through M. Harris and Sons, 24 April 1918, £40.

References: **1** J. Hall, *Dictionary of Subjects and Symbols in Art*, 1974. The same story embroidered in a different design was formerly in Sir Frederick Richmond's collection, *Connoisseur*, May 1935, opp. p. 283.

1928 Catalogue no. 14.

The mythological story of Venus and Adonis has been embroidered from the bottom left-hand corner upwards. It shows the blindfolded cupid aiming his dart at Venus who is vainly trying to prevent Adonis setting off with his pack of dogs. Above Adonis lies dead from the boar's attack, while in the top left corner Venus, after having heard her lover's groans comes down to aid him, but too late.[1] The figures are surrounded by plants and flowers popular in the seventeenth century including bluebells and the ever popular borage (in the centre). The embroidery displays fine workmanship and probably continues a small way underneath the mount.

LL5238

LL5239 (WHL3465)

## The Five Senses

Second half of the seventeenth century

*Satin worked with silk and metal thread in long and short, satin, stem and running stitches with couched metal and silk threads and purl, with attached mica and a single glass bead, surrounded by a silver thread braid border.*

Allegorical groups representing the five senses are often found on seventeenth century embroideries.[1] The theme itself featured frequently on sets of Netherlandish engravings in the sixteenth and seventeenth centuries. The design for LL5239 is more likely to derive from a seventeenth-century series, as Touch is shown with a bird pecking her fingers, a more common depiction in this century than in the previous century when Touch is usually shown holding a hedgehog or an ermine. Some pictorial embroidery designs used the popular series engraved by Adriaen Collaert after Martin de Vos, published *c.* 1600.[2] But the design for LL5239 is more likely to have been adapted from a less complex series of single figure subjects such as Jost Amman's, published in 1586,[3] though this did not depict the animal attributes of the senses (the dog associated with Smell, the ape eating an apple associated with Taste and the stag associated with Hearing), which were shown in both the Collaert prints and LL5239. Along with the animals some of the identifiable plants and flowers may also have symbolic connotations, the sunflower(?) with Sight, tulip and anemone(?) with Touch and the pear tree with Taste. The braiding around LL5239 and its size suggests that it once formed the top to a casket. LL5239 was not the only pictorial embroidery of this theme owned by Leverhulme, another piece was sold in 1926 and is now in the

29.5 × 40 cm

Provenance: purchased through M. Harris and Sons, 24 April 1918, £35.

Exhibited: Platt Hall, Manchester, 21 June–7 November 1955.

References: **1** An example of a piece fairly closely related to LL5329 is a small panel formerly owned by another collector of pictorial embroideries, Sir Frederick Richmond. Christie's, 23 June 1987, lot 152; also see the two figures (Hearing and Smell) on a stumpwork picture in the National Museum of Wales, 14.297, F.G. Payne, *Guide to the Collection of Samplers and Embroideries in the National Museum of Wales*, 1939, illus. pl. II. **2** Y. Hackenbroch, *English and other Needlework, Tapestries and Textiles in the Irwin Untermyer Collection*, 1960, Lix, fig. 82. **3** *The Illustrated Bartsch*, vol. 20, pt. 1, p. 43, 44. **4** See Appendix AG2, lot 261; Y. Hackenbroch, as above., p. 40, fig. 114, pl. 79.

1928 Catalogue no. 52.

LL5239

Metropolitan Museum of Art, New York,[4] and four of the five senses can be found on a casket still in the collection, LL5262 (p. 184).

LL5240 (WHL3473)

## Justice and Truth

Second third of the seventeenth century

*Satin worked with silk in long and short, satin and stem stitch with couched silk thread.*

These allegorical figures, standing under schematic arches which are entwined with flowers, resemble those sometimes found on book covers of this period.[1] They are most closely comparable to the Justice and Mercy entwined with flowers embroidered on the cover of a 1648 Bible in the Bible Society's collection,[2] in which Mercy holds a broken column in her left hand and carries the rest of the column across her back. The combination of these figures is traditional and often found in psalters illustrating Psalm 85:10 – 'Mercy and truth are met together, righteousness [justice] and peace have kissed each other'. LL5240, however, was probably not worked as a cover to a psalm book as it lacks the necessary central band to cover the spine. The small panels are more likely to have been intended for the interior doors of a cabinet.

15 × 27.5 cm

Provenance: purchased through M. Harris and Sons, 24 April 1918, £20.

References: **1** G.S. Seligman and T. Hughes, *Domestic Embroidery*, 1926, pls. 63–4. **2** A.S. Herbert, *Historical Catalogue of the Printed Editions of the English Bible*, 1968, No. 610.

1928 Catalogue no. 47.

LL5240

LL5241 (WHL3476)

## The Expulsion of Hagar and Ishmael by Abraham

Second half of the seventeenth century

*Satin worked with silk in fine long and short, satin and stem stitch and French knots with a small amount of silk threads couched in brick and lattice patterns.*

The expulsion of Abraham's mistress, Hagar, and his illegitimate son, Ishmael, from Abraham's home was one of the most commonly embroidered scenes of the century. Many of these embroideries, like LL5241, were adapted from an engraving published by Gerard de Jode after a painting (*c.* 1562–3) by Martin de Vos[1] (fig. 4). The popularity of the scene as an embroidery design may derive from the nature of the subject, which related to a woman's power within marriage.[2] It is tempting to suggest that the story of Sarah (shown under the tent in the background) demanding of her husband, Abraham, the expulsion of his concubine Hagar and his son (Genesis 21:8–21) may have been seen as a peculiarly appropriate moral to instil in young minds approaching

34 × 54 cm

Provenance: purchased through M. Harris and Sons, 24 April 1918, £40.

Exhibited: Platt Hall, Manchester, 21 June–7 November 1955.

References: **1** Gerard de Jode, *Thesaurus Sacrarum Historiarum Veteris Testamenti*, Antwerp 1585; Martin de Vos, *The Expulsion of Hagar*, Christie's, 21 July 1989, lot 120; A. Zweite, *Marten de Vos*, 1980, Cat. 9 pl. 10. Nancy Cabot, 'Pattern Sources of Scriptural Subjects in Tudor and Stuart Embroideries', *Bulletin of the Needle and Bobbin Club*, 1946, vol. XXX, nos. 1 and 2, p. 33. She identified thirteen embroideries in the UK and US collections using the same print source. See also LL5243. Mayhew's survey (see University of St Andrews thesis, 1988) found twenty-three embroideries with the theme. Other well-known embroidery collectors of the twentieth century had several pieces depicting the theme, for example, Rous Lench, Sotheby's, 4 July 1986, lot 605; Sir Frederick

LL5241 (see also colour plate 4)

Figure 4 The engraving of the Expulsion of Hagar and Ishmael by Abraham published after a painting by Martin de Vos. (*Courtesy of the British Museum*)

Richmond, Christie's, 23 June 1987, lots 102, 132, 147. **2** Roszika Parker, *The Subversive Stitch: Embroidery and the Making of the Feminine*, 1984, p. 96; Mayhew, as above, p. 28.

1928 Catalogue no. 33.

marriageable status, as well as reinforcing the sinful nature of adultery. But the plight of the young Ishmael, saved from dying of thirst in the desert by an angel showing Hagar a well, must also have attracted the sympathy of the youthful embroiderers. Among the flowers interspersing the narrative are a cornflower and a tulip.

LL5243 (WHL3684)

**Flat silk and raised-work picture**

## *The Expulsion of Hagar and Ishmael by Abraham*

Second half of the seventeenth century

LL5243

*Satin worked with silk in long and short and chain stitches, and couched thread and cord with a small amount of raised-work including a variety of raised stitches, French knots and purl.*

A contracted version of LL5241, depicting only the key figures from the expulsion scene. A similarly abbreviated scene was found on a seventeenth-century embroidered Bible covering owned by Percival Griffiths,[1] a leading collector of furniture and needleworks. The figures are interspersed with fruit trees and flowers including a daffodil, a pink and a tulip.

25 × 37 cm

Provenance: purchased through M. Harris and Sons, 23 October 1918, £38; first displayed at The Hill, Hampstead.

References: **1** A.J.B. Wace, 'Exhibition of Early English Needlework', *Old Furniture*, April 1928, p. 232.

1928 Catalogue no. 41.

## LL5247 (WHL3774)

### *The Reception of the Queen of Sheba by King Solomon with the Four Elements*

Second half of the seventeenth century

*Satin worked with silk, metal purl and silk pile in a variety of stitches including satin, stem, running, and long and short stitches with couched threads, coiled silk pile and French knots and a small amount of padded, detached buttonhole and filling stitches. It is perished along the top edge and right-hand side and is badly stained.*

The central scene showing the queen offering gifts to the king was the usual way in which this Old Testament story (1 Kings 10:10) was illustrated. Compared with the other versions of the theme in the collection, LL5247 bears the closest resemblance to Gerard de Jode's published print of the subject, with the embroidered figures reversed from the print, although the similarity is tenuous (fig. 5). The figures of the royal couple and their entourage are identical but in

41 × 55 cm

Provenance: purchased through M. Harris and Sons, 22 April 1919, £90 and displayed at The Hill, Hampstead.

References: **1** For a discussion of the way in which the theme is commonly depicted see LL5230 (Canvas-work picture p. 22). **2** National Gallery of Art, Washington, *Treasure Houses of Britain*, 1985, Cat. no. 75. **3** See John Dunstall's book of etched slips of flowers in Alexander Globe, *Peter Stent, London Printseller*, Vancouver, 1985, pl. 248, or A. Collaert's *Florilegia*, 1590, reproduced by John Johnstone in the seventeenth century.

1928 Catalogue no. 28.

Figure 5   Print of the Reception of Sheba by Solomon published by Gerard de Jode. (*Courtesy of the British Museum*)

LL5247

reverse from those in LL5274 (p. 74).[1] The four allegorical figures in the corners probably represent (from the top left, clockwise) the four elements of Fire, Air, Earth and Water, the latter represented by a human-headed reptile pouring water. The two upper figures, which are similar to figures on an embroidered cabinet *c.* 1670 at Groombridge Place,[2] may derive from unidentified prints depicting the sun god Apollo and the goddess Juno, whose chariot was pulled by a peacock. Some of the flowers which fill the outer spaces, particularly the rose, the pink, and the campanula, look as though they could be drawn from one of the many sheets of flower studies sold by print sellers in the second half of the century.[3]

LL5247 was probably once part of a casket or workbox. The frame drawn on the silk around the picture is still visible and the faces of the four elements have not been embroidered.

LL5339 (H51)

## *The Old Man and Death*(?) *with a Floral Border*

Seventeenth century

*Satin worked with silk, metal thread and metal coil in satin stitch, split stitch and couched threads. The satin is worn through in several places.*

The scene may be meant to illustrate the fable of 'The Old Man and Death' by Aesop (retold by La Fontaine), in which an old man wearying of his burden of wood calls upon Death to release him but is horrified when Death actually appears. However, LL5339 lacks the important pile of sticks which appears in the frontispiece of Francis Barlow's second edition of *Aesop's Fables* published in 1687 and the man does not appear very old. LL5339 may be related to two other small embroidered satin panels in the collection along with which it was purchased, which do illustrate Aesop fables[1] and it may have been a book cover. The floral border is stylistically similar to embroidery of the first half of the seventeenth century. All three embroideries (LL5399, LL5426, LL5427) may be continental.

11 × 9 cm

Provenance: 'Property of a Gentleman'; sold Puttick and Simpson, 12 July 1906, lot 168, with the suggestion that the panel was probably once a book cover; bought M. Harris for £3.3.0. Kept at The Hill, Hampstead.

References: **1** See *The Fox and the Crow*, LL5426, and *The Wolf and the Crane*(?), LL5427.

Not previously catalogued.

LL5339

LL5426 (H52)

# The Fox and the Crow

Second(?) half of the seventeenth century

*Satin worked in silk in long and short, encroaching gobelin, and satin stitches, knots and couched metal thread.*

The picture probably illustrates the Aesop fable of 'The Fox and the Crow'. The fox tricks the bird out of its piece of cheese by telling it that it has a beautiful voice whereupon the bird, unused to such flattery, opens its mouth to sing and lets drop the food. The embroidery is similar enough to have had as its design source the prints by Hollar and Barlow which illustrated John Ogilby's popular *Aesop's Fables Paraphrased* of 1665 and 1666 (see fig. 6).[1] The distinctive use of metal thread and silk in a form of encroaching gobelin stitch could be an attempt to reproduce the qualities of Hollar and Barlow's etchings. LL5426, like its pair LL5427, may have been intended as a book cover or perhaps more likely, bearing in mind its small size and fragility, a panel for a casket door.

8.2 × 6 cm

Provenance: 'Property of a Gentleman'; sold Puttick and Simpson, 12 July 1906, lot 159; bought M. Harris for £1.9.0. and kept at The Hill, Hampstead.

References: **1** John Ogilby, *Aesop's Fables Paraphrased*, 1665, p. 9, pl. 5.

Not previously catalogued.

Figure 6 The illustration of 'The Fox and the Crow' from John Ogilby's *Aesop's Fables Paraphrased* of 1665 and 1666. (*Courtesy of the British Library*)

LL5426

LL5427 (H52)

## *The Wolf and the Crane(?)*

Second(?) half of the seventeenth century

*Satin worked with silk in florentine and long and short stitch, with couched metal thread and coil, knots and purl. The silk ground is very frayed.*

Like its pair (LL5426), this picture probably shows one of Aesop's fables.[1] It may illustrate the story of the wolf and crane, in which the wolf asks the crane to help him remove a bone from his throat in return for a reward. Once the crane has helped him the wolf maintains that the reward was that the crane's head had not been bitten off. However, the fable

9.6 × 6 cm

Provenance: 'Property of a Gentleman'; sold Puttick and Simpson, 12 July 1906, lot 160; bought M. Harris for £2.

References: **1** See also *The Old Man and Death(?) with a Floral Border* (LL5339).

Not previously catalogued.

LL5427

makes no mention of the soldier shown in the background of the embroidery and neither does the fable of 'The Fox and the Stork', which is the title it was given when it was sold with LL5339 and LL5426 in 1906.

## LL5248 (WHL4048)

### *Landscape with the Stoning of St Stephen*

Flemish, seventeenth century

*Satin worked with silk in a wide variety of fine straight stitches including long and short, split, running and satin stitch with very fine knots and speckling stitches. Some details are in herringbone and brickwork patterns. The threads used to create the dark clouds appear to have been painted before being couched down with pale threads in very fine straight stitches.*

When the picture was first catalogued along with its pair, LL5249, it was considered 'foreign', possibly South German, and dated *c.* 1675.[1] Nothing comparable seems to have been produced in Britain and it is possible that both embroidered

31.1 × 48.2 cm

Provenance: Miss Hilton Jones, 39 Norland Square, Holland Park; sold Christie's, 31 July 1919, lot 128 as a pair with LL5249, £73.10.0, bought through M. Harris and Sons, 5 August 1919 and originally displayed at The Hill, Hampstead.

References: **1** A. Carlyle Tait, 'English Needleworks in the Lady Lever Art Gallery – Part II', *Apollo*, vol. 45, July 1947 p. 3. **2** Vibeke Woldbye, 'Scharloth's Curious Cabinet', *Furniture History Society Journal*, 1985, vol. xxi, pp. 68–74. **3** See *Le Paysage Brabancon au XVII siècle*, Musées Royaux, Brussels

LL5248

pictures come from a professional workshop in Flanders, perhaps from somewhere like Antwerp which specialized in making cabinets faced with finely worked embroidered panels.[2] The thickly forested landscape with tall twisting trees and vistas through to lakeside settlements bears a strong resemblance to the work produced by the Flemish artist Gillis van Coninxloo III (1544–1607) and his followers such as David Vinckboons (1576–1630/3) and Denis van Alsloot (1570–1628).[3] Drawings by Vinckboons from the first decade of the seventeenth century are very close to the embroidered landscapes (LL5248, LL5249).[4] They usually depict biblical stories in which small figure groups, placed to one side, are surrounded by twisting trees and vegetation, and distant townscapes, viewed across water, dominate the horizon. In particular, an engraving by Nicolaes de Bruyn after Gillis van Coninxloo's *Landscape with the Prophet Elisha* has the same compositional format and a very similar mountainous village and mill.[5] The pair to LL5248, *Landscape with the Meeting of Jacob and Esau*, is after Gillis van Coninxloo.

13 October–5 December 1976, pp. 16, 20; *The Age of Brueghel: Netherlandish Drawings in the Sixteenth Century*, National Gallery of Art, Washington, 7 November 1986–18 January 1987. pp. 298–300. **4** Wegner and Pée, 'Die Zeichnungen des David Vinckboons', *Münchener Jahrbuch der Bildenden Kunst*, vol. 31, 1980, pp. 49, 58, 66, cat. 1, 11, 18. **5** Rijksprenten Kabinet, Amsterdam, *The Age of Brueghel* as above, p. 29, fig. 2.

1928 Catalogue no. 83.

## LL5249 (WHL4047)

## Landscape with the Meeting of Jacob and Esau

Flemish, seventeenth century

*Satin worked with silk in a wide variety of fine straight stitches including long and short, split, running and satin stitch and knots. Some straight stitches are in herringbone and brickwork patterns.*

Like its pair (LL5248) this embroidered picture was most probably embroidered in a Flemish or Dutch professional workshop. Its composition has been lifted almost completely from an engraving by Boetius a Bolswert after a painting by Gillis van Coninxloo, *c.* 1598[1] (see fig. 7).

32 × 48.5 cm

Provenance: Miss Hilton Jones, 39 Norland Square, Holland Park; sold Christie's, 31 July 1919, lot 128, as pair with LL5248 £73. 10. 0; bought through M. Harris and Sons, 5 August 1919 and originally displayed at The Hill, Hampstead.

References: **1** *Bulletin Musées Royaux des Beaux Arts de Belgique*, 1968, vol. 1/2, p. 33 fig. 20; Rijksmuseum Stichting, Amsterdam.

1928 Catalogue no. 81.

LL5249 (see also colour plate 5)

Figure 7 Engraving by Boetius Bolswert of the Meeting of Jacob and Esau, after a painting by Gillis van Coninxloo. (*Courtesy of the Rijksmuseum Stichting, Amsterdam*)

LL5253 (WHL4238)

**Flat silk and raised-work picture**

## *The Figure of Charity(?) with Three Children*

Flemish(?), mid-seventeenth century

*Satin worked with silk, metal thread and rouleau, parchment and patterned metal braid, in flat-work and high relief in stitches including long and short, satin, split and stem, with speckling and couched metal thread and cord, purl and bullion and attached spangles. A green selvedge strip runs down the right side.*

A composition with exactly the same group of a seated woman with three children, one holding a spoon the other a cross, is found reversed, within an oval scrolling cartouche, in the collection at Historic Deerfield, Massachusetts.[1] There the

33 × 43 cm

Provenance: purchased through F. Partridge, 22 June 1920, £35 and first displayed at The Hill, Hampstead.

References: **1** # 1048. Illustrated in M Swain's, *Embroidered Stuart Pictures*, Shire Album, 1990, p. 30. **2** See for example the Raphael Tondo, Terranuova Madonna, Berlin-Dahlem, *Catalogue of Paintings*, 1988, p. 342. **3** Patricia Wardle, 'Belgium: Ecclesiastical Embroidery in the Seventeenth Century', in Harriet Bridgeman and Elizabeth Drury ed., *Needlework an Illustrated History*, 1978, pp. 170–71. **4** Rockoxhuis, Antwerp,

LL5253

illustrated pl. 68, Bridgeman and Drury, as above. **5** Possibly when (according to a note in Gallery files) the tortoiseshell frame and a backing of 'manson cloth' [*sic*] was supplied by Pawsey and Payne.

1928 Catalogue no. 89.

central group is obviously meant to represent Charity, for it is set between figures representing Hope and Faith. LL5253 may also represent the virtue, but the grouping of the figures and the attributes they hold, is also very reminiscent of Italian paintings of the Virgin and Child with St John the Baptist and other infant saints. A comparison strengthened in the case of LL5253 by the rather Italianate landscape in the background, which is not present in the Deerfield embroidery, and the prominent raised pomegranates and cherub heads on the oval cartouche. As a Madonna and Child with infant saints it could be derived from a print after an early sixteenth-century Italian painting.[2] The oval cartouche and surround of cherubs, pomegranates and tulips is Flemish in style and appears to be of professional quality with the use of a great deal of metal thread.[3] A similar type of surround, though not as highly raised, can be seen on LL5281 (p. 55) and on a seventeenth-century Antwerp cabinet mounted with small panels of birds, animals and fruit baskets.[4] At some point LL5253 appears to have been substantially restored, though when purchased it was said to be a very fine piece.[5] The raised oval frame to the central picture may also have been attached later.

LL5280 (WHL3467)

**Silk-work picture with raised-work motifs**

## *Ahasuerus Receiving Esther*

Mid-seventeenth century

31.5 × 43.2 cm

Provenance: purchased through M. Harris and Sons, 24 April 1918, £29.10.0.

References: **1** According to Charlotte Mayhew's survey of seventeenth-century embroidery themes, in over 500 pieces in British and American collections 27 shared the Esther theme. **2** Roszika Parker, *The Subversive Stitch: Embroidery and the Making of the Feminine*, 1984, p. 98, fig. 56. **3** See Jost Amman, *Opera Josephi*, 1580 and tent stitch panel sold Sotheby's, 6 May 1987, lot 193. **4** 'And God changed the spirit of the King into mildness and in alarm he sprang up from his throne and raised her in his arms until she came to herself again and comforted her with reassuring words', Esther, apocryphal additions to Chapter 15. **5** V&A no. 338–1866. G. Wingfield Digby, *Victoria and Albert Museum, The Tapestry Collection; Medieval and Renaissance*, 1980, cat. no. 30. **6** See Jost Amman, 'Esther before Ahasuerus', *Opera Josephi*, 1580 and his illustrated *Biblia*.

1928 Catalogue no. 37.

*Satin worked with silk in long and short, detached buttonhole and lace stitches, split stitch, and French knots, with applied canvas slips in rococo and tent stitches and a small amount of purl, couched metal thread and beads; some motifs are raised with padding.*

The story of Esther was the most popular Old Testament theme among seventeenth-century embroideresses.[1] Esther represented one of those biblical women (Judith and Jael were others) whose courageous acts saved their people. Esther's dangerous but successful intervention on behalf of her fellow Jews, with her husband the Persian King Ahasuerus, symbolized women's beneficial power within marriage and was used to exemplify this in anti-misogynist tracts of the time.[2] It was also an image invoked during times of danger by persecuted minorities, such as the Puritans, the Royalists under the Republican Commonwealth, Dissenters, and Jacobites in Charles II and William and Mary's reign.

The sceptre scene, in which the king by extending his sceptre to Esther accepts her intervention and saves her life, was the most commonly depicted and embroidered event in the story of Esther,[3] but LL5280 may represent the event

LL5280

immediately after (related in the apocryphal additions to the
Book of Esther), when the king is described as raising her in
his arms and assuring her of her safety.[4] Esther's subsequent
reception is shown in the upper left corner of an early
sixteenth-century Brussels tapestry in the Victoria and Albert
Museum.[5] The lack of gifts or crown would suggest the
figure does not represent the Queen of Sheba, representations
of whom are often confused with Esther. The courtier in
classical military garb, probably here representing Esther's
relative, Mordecai, was a stock motif in Stuart embroidery
and may be derived from a late sixteenth-century print,
where this type of military dress and posture are common.[6]
As is typical in these pictures the king and other figures are
clothed in contemporary dress.

LL5281 (WHL4066)

## Silk-work picture with raised-work framing

## *The Revenge of Queen Thomyris over Cyrus the Great*

Mid-seventeenth century

43 × 53 cm

Provenance: purchased through M. Harris and Sons, 3 September 1919, £65; first displayed at The Hill, Hampstead.

References: **1** Herodotus, *Histories*, Book I, 205–14. **2** M.C. Garcia Gainza, 'Un programa de "Mujeres Ilustres" del Renacimiento', *Goya*, 1987, vol. 199–200, pp. 6–13. **3** V&A T.14–1971; Bath, Holburne Menstrie Museum, F. 97,

*Satin worked with silk in long and short, satin, split, stem and speckling stitches, with French knots, cut silk pile, and coiled silk pile; and also with metal threads, wire, purl and coil in patterned laid and couched work, with applied seed pearls and silk-wrapped parchment. The satin edges are badly frayed.*

The embroidered picture is a fairly close copy of a Rubens painting (now in Boston Museum of Fine Arts), depicting the

LL5281

revenge of Queen Thomyris over her sworn enemy Cyrus the Great of Persia, as related by Herodotus.[1] The queen in order to avenge the suicide of her son, caused by Cyrus's trickery, had the king slain in battle and ordered that his head be severed and dipped in a container of blood. The scene itself was considered symbolic of justice, while Queen Thomyris of the Massagetae was one of the famous women warriors of the Renaissance.[2] There are at least three embroideries derived from the Rubens picture of *c.* 1626. Two of them, one in the V&A and one dated 1655 at Bath[3] are almost exact copies of the Paulus Pontius engraving of the Rubens work, published in 1630[4] (see fig. 8). The quality of the embroidered reproduction suggests that they could both be examples of a professional workshop. Unlike LL5281, both have the same Latin motto running along the bottom edge of the rectangular panel and in neither is the scene set within an embroidered oval cartouche and outer border.[5] However, the third panel, formerly in the collection of Baron William Plender (1861–1946), is much closer to LL5281 in design and quality of work, which is less finely detailed in the representation of features.[6] In both cases the narrative scene is set within a similar raised purl frame and the border is embroidered with the same animals, a leopard, a lion and eagle-like birds, though the Plender panel does not have the prominent corner flower motifs of tulip, marigold, iris and daffodil or the raised cherubs found on LL5281.[7] Both the Lever and the Plender panels depict the scene the same way round as the painting, with the queen on the left rather than reversed as in Pontius' engraving. As both needlework pictures replace the twisted salomonic columns, balcony and plain floor of the painting with fluted columns, wall and mosaic floor, their designs are most probably derived from either an engraving reversing the Pontius print or adapted from a professionally embroidered panel, rather than from the painting itself. Overall LL5281 is a more faithful rendering of the Rubensian scene than the Plender panel, though the foreground dog is a distinctly different type to that in the painting. Also introduced to the centre of the scene is a mustachioed man looking out at the viewer. He neither features in the painting or engraving nor in any other of the embroideries and may well have been inserted at the whim of LL5281's designer or embroiderer.

Figure 8 Paulus Pontius' engraving of Rubens' *Revenge of Queen Thomyris over Cyrus the Great*, published in 1630

(48.3 × 61 cm). A further one is in a private collection in New Zealand according to V&A files. **4** C. Rooses-Reulens, *L'Oeuvre de Rubens*, vol. IV, pp. 3–5, pl. 252. **5** The raised-work cherub-head motifs were used particularly in the mid-1630s, while the oval cartouche with stylized foliage and palms bears a slight resemblance to the panel of 1654–60 at Blair Castle, designed by John Nelham. P. Wardle, 'English Pictorial Embroidery of the 17th century', *Antiques International*, 1969, p. 286; M. Swain, 'John Nelham's needlework panel', *Bulletin of the Needle and Bobbin Club*, 1982, p. 8. **6** 'An Exhibition of Old English Needlework', *Old Furniture*, vol. II, 1927, p. 115. Plender's was a well-known embroidery collection, a very small part of which, excluding the *Thomyris* panel was sold at auction Sotheby's, 26 June 1970, lots 31–4. **7** In the Metropolitan Museum another embroidery adapted from a print after a Rubens work, *The Feast of Herod* also depicts the scene within a slightly plainer oval compartment surmounted by cherubs' heads and surrounded by animal motifs typical of the amateur embroideries of the second half of the century. Y. Hackenbroch, *Untermyer Collection*, fig. 87, pl. 58. The embroidery was formerly in the collection of Lord Tweedsmouth. The painting *The Feast of Herod*, Edinburgh, National Galleries of Scotland, Inv. no. 2193, was in Lever's collection when he purchased LL5281, but he was unaware that the embroidery also represented a Rubens painting.

1928 Catalogue no. 57.

# Raised-work Pictures

LL5270 (WHL1346)

*The Story of David and Bathsheba*

Dated 1665

LL5270 (see also colour plate 6)

*Satin worked with silk, metal thread and silk-covered wooden moulds for fruit and statuary, with examples of a variety of flat, couched and raised stitches including long and short, stem, chain, running, detached buttonhole and lace. Pieces of mica, metal rouleau and loops, purl, seed pearls, coiled silk pile, parchment, bobbin lace and woven textile have been applied to the satin ground, which has a green selvedge.*

The embroidery is dated on the letter proffered by the maid, which is also inscribed 'Bashee boy' [*sic*]. The story of David and Bathsheba (2 Samuel:11–12) was a commonly embroidered one. At least nine versions in raised- and canvas-work are known in major British and American collections.[1] A number of these,[2] in common with LL5270, depict the whole story using five scenes whose figures were lifted from four engravings published in Gerard de Jode's *Thesaurus Sacrarum Historiarum Veteris Testamenti*, Antwerp, 1585 (figs. 9–12).[3] They all place Bathsheba bathing as the central scene with the rest of the story related through surrounding vignettes: King David catching sight of Bathsheba and arranging an adulterous meeting with her (top left); David attempting to

43 × 53 cm

Provenance: D.L. Isaacs and Sons, 23 June 1914; purchased Lever, 15 July 1914,[6] £48 and first displayed at The Hill, Hampstead.

Exhibited: Platt Hall, Manchester, 21 June – 7 November 1955.

References: **1** V&A T.253–1927 dated 1661, T.52–1934 dated 1656; Fitzwilliam, Cambridge T.5–1954 dated 1700; Metropolitan Museum, Untermyer Collection, Hackenbroch, fig. 85; Burrell Collection, Glasgow 29/58; Minneapolis Institute of Arts, no. 47.1; Sir Frederick Richmond's collection, sold Christie's, London, 23 June 1987, lots 115, 121; Frank Partridge and Sons, July 1934, fig. 1. **2** LL5270 has closest affinities with the pieces in the V&A, T.52–1934, Fitzwilliam, Burrell, and Untermyer collection. It differs from these only in slight rearrangements of the disposition of the figures and differing fountains. **3** M.H. Swain, 'Embroidered Pictures from Engraved Sources', *Apollo*, 1977, p. 122–3. **4** Kerrich, *Catalogue of Marten van Heemskerk*, 1829, p. 4. **5** G. de Tervarent, *Attributs et Symboles dans l'art Profane*, 1959, vol. II, p. 334. **6** LL5270 must have been one of the earliest purchases after the arson attack on The Bungalow, Rivington which destroyed much of Lever's original embroidery collection.

1928 Catalogue no. 15.

Figure 9   David catching sight of Bathsheba bathing and arranging an adulterous meeting with her, from Gerard de Jode's *Thesaurus Sacrarum Historiarum Veteris Testamenti*. (*Courtesy of the British Museum*)

Figure 10   David discussing the conduct of the war with Uriah, from Gerard de Jode's *Thesaurus Sacrarum Historiarum Veteris Testamenti*. (*Courtesy of the British Museum*)

Figure 11   Uriah's death in battle, from Gerard de Jode's *Thesaurus Sacrarum Historiarum Veteris Testamenti*. (*Courtesy of the British Museum*)

Figure 12   Nathan the prophet relates the parable of the poor man and his ewe lamb to David, from Gerard de Jode's *Thesaurus Sacrarum Historiarum Veteris Testamenti*. (*Courtesy of the British Museum*)

persuade Bathsheba's husband Uriah to stay home (top right) and subsequently engineering his death in battle (lower left); and the prophet Nathan relating the parable of the poor man and his ewe lamb which leads David to repent his sins (lower right). The frequency of the narrative as a subject for embroidery may stem from its use as an illustration of the seventh commandment, thou shalt not commit adultery.[4]

Unlike LL5270, none of the other embroidered versions have a border in which four allegorical or mythological figures are shown within oval cartouches interspersed with animals, birds, insects and flowers, including cornflowers, carnations, tulips, fritillaries and strawberry plants. Macquoid identified the figures as Venus, Juno, Diana and Ceres without specifying who was who. However, the additional attribute of a dragon or salamander on which Venus sits suggests that the goddesses might also represent the four elements:[5] Venus, along the top border, representing fire and (clockwise) Juno, air, Diana, water, and Ceres, earth.

## LL5229 (WHL2795)

### The Drowning of the Pharaoh in the Red Sea

Worked by Damaris Pearse, c. 1669–75[1]

*Satin worked with silks, metal thread and rouleau, purl, cut silk pile, and attached spangles, mica and seed pearls in long and short, stem, split, and running stitches, French and bullion knots and a wide variety of detached buttonhole and lace stitches over wooden moulds and raised wool stuffing. Green selvedge strips run down both sides.*

Although LL5229 is not signed[2] there are good reasons to believe that it was worked by Mrs Damaris Pearse (1659–79), the pious daughter of a Nonconformist minister in Ermington, Devon. When purchased the embroidery was accompanied by a small leather-bound book, *A Present for Youth and an Example for the Aged: or the Remains of Damaris Pearse*, published by William Pearse in 1683 in memory of his daughter's Christian life and devotion, and as an encouragement to others.[3] The book's introduction describes Damaris as being, 'but young and of very plain and ordinary education, (only taught fine needle-work, wherein she was ingenious)'. Her attributes are expanded upon elsewhere in the book:

Concerning her endowments, and attainments, besides her skill in, and her ingenious dexterity, ready invention, quick dispatch, and curious putting out of hand, the choicest sort of needleworks and most other kinds of fine works, such as young women often are exercised in whether with silk,

34 × 55.5 cm

Provenance: purchased through D.L. Isaacs, 25 May 1916, £50; displayed at Thornton Manor.

Literature: A. Carlyle Tait, 'English Needleworks in the Lady Lever Art Gallery – Part I', *Apollo*, 1947 p. 115; Patricia Wardle, 'English Pictorial Embroidery of the Seventeenth Century', *Antiques International*, 1969, p. 279, illus. 9; H. Bridgeman and E. Drury ed., *Needlework, an Illustrated History*, 1978, p. 45. Lanto Synge, *Antique Needlework*, 1982, p. 75; Muriel Best, *Stumpwork: Historical and Contemporary Raised Embroidery*, 1987, p. 43 fig. 17; Margaret Swain, *Shire Album No. 246: Embroidered Stuart Pictures*, 1990, pp. 28–9, illus.

References: 1 For four years before her death in 1679 Damaris Pearse was severely ill making it unlikely that LL5229 could have been embroidered later than 1675 when she was 16 years old. 2 LL5229 was last unframed sometime before the 1928 catalogue was published. It was then said to be unsigned. 3 The Pearses appear to have been a long-standing local Ermington family; letter, Ann Chiswell, 17 March 1989; Edmund Calamy, *Account of the Ministers and others Rejected and Silenced*, 1660–62, pp. 340–45; A.G. Matthews ed., *Calamy Revised*, 1934, p. 24. 4 *A Present for Youth*, as above, p. 57, p. 18, p. 66. 5 A photograph taken in the 1930s(?) in the Gallery's files shows Moses' sceptre in place on the embroidery. The sceptre is now lost. 6 John Morill, 'The Stuart Period' in *The Oxford Illustrated History of England*, 1986, p. 327. 7 Alexander Globe, *Peter Stent, London Printseller*, Vancouver, 1985, p. 116 no. 399. 8 Simon Schama, *The Embarrassment of Riches*, 1987, p. 104–5.

LL529 (see also colour plate 7)

thread or other materials, so great variety, and plenty and so excellently done, as is scarce credible of one so young, as when by her made and finished; and as in these, so she was skilled in writing (right spelling) reading, and of good understanding, and all learnt by little instruction.

The book's text, consisting mainly of speeches Damaris made to her family during a long illness, throws some further light on the type of embroidery she created and, in a brief aside, the economic reasons behind her work: 'I have many good books and I made many ★shifts (that is according to the flesh) to get them:

★She privately earned some small matter with her needle (when able) and it was to bestow it in books, as she did every penny thereof.'

Damaris Pearse would, therefore, have been quite capable of producing something of the quality of LL5229. It could be possible that, like the embroidered women's smocks or shifts, it was made for sale, were it not for another statement in the book indicating the importance Damaris attached to the particular scene of the Israelites' safe crossing of the Red Sea. Like many children of the age, and particularly as a dissenting minister's daughter, she was well versed in the scriptures, especially the Old Testament chapters, which she would often run through in their entirety:

9 A. Zweite, *Marten de Vos*, 1980, Cat. 107, p. 1136. Another Marten de Vos painting combines the drowning with the scene on land (Zweite, cat. Z6 p. 1149) but is not the source for the embroidery. Neither do the foreground figures bear much resemblance to de Jode's illustration to Exodus 12 for the *Thesaurus Sacrarum* and there are only slight similarities with a print by J.V. Stalburch after Frans Floris, 1556, F.W.H. Holstein, *Dutch and Flemish Etchings and Engravings, 1450–1700*, vol. 28, p. 38. 10 G. De Tervarent, *Attributs et Symboles dans l'art Profane, 1450–1600*, vol. II, p. 356.

1928 Catalogue no. 58.

Figure 13   The Israelites safely across the Red Sea, Moses calling on God to close up the sea, from Gerard de Jode's *Thesaurus Sacrarum Historiarum Veteris Testamenti.* (*Courtesy of the British Museum*)

Figure 14   The drowning of Pharaoh in the Red Sea, from Gerard de Jode's *Thesaurus Sacrarum Historiarum Veteris Testamenti.* (*Courtesy of the British Museum*)

Once she talked long concerning the Israelite bondage in Egypt, and miraculous deliverance from thence, and their passage thorow the Red Sea, and preservation and supportment in the wilderness, and safe conduct into Canaan: (As she proceeded besides other hints, she made some observation on Aarons making the Molten Calf, both condemning the sin, and likewise, showing how people now living should improve it, that it should teach all to be watchful against sin, not only inferiors, but also those in high place and dignity: Considering what Aaron was, and yet how grievously he sinned.)[4]

The Israelites are shown enjoying the fruits of Canaan, in the left-hand corner of LL5229 while Moses, with Aaron beside him, calls down God's power with his sceptre to drown the Pharaoh and his troops (Exodus 14, 15).[5] The underlying anti-clericalism and egalitarianism of Damaris's comments above indicate the importance to her of the scene depicted in the embroidery. The drowning of the Pharaoh had particular significance to followers of Cromwell in the Commonwealth period, who associated it with the execution of Charles I, and saw Cromwell as their Moses.[6] It is quite possible that it was meant for the Pearse family home, to be displayed as a picture or used on the lid of a work-box.

As for the design source of LL5229, the central scene of the Pharaoh overwhelmed along with his chariot and bodyguard is almost directly derived from an engraving illustrating Exodus 14 in Gerard de Jode's *Thesaurus Sacrarum Historiarum Veteris Testamenti* first published in Amsterdam 1585 (see figs. 13, 14). The *Thesaurus* itself became a principal source of illustrations for the *Piscator Bible*, first published in Amsterdam in 1643, and an unlocated engraving of the *Pharaoh Drowning in the Red Sea* was advertised for sale by one of London's leading print sellers in 1662 and 1673.[7] This particular biblical event was for patriotic reasons a popular subject among Dutch printmakers, from whom many known embroidery design sources derived, for they related it to the Dutch defeat of the Spanish troops by flooding their besieged land.[8] So far the print source for the subsidiary scenes of the resting Israelites with Moses calling on God's power (in the left-hand corner) has not been found, although the woman suckling her child, in the background of the embroidered group, may be based on a similar suckling figure taken from a work by Marten de Vos painted in 1602.[9] The intrusion on the scene of a mermaid, above the Pharaoh's head, might be a whimsical introduction by Damaris Pearse of a motif commonly found on embroidered mirror-frames and pictures of the period. But bearing in mind Damaris's Protestant and dissenting background it could symbolize life's adversities or be a reference to the Harlot of the Apocalypse, seated upon the waters combing her hair and admiring the reflection in her mirror.[10]

LL5236 (WHL3426)

## Cavalier and Lady with Central Vignette of Men Fishing

Second half of the seventeenth century

*Satin worked with silk and metal thread in detached lace stitches, long and short stitch, with purl, running stitch, French knots and other raised stitches over padding, with silk-wound parchment, padded, knitted fabric and an applied canvas tent stitch motif in the centre, with attached mica and bits of woven cloth.*

When acquired LL5236 was described as the 'Court of Elizabeth' and the figures of the cavalier and the lady were

52 × 59.2 cm

Provenance: Mrs J.W. Anson; presented 31 July 1861 to the Royal Dramatic College [*sic*];[3] purchased through M. Harris and Sons, 1 March 1918, £100; displayed at The Hill, Hampstead.

References: **1** *Connoisseur*, vol. XVI, November 1906, p. 180, illus. p. 178; also see a similar picture with central vignette,

LL5236

National Museums of Scotland, A1987.143 and unmounted slip, V&A, T.132a–n.1878. Lever also owned other pictures similar to the central vignette, see Appendix AG1, lot 79. **2** This was probably done after Lever's purchase. **3** Information found in old Lady Lever inventory. The college cannot be identified with either RADA or the London Academy of Music and Drama.

1928 Catalogue no. 22.

26.7 × 28 cm

Provenance: purchased as one of a pair with LL5238 through M. Harris and Sons, 24 April 1918, £40.

References: **1** Daniel 6:16–22; *Bel and the Dragon* verse 36. **2** F.W.H. Hollstein, *Dutch and Flemish Etchings and Engravings, 1450–1700*, vol. VII, p. 170.

1928 Catalogue no. 19.

described as the Earl of Leicester and Queen Elizabeth. This fanciful description may have been attached when the embroidery was owned by the 'Royal Dramatic College'. The title could also acknowledge the fact that the central tent stitch cartouche might be earlier than the surrounding work, though almost certainly not datable to the sixteenth century as suggested by the Macquoid catalogue. A comparable central cartouche depicting a fisherman, shepherd and shepherdess surrounded by tent-stitch motifs was at Hengrave Hall, Suffolk.[1] LL5236 has suffered a great deal of damage. Much of its original silk satin ground has rotted away and subsequently been replaced with a modern backing,[2] while the canvas flowers have lost most of their tent-stitch work.

## LL5237 (WHL3463)

### *Daniel in the Lions' Den with Habakkuk and the Angel*

Mid-seventeenth century

*Satin worked with silk in long and short stitch, satin and running stitch with a variety of purl and some padded figures with French and bullion knots and attached glass beads for the lions' eyes.*

The story of Habakkuk's flight through the air, guided by an angel, to save Daniel from the lions' den, does not appear in the Bible but was related in the apocryphal and popular *Bel*

LL5237

and the Dragon.[1] It was not a commonly embroidered subject although the two scenes were sometimes depicted together on the same engraving, with Daniel and the lions in the foreground and Habakkuk with the angel in the distance, as occurs in the engraving by Jacob de Gheyn II (1565–1629) after Dirk Barentsz.[2] This does not form the basis for LL5237. Part of the design around Daniel's head and arms and the 'cave' or rock behind him have not been embroidered over; the panel was probably left unfinished.

The embroidery was acquired along with LL5238, *Venus and Adonis with Cupid* (p. 39), which also has the same type of mount.

LL5259 (X795)

## Lady and Gentleman Singing and Playing the Lute with the Seasons

Third quarter of the seventeenth century

*Much restored and worn satin worked with silk in satin, long and short, stem and split stitch with French knots and a variety of detached buttonhole, lace and couched stitches in silks and metal thread with applied silver thread brocade, cut silk pile, mica and glass beads.*

The central melodious couple are seventeenth-century forerunners of the typical arcadian couple of the next century.

31 × 41 cm

Provenance: purchased through D.L. Isaacs, 20 August 1915, £18, at the same time as LL5381 (p. 111), and first displayed at Thornton Manor.

References: **1** V&A *Catalogue of Wallpapers*, p. 97, no. 26 showing the Arms of the Haberdashers' Company, E203, 204–1913. **2** M. Jourdain 'Packwood House and its Collection', *Apollo*, vol. 43 (1946), p. 5, fig. VI. Stent and Overton advertised four plates of the seasons by George Glover (unlocated) in 1653, 1662 and 1673. Alexander Globe, *Peter Stent, London Printseller*, no. 486. **3** Mary Schoeser, *Printed Handkerchiefs*, Museum of London, June–September 1988, figs. 5, 6.

1928 Catalogue no. 43.

Figure 15 The Four Seasons, from a block-printed piece of wallpaper. (*Courtesy of the Victoria and Albert Museum*)

LL5259

The representation of the four seasons placed in the corners of the embroidered panel are very similar to those found on a block-printed piece of wallpaper *c.* 1689–1702 in the Victoria and Albert Museum (fig. 15),[1] even down to the cat seated on one side of Winter's blazing fire. Both wallpaper and needlework depict Autumn pruning trees rather than the more usual continental scene of the wine harvest. When the printed wallpaper was discovered as a lining to a drawer it was thought that it might have been of the type sold by Peter Stent.[2] All the figures except Summer are similar to those found on a mirror frame in the collection, LL5222 (p. 197). Neither pieces relate to the representations of the months after Wenceslas Hollar on a silk handkerchief, printed *c.* 1675–80, in the Museum of London.[3] LL5259 has been mounted and padded as if it were a cushion.

LL5260 (WHL3462)

## Paris and Pallas (Athene) with the Four Continents

Second half of the seventeenth century

*Satin worked with silk in satin, long and short, stem, detached buttonhole and lace stitches and other surface and raised stitches with attached purl, mica and silk-wrapped parchment strips simulating laurel wreaths. The satin has split in places and has been conserved by mounting on linen backing. The selvedge is green.*

The smooth cream-coloured satin on which the figures have been worked is divided up into square and oblong panels drawn in ink. These divisions suggest that the panels which form LL5260 were originally intended to be mounted as a mirror frame; the four continents in the corners with the central couple along the top and bottom. As the panels were never cut out for use they have retained their identifying titles, written in ink below the roundels and ovals. The two central figures are named as Pallas (Athene), the goddess of all the arts, including domestic embroidery, wearing her plumed helmet, and Paris, the Trojan prince and shepherd. Originally the raised-work figure of Paris held a three-dimensional 'spud' (used to protect sheep from marauding animals) to denote his shepherd's occupation, but (as with a figure in LL5267) this is now lost and only the drawing remains on the fabric ground. The four continents are (from upper left clockwise) America with bow and arrow, Europe holding a book (Bible?) and sceptre, Asia with a veil and censer and Africa seated in front of the globe. The figures are not exactly

30 × 71 cm

Provenance: the Misses Lawrence; sold for the benefit of the Red Cross Society and the Order of St John of Jerusalem, Christie's, 12 April 1918, lot 686; purchased through M. Harris and Sons, £231 along with the raised-work panel LL5265, p. 70.[2]

References: **1** Christie's, London, 23 June 1987, lot 168, pl. 8. **2** Lever complained of the artificially high prices brought by the Red Cross sale saying that he would 'rather have let the needleworks go past me'. Letter in archives 15 April 1918. LL5265 was also presented for sale by the Misses Lawrence, Louisa and Mary, sisters to Sir Trevor Lawrence (see LL5101 p. 84) and friends of Viscountess Wolseley (see LL5397–8, LL5410, LL5420–21 pp. 257–9, 186, 269, 271).

1928 Catalogue no. 29.

LL5260 (see also colour plate 8)

equivalent to those found on a Lady Lever mirror frame (LL5219, p. 193), which appear to be based on a set of prints published by William Marshall, but they are almost exactly the same as those on a casket formerly in Sir Frederick Richmond's collection.[1]

LL5267 (WHL3522)

## Apollo(?) and Minerva(?) Surrounded by Cherub Heads

Third quarter of the seventeenth century

*Satin worked with silk, metal thread and coloured beads in fine long and short, satin and stem stitch with French knots, detached buttonhole stitch and purl, and applied padded tent stitch motifs, with silk-wrapped parchment simulating a leafy oval border.*

When catalogued in 1928, this embroidery was described as a covering to a casket and titled Apollo (the god of creative arts)

37.5 × 54.5 cm

Provenance: purchased through Cyril Andrade, 10 May 1918, £60 and first displayed at The Hill, Hampstead.

Exhibited: lent to East Riddleston Hall, Yorkshire, 29 June 1950.

LL5267 (see also colour plate 9)

and Minerva (the goddess of domestic arts including weaving and embroidery), although no identifying names had been provided on its purchase. Apollo is sometimes shown, holding a shepherd's 'spud' and Minerva is usually shown armed with shield and helmet. However, the figures could also represent Mercury, the messenger of the gods, wearing his winged helmet and holding a baton, and the princely shepherd Paris, whose spud has slipped in front of his face. Another raised-work panel in the collection (LL5260) specifically identified a figure with a spud as Paris.[1] A similar, unidentified, helmeted figure holding a baton is found on the inside to a door of a cabinet on a stand, dated about 1670, at Groombridge Place, Sussex.[2] The way in which the embroidery is disposed on LL5267 makes it unlikely that it was meant to cover a casket or a mirror frame (like LL5260) but it was obviously not intended as a picture. When sold to Lever, LL5267 was said to be 'a very rare and unique specimen'.[3] Lever had, in fact, less than a month earlier, purchased a similar piece, LL5260.

References: **1** Other embroidered figures holding this individual looking spade are also identified as Paris. Nevinson, *Catalogue of English Domestic Embroidery in the Victoria and Albert Museum*, 1938, T.142–1931. **2** Exhibited *Treasure Houses of Great Britain*, Washington, 1985–86, cat. no. 75, illus. p. 151. **3** Letter from Cyril Andrade, 4 May 1918, in Gallery archives.

1928 Catalogue no. 32.

LL5261 (WHL4308)

## The Return of Jephthah from the War

Second half of the seventeenth century

*Satin worked with silk and metal thread in long and short, stem, and split stitch, with purl and couched metal thread and strips and silks in a lattice pattern, with a few attached padded, tent stitch motifs, braided silk ribbons, spangles and a border of silver lace.*

35.5 × 42.5 cm

Provenance: unknown. Found at The Hill, Hampstead, 29 August 1921, possibly acquired sometime after November 1912.

References: **1** For example Christie's, 23 June 1987, lot 73, formerly Sir Frederick Richmond's collection; Y. Hackenbroch, *English Needlework in the Irwin Untermyer Collection*, 1960, fig. 64, pl. 41. **2** See Y. Hackenbroch, above, fig. 64, pl. 41 for an explicit linking of the two stories; and 'The Old House', Clavering, Essex where the two were frescoed on to the staircase *c.* 1690. **3** Letter to the Hebrews 11:32.

1928 Catalogue no. 59.

LL5261

The scene depicted derives from the Old Testament story of the warrior Jephthah (Judges 11:34–9), who in order to secure victory in battle made the rash promise to God that he would sacrifice the first one to greet him on his return home. The scene in which he arrived to be met by his only daughter and her companions, was embroidered fairly frequently in the seventeenth century, though usually with many more figures than employed here.[1] The story was regarded as the female equivalent of Abraham's sacrifice of Isaac,[2] though more tragic, as Jephthah ultimately fulfilled his vow and was thus included in the category of great people of the faith.[3]

The contemporary metal lace trim to the picture suggests that LL5261 may originally have been the front of a sachet.

## LL5268 (WHL4151)

### Jacob, Rachel, Leah and Laban

Second half of the seventeenth century

*Worn and perished satin worked with silk and metal thread in long and short, stem and tent stitch with detached buttonhole and lace stitch and applied seed pearls. Mounted in a painted box frame.*

Theresa Macquoid suggested that this picture depicted the Old Testament episode of Jacob's meeting with Rachel and Leah (Genesis 29:15–20). No title was attached to the embroidery on its purchase. Laban is shown in the corner, with his camels, offering Jacob his elder daughter Leah in marriage instead of the younger, Rachel with whom Jacob was in love. This would account for the rather startled expression on Jacob's face. In the seventeenth century the story of Jacob and Rachel was treated as a moral example illustrating the constancy of love. Another finer representation of the theme is LL5233 (p. 36).

31.8 × 42.5 cm

Provenance: purchased through M. Harris and Sons, 11 March 1920, £58.14.0, and first displayed at The Hill, Hampstead.

1928 Catalogue no. 66.

LL5268

LL5265 (WHL3461)

## Two Ladies under Canopies

Second half of the seventeenth century

*Satin worked with silk and metal thread in long and short, satin, brick and running stitch with a wide variety of applied bobbin lace, detached buttonhole and needle-weaving stitches, tassels, purl and ravelled silk, with other raised stitches. Pieces of lace and embroidered textile have been applied over padding. The right-hand panel has a green selvedge.*

In common with the other raised-work picture purchased by Lever from the same collection,[1] the two figures along with the small waterscapes beneath them were probably originally mounted around the sides of a mirror. After they were detached from the mirror they were tacked together to form one picture. As one of the ladies holds what could be an apple (whose threads have rotted), and the other was intended to hold a sceptre (now lost), the two figures may have been meant to represent the goddesses, Venus and Juno. In several areas the embroiderer has not followed the original pattern drawn on the silk.

44.5 × 34.5 cm

Provenance: the Misses Lawrence; sold Christie's, 12 April 1918, lot 685 for the benefit of the Red Cross Society and the Order of St John of Jerusalem; purchased through M. Harris and Sons, 24 April 1918, £162.15.0; first displayed at The Hill, Hampstead.

Exhibited: lent to East Riddleston Hall, Yorkshire, 29 June 1950.

References: 1 LL5260 (p. 66), the Misses Lawrence. Both pictures are framed in the same wooden frames, carved with acorns, and both are rendered in a very similar variety of stitches, though the quality of work in LL5260 is finer.

1928 Catalogue no. 65.

LL5271 (WHL3732)

## Judith and Holofernes

Second half of the seventeenth century

*Satin worked with silk, metal thread in long and short, split and stem stitches with a variety of knotted, couched and raised lace and detached buttonhole stitches, and applied silk-covered wooden moulds and purl, beads, spangles, seed pearls, and cut silk pile.*

Judith is shown having beheaded Holofernes, the Assyrian general who had attempted to rape her and laid siege to her people's city. Her maid-servant approaches with a sack in which to hide the general's head. The sword and the head, presumably both three-dimensional, have been lost. The story of this patriotic heroine from the Old Testament Apocrypha (Judith 13) was frequently illustrated throughout the sixteenth and seventeenth centuries. The gruesome decapitation was a favourite scene. The main figures of LL5271 were adapted from the foreground and some background elements of the print published by Gerard de Jode in *Thesaurus Sacrarum Historiarum Veteris Testamenti*, Antwerp, 1585 (fig. 16). The story's culminating scene when Holofernes' head is hung on a pole from the battlements is shown in the embroidery's top right corner, where the unworked ink

22 × 33 cm

Provenance: purchased through M. Harris and Sons, 5 February 1919, £75.

References: 1 Erhard Schoen, *c.* 1533, *Illustrated Bartsch* vol. 12, p. 242; Hans Sebald Beham, *Illustrated Bartsch*, vol. 15 p. 158; Jost Amman *Biblia* and *Opera Josephi*, 1580, *Illustrated Bartsch*, vol. 20 pt. 1, p. 298, fig. 1. 96; and Virgil Solis's picture-book version of the Bible, *Biblische Figuren* published in 1560. 2 See T. Heywood, *The Exemplary Lives and Memorable Acts of the Nine Most Worthy Women of the World*, 1640, in which the inscription under her image ran:

> Where ever was such a Virago Knowne,
> As Judeth, shee who single and alone
> W$^{th}$ his owne sword Great HOLOPHERNES slewe,
> By w$^{ch}$ the ASSIRIAN hoast shee overthrewe.

The printed image was being advertised for sale by Stent and Overton in 1662 and 1673.

1928 Catalogue no. 16.

LL5265

LL5271

under-drawing for the head is visible. The scene is not included in de Jode's engraving but features prominently in several other printed examples from which the embroidery designer could have borrowed.[1] Judith was one of the 'women worthies' of biblical, classical and Jewish history[2] and, as such, she was a pre-eminent example to set before young ladies of female valour and virtue triumphing over male vice.

Figure 16   Judith and Holofernes published by Gerard de Jode in the *Thesaurus Sacrarum Historiarum Veteris Testamenti*. (*Courtesy of the British Museum*)

LL5272 (WHL4063)

## *Peace(?) and Plenty with Lion and Griffin*

Second half of the seventeenth century

33 × 43 cm

Provenance: purchased through M. Harris and Sons, 3 September 1919 and first displayed at The Hill, Hampstead.

References: **1** G. de Tervarent, *Attributs et symboles dans l'art profane*, 1959, vol. II, p. 282. **2** Y. Hackenbroch, *English Needlework in the Irwin Untermyer Collection*, 1960, fig. 115, pl. 80.

1928 Catalogue no. 11.

*Satin worked with silk and metal thread in a wide variety of fine lace and detached buttonhole stitches and knots with attached purl, glass beads, and glass griffin's beak, seed pearls, and lace with some long and short and stem stitch and twisted silk pile. The right-hand edge has a green selvedge.*

The two ladies in seventeenth-century dress who stand holding a cornucopia of fruits and a bunch of leaves and branches were identified by Macquoid as the goddesses Ceres and Venus; the latter's bouquet was considered to represent the myrtle plant, which is closely associated with Venus.[1] If the plant is identified as an olive branch the two women probably represent allegorical figures of Peace and Abundance. The raised-work picture in the Untermyer collection of two ladies facing each other, which is said to be similar to LL5272, is not related to the Lady Lever piece.[2]

LL5272

LL5274 (WHL2878)

## The Reception of the Queen of Sheba by King Solomon

Second half of the seventeenth century

*Satin worked with silk, metal thread and purl in long and short, satin, running, and stem stitch with French knots and applied canvas motifs worked with wool and silk in tent and rococo stitches and attached seed pearls and mica with a variety of detached buttonhole and lace stitches over raised wool padding.*

The composition of LL5274 is the reverse of LL5247 (silk-work picture p. 44) and worked with a much cruder, more schematic delineation of the figures' features and bodies. The

43 × 52 cm

Provenance: purchased through D.L. Isaacs, 26 July 1916 and displayed at The Hill, Hampstead.

Exhibited: Platt Hall, Manchester, 21 June – 7 November 1955.

1928 Catalogue no. 24.

LL5274

four large canvas floral slips applied in the corners, (a peony(?), an anenome, a narcissus and a tulip) and the carnation embroidered onto the satin on the left, are of a size and degree of detail to have been adapted from an illustrated botanical book or florilegium, such as Crispin de Passe's *Hortus Floridus*, published in 1614 in four different languages including English.

LL5276 (WHL3189)

## Lady Holding Flower and Gentleman with Bird on Wrist

Second third of the seventeenth century

*Satin worked entirely with green-coloured looped metal purl with some detached lace stitch, braiding, couched silk threads, applied beads and mica. The original silk covering the wooden face and arm moulds has perished.*

The lady and gentleman are surrounded by the floral, animal, insect and architecture motifs commonly found on pictures of couples sometimes considered engagement pictures (see LL5295; LL5343 pp. 29, 91). A handwritten label on the picture's back states that it was worked by the 'twice Greatmother of George Washington of America'.[1] Washington's great-great-grandmother was Amphilis Twigden who married the Reverend Lawrence Washington in 1632 when he became rector of Purleigh, Essex. She died in 1654, two years after her husband had died a pauper having been turned out of his living for royalist sympathies. Sulgrave Manor, the Washington family's ancestral home also owns a raised-work picture with animals, fruit and flowers and painted figures of Adam and Eve, dated to about 1640, on the reverse of which is a similarly inscribed label referring to a 'twice great grandmother'.[2]

22.2 × 36 cm

Provenance: Edward Washington(?), Hampton, Middlesex; Mr J.J. Briginshaw, Ongar, Essex; sold Christie's, 4 July 1916, lot 129; purchased through M. Harris and Sons, 30 May 1917, £19 (along with a raised-work 'stumpwork' picture of Lot's wife also priced £19) and first displayed at The Hill, Hampstead.

References: **1** Label reads 'Worked by twice Greatmother of George Washington of America, left to Edward Washington of Hampton, Middlesex, first cousin to George Washington.' **2** Presented to Sulgrave by Viscountess Lee of Fareham; Harold Clifford Smith, *Sulgrave Manor and the Washingtons*, 1933, p. 128; letter Martin Sinot-Smith, Sulgrave Manor, 8.12.89.

1928 Catalogue no. 40.

LL5276

LL5277 (WHL3204)

## The Four Seasons

Third quarter of the seventeenth century

*Satin worked with silk and metal thread in satin, long and short, detached buttonhole and lace stitches, with French knots, couched threads, purl, and applied beads, pearls, tent stitch canvas motifs and padded features. The satin ground is split and much worn.*

The figures of the seasons are (from upper left clockwise) Autumn, holding a glass of wine, Winter, Summer and Spring. As a group they do not relate closely to other versions in the collection, on a mirror frame (LL5222 p. 197) and another raised-work picture (LL5259), although the figures of Winter and Summer are close to those on LL5259 (p. 64). The figures are surrounded by the creatures, birds, flowers and turreted buildings commonly found on such pictures, among which are a peacock, carnation, rose and a mermaid similar to one on a sampler from the second quarter of the seventeenth century.[1]

26 × 38 cm

Provenance: purchased through M. Harris and Sons, 28 June 1917, £40 and first displayed at The Hill, Hampstead.

Exhibited: on loan East Riddleston Hall, Yorkshire, 29 June 1950.

References: **1** Leigh Ashton, *Samplers*, 1926, fig. 14.

1928 Catalogue no. 21.

LL5277

LL5278 (WHL3368)

## *The Servant Eliezer Taking his Leave of Abraham; a Camel and a Fountain*

Second half of the seventeenth century

12.5 × 19.3 cm

Provenance: purchased through M. Harris and Sons, 13 November 1917, £20.

References: **1** New York, Cooper Hewitt Museum (1962.52.10); Y. Hackenbroch, *English Needlework in the Untermyer Collection*, 1960, p. xxxi, fig. 28.

1928 Catalogue no. 13.

*Satin worked with silk in satin, long and short, chain and detached buttonhole and lace stitches with French knots and an applied tent stitch motif. Several of the drawn motifs have not been embroidered.*

The two main figures were probably intended for a scene representing Eliezer's departure from Abraham in search of a wife for Isaac (Genesis 24:1–10). The scene is depicted on the side panel of a casket (LL5256, p. 179) by two men in the same postures. The figure of Abraham is in fact the same figure as that commonly used to represent Winter but without his fire (see for example LL5259 and LL5277, pp. 64, 76). The camel and the fountain, whose male water god was left unembroidered, also feature in the narrative of Eliezer's encounter with Rebecca and the rounded fragments may have been intended for the bottom of a scalloped-edge embroidered mirror frame relating this story. A similar water god fountain can be found on an unfinished embroidered picture derived from a Gerard de Jode print.[1]

LL5278

LL5279 (WHL3370)

## Oaktree in Landscape with Lion, Leopard and Stag

Third quarter of the seventeenth century

*Linen worked almost entirely with couched metal thread and coiled silk pile with a number of wooden moulds stitched over with a wide variety of detached buttonhole and lace stitches and French knots and a few straight stitches in silk with applied mica.*

The picture showing an oaktree with its three-dimensional acorns, is unusual for its lack of narrative content. As it is surrounded by three royal beasts it was possibly meant to be symbolic of Charles II's successful return to power. A slightly similar depiction of a solitary tree but with a salamander below, is thought to have been North European in origin and

30 × 41.5 cm

Provenance: purchased M. Harris and Sons as a 'Charles II Stumpwork Picture' on 13 November 1917, £75.

References: 1 New York, Cooper Hewitt Museum, gift of Marian Hague 1959. Adolph Cavallo, *Needlework*, 1979, p. 35, fig. 33. Letter 19 May 1989. The Macquoid catalogue dated LL5279 to *c.* 1620.

1928 Catalogue no. 20.

LL5279

to have once been mounted on the inner door of a cabinet on a stand, dated about 1575–1625.[1] LL5279 could also have performed this function, although it is more likely to have formed the top of a casket, and the laid metal ground is strongly influenced by Flanders and northern France.

## LL5282 (WHL4146)

### *Lady Standing under Arched Canopy with Flowers*

Second half of the seventeenth century

*Satin worked with silks in satin, long and short, stem, running, and tent stitches, and a variety of detached lace and buttonhole stitches, French knots and twisted silk pile; also with coloured metal purl and applied black beads forming a necklace. Like its pair it has a border made of metal thread and strips.*

Like her companion (LL5283) the lady is shown standing on a grassy knoll holding a fruit-bearing branch surrounded by

30 × 23 cm

Provenance: Viscountess Wolseley(?), Wolseley Hall, Stafford, but not sold at the Puttick and Simpson sale of 12 July 1906, unless it is identifiable as lot 128, see LL5397–8, 5410, 5420–21. pp. 257–9, 186, 269, 271; Mrs Percival Griffiths, Sandringbury, St Albans, sold along with LL5283 Christie's, 2 March 1920, lot 92; purchased through M. Harris and Sons, £39.18.0 the pair.

LL5282

entwined flowers and fruits, among them a tulip, pink, eglantine rose, strawberry plant and pea pod. Female figures under flowering bowers or arches were often embroidered throughout the seventeenth century.[1] Occasionally, as in a panel at Bath[2] the figures were allegorical, though this is probably not the case with the Lady Lever panels. These two pieces may originally have been mounted on the inside of casket doors as are similar figures, representing the elements, on a casket in Cambridge, or they could possibly have acted as the doors to a covered mirror.[3]

References: 1 For example, two panels, one from the first half, the other from the second half of the century, formerly in Sir Frederick Richmond's collection, Christie's, 23 June 1987, lots 105, 122. Figures standing under flowering arcades were common Sheldon tapestry motifs. 2 Holburne Menstrie Museum, F.233. 3 Fitzwilliam Museum, T.8–1945; G.S. Seligman and T. Hughes, *Domestic Embroidery*, 1926, pl. 73d.

1928 Catalogue no. 54.

## LL5283 (WHL4147)

### Lady Standing under Ornamental Canopy with Flowers

Second half of the seventeenth century

*Same technique as LL5282 except that seed pearls are substituted for black beads to form the necklace. The satin is frayed around the edge and over the lady's padded features.*

30 × 23 cm

Provenance: Mrs Percival Griffiths,[3] Sandringbury, St Albans sold along with LL5282 Christie's, 2 March 1920, lot 92, purchased through M. Harris and Sons £49.18.0.

References: 1 Puttick and Simpson, 12 July 1906, lot 128? (possibly LL5282) 'stump needlework picture, lady under a canopy' raised £38. 2 Lever bought mainly small costume accessories, purses, shoes and trinket boxes, LL5397–8, LL5410, LL5420–21. A letter in gallery archives from Arthur Edwards, dealer, offering at Lady Wolseley's suggestion, a 'Stuart' casket, dated 1659, and a picture. 3 The widow of Percival Griffiths another leading collector of Stuart and Georgian embroideries and a contemporary of Lever's.

1928 Catalogue no. 54.

LL5283

LL5283 was purchased as a pair with LL5282. A newspaper cutting on the reverse of the panel implies that it (and presumably its pair) were once in the collection of Viscountess Wolseley, an early collector of seventeenth-century embroidery. The sale of her collection in 1906 realized relatively high prices for Stuart embroideries and is thought to have first attracted the attention of other collectors and the public to this type of material.[1] Lever bought several items from the sale (though probably not LL5283) and shortly afterwards dealers with suitable Stuart items were being directed to him, as a likely purchaser, by Viscountess Wolseley.[2]

25 × 27.5 cm

Provenance: purchased through M. Harris and Sons, 22 July 1920, £20.

Exhibited: Yorkshire, East Riddlesden Hall, 29 June 1950.

References: **1** Alexander Globe, *Peter Stent, London Printseller*, 1985, fig. 519, pl. 238. **2** Globe, as above, p. 141, fig. 525–32. In 1673 Overton advertised an expanded edition of 'Five Hundred New Sorts' with the addendum 'and he is doing more

LL5285 (WHL4267)

## Man Rowing a Boat with Dolphins and other Animal Motifs

Second half of the seventeenth century

*Satin worked mainly in metal thread in a variety of green-coloured purl, also with silks in satin, split and detached buttonhole stitches and applied tent stitch in silk and wool on canvas motifs, French knots, couched threads and twisted silk pile.*

The picture's technique which makes great use of green-coloured purl to depict luxuriant foliage is similar to that found on two thin rectangular panels in the collection (LL5301, LL5302, p. 82), thought to be fragments or side

LL5285

panels from a casket. A few dolphins appeared in Wenceslas Hollar's *A New Book of Flowers and Fishes*, published by Stent in 1662.[1] From 1671 onward a greater variety of dolphins of different sizes were published in John Overton's fragmentary collection *A New Book of all Sorts of Beasts*, which was advertised as providing 'Four hundred new sorts of Birds, Beasts, Flowers, Fruits, Fish, Flyes, Worms . . . Lively coloured for all sorts of Gentlewomen and School-Mistresses Works'.[2] However, the latter does not seem to have been the source for the animals found in LL5285. Illustrations of monstrous and amazing beasts, such as dolphins and whales, were common in the seventeenth century and whole pages depicting them can be found in Randle Holmes' encyclopaedia, the *Academy of Armory*.[3]

as fast as time will permit'. **3** Randle Holme, *Academy of Armory*, 1688, Ch. XVI, p. 361.

1928 Catalogue no. 8.

## LL5301 (WHL4116)

## *Fountain with a Dog Chasing a Duck*

Mid-seventeenth century

*Satin worked mainly with metal thread couched in spirals of coloured purl and spangles; also in silks in raised, detached buttonhole, running, and long and short stitches and couched thread.*

The shape of both LL5301 and its pair (LL5302) and the remnants of stitch-holes along the lower edge suggest that the panels could originally have been mounted along the sides of a casket lid. They would appear to have been too large to have acted as drawer fronts, as some similarly shaped panels did.[1] The luxuriant flowers and vegetation of the panels are similar in style to those found on the embroidered picture of *Man Rowing a Boat with Dolphins and other Animal Motifs* (LL5285, p. 81).

15.5 × 53 cm

Provenance: purchased through M. Harris and Sons as a pair to LL5302, 25 February 1920, £50, first displayed at The Hill, Hampstead.

References: **1** Rous Lench Collection, Sotheby's, 4 July 1986, lot 619.

1928 Catalogue no. 26.

LL5301

LL5302 (WHL4117)

## Dog Chasing Hare among Trees and Flowers

Mid-seventeenth century

16 × 53 cm

Provenance: refer to LL5301.

1928 Catalogue no. 31.

*Same technique as LL5301 but without the straight stitches in silk. Some purl along the upper edge has been lost revealing the ink under-drawing of the clouds.*

This type of hunting scene appeared frequently on tapestries and needleworks throughout the late sixteenth and seventeenth centuries and earlier.

LL5263 (WHL2282)

## King Charles I, Henrietta Maria and Three Royal Children within a Floral Border

Third quarter of the seventeenth and early eighteenth century

38 × 80.5 cm

Provenance: Mrs Hillier, Cautley Avenue, Southside Clapham Common; sold Christie's, 21 July 1915, lot 249; bought through D.L. Isaacs, 28 July 1915, £18.9.0, and first displayed at The Hill, Hampstead.

References: **1** *Illustrated Catalogue of Ancient Framed Needlework Pictures in the Possession of Mrs S.H. Lilla Hailstone*, 1897, pl. 1 no. 75. **2** Arthur Hind, *Engraving in England in the Sixteenth and Seventeenth Centuries*, 1964, Vol. III, p. 108, no. 23, pl. 54.

1928 Catalogue no. 17.

*Satin worked with silk and metal thread. A central panel of raised-work with examples of long and short, tent, detached buttonhole and lace stitch and purl. The outer border also of satin was worked later in long and short and stem stitch and is badly frayed and stained.*

The picture consists of two embroidered panels of different styles worked at different times. The outer border of trailing flowers and oriental birds was probably worked on to the earlier panel sometime in the early eighteenth century. In several areas its flower stems and leaves have been applied to overlap the border between the two panels. The inner panel has its own border of 'royal beasts' (lion, leopard, stag and unicorn), hare and hound, squirrel, snail, birds and insects interspersed with flowers such as tulips, roses, and cornflowers.

LL5263

The under-drawing of the faces is clearly visible on the fabric.

The central image depicts Charles I with his wife and three of his children, presumably Charles and Mary (standing outside the tent) and the young prince James. Another example of exactly the same embroidered composition, even down to the horse and boar worked above the heads of Charles and Mary, was in the collection of Mrs Lilla Hailstone in 1897.[1] The design may have been adapted from an engraving by William Marshall (worked 1617–50), of the royal parents with their five children standing and in cots on a draped terrace, although the throne stool with crown and sceptre displayed in the embroidery does not appear in the print.[2] The attraction of a picture depicting the future Charles II and Queen Mary would have been great in the final third of the seventeenth century.

LL5101 (WHL2819)

## Adoration of the Holy Family and the Holy Trinity by St Elizabeth, the Infant St John and St Peter(?) as Pope

Central European, second half of the seventeenth century

*Linen worked in silver and gold thread and silk couched so as to entirely cover the ground, with purl and seed pearls and wooden or plaster moulds covered in silk with some silks in detached buttonhole stitches and knots.*

26 × 25 cm

Provenance: Sir Trevor Lawrence, Bt., KCVO, deceased, of 57 Princes Gate and Burford, Dorking;[3] sold Christie's, 29

May 1916, lot 238; bought through D.L. Isaacs, 2 June 1916 for £55.9.0 and kept at The Hill, Hampstead.

Literature: Muriel Best, *Stumpwork: Historical and Contemporary Raised Embroidery*, 1987, p. 20, illus. 9.

References: **1** Harriet Bridgeman and Elizabeth Drury ed., *Needlework: an illustrated history*, 1978, pp. 210, 214, 221; Lanto Synge, *Antique Needlework*, 1982, p. 61. **2** See *The Revenge of Thomyris* (LL5281 p. 55) and the hood of a cope embroidered in raised-work cherubim and sunbursts in the collection of the Dean and Chapter of Durham Cathedral, Muriel Best, as above, p. 21, illus. 10; Patricia Wardle, 'English Pictorial Embroidery of the Seventeenth Century', *Antiques International*, 1969, p. 286. **3** Sir James John Trevor Lawrence (1831–1913), from whose sale in 1916 Lever also acquired most of his Chinese *cloisonné* enamel collection and a Wedgwood inkstand. Sir Trevor Lawrence was well known as a collector of Japanese lacquer furniture and was the brother of the Misses Lawrence, for whom see LL5260 and LL5265 (pp. 66, 70).

1928 Catalogue no. 78.

LL5101 (see also colour plate 10)

The picture is in very high relief with heads, limbs and torsos seemingly carved from wood or plaster and covered in silk, before having their features painted on. When it was acquired at auction LL5101 was described as Spanish, seventeenth-century work. However, it bears a much closer resemblance to the highly embossed ecclesiastical vestments, often encrusted with seed pearls, which were produced by workshops in Hungary, Bohemia and central Europe.[1] It was probably worked after an as yet unidentified Baroque Italian or possibly Flemish painting. The cherubs' heads on the mock picture-frame are similar to those found on Flemish embroidered pictures and English ecclesiastical work of the mid-1630s.[2]

LL5284 (WHL4210)

**Raised-work collage**

## *Abigail Providing Food for King David and his Troops*

Nineteenth century

*A collage of woven silks, brocades, velvets and padded kid leather with some floss silks worked in a variety of knots.*

When purchased LL5284 was said to date from *c.* 1680. In fact it is probably a nineteenth-century imitation of a raised-work picture, perhaps continental in origin, or it could have been made as a 'shadow box', typically produced in Britain from *c.* 1865 onwards, in which heavily raised figures of felt and paper were placed in deep box frames against a flat background.[1] The story of Abigail and David was often depicted in seventeenth-century needleworks.

19.5 × 22 cm

Provenance: purchased through Frank Partridge, 29 May 1920, £13.

References: **1** Ayles, *The Art of the People in America and Britain*, Cornerhouse Art Centre, Manchester, 23 November 1985– 5 January 1986.

1928 Catalogue no. 45.

LL5284

LL5275 (WHL3179)

**Raised-work fragments**

## Lady and Gentleman with Castle, Animals and Flowers

Late nineteenth century

*Padded, knitted and tent stitch motifs in wool with lace, velvet and glass beads applied to a much perished silk ground.*

The Macquoid catalogue described it as a crude modern copy of a stumpwork picture. LL5275 in fact consists of some original seventeenth-century motifs randomly distributed across a satin ground and probably worked up and mounted in its walnut frame sometime at the turn of the nineteenth century as a pastiche of English raised-work pictures which were then coming into vogue as collectable items. According to gallery files it was entitled 'Charles I and Queen'.

37.5 × 30 cm

Provenance: purchased through M. Harris and Sons, 1 May 1917, £35.

1928 Catalogue no. 61.

LL5275

# Beadwork Pictures

LL5257 (WHL503; H55)

## King and Queen with Floral and Animal Motifs

Worked by Anne Mairy Sawell December 1672(?)

*Satin backed with linen canvas and worked with fine multi-coloured opaque, clear and dyed(?) beads, purl, metal thread and a little silk and trimmed with metal thread braid. The faces and hands are raised over moulded leather(?) as is the entire central section while the acorns and fruit are padded with wool. The box beneath is lined with pale blue silk.*

LL5257 is a form of protective mirror frame, its central section lifts to reveal a small mirror on the underside and a larger one on the base of a shallow box. The embroiderer's name and the inscription 'Good. Anno. December 167[?]' are

39.8 × 43.5 cm

Provenance: unknown. Acquired by January 1907 and kept at The Hill, Hampstead before 1911.

Literature: Muriel Best, *Stumpwork: Historical and Contemporary Raised Embroidery*, 1987, illus. fig. 16.

References: **1** Y. Hackenbroch, *English Needlework in the Irwin Untermyer Collection*, 1960, fig. 107, pl. 73; N.M.S., 1931.60. Another undated royal couple is in the Chicago Art Institute, acq. 1980.130.

1928 Catalogue no. 3.

LL5257

written on the book held by the king. In the 1928 catalogue the date was read as 1672 and the royal couple were identified as Charles II and Catherine of Braganza standing beneath a pair of oaks. If it is intended to be the couple the picture might have been embroidered to commemorate their tenth wedding anniversary celebrated in 1672. Identical beadwork pictures dated generally to the third quarter of the seventeenth century are in the Untermyer Collection of the Metropolitan Museum, New York and the National Museums of Scotland.[1] The beads are much finer and more sophisticatedly shaded than those found on the beadwork basket (LL5343, p. 91) and have been carefully worked, one bead threaded at a time and looped to the previous row, to reproduce the folded fabrics worn by the queen.

## LL5264 (WHL3423)

### Adam and Eve

Second half of the seventeenth century

*Satin worked with large multicoloured and striped beads. The padded faces have features embroidered in stem stitch and there is a broad metal thread braided border. Some beads have been lost revealing the under-drawing in the top right-hand corner.*

The four beasts accompanying the couple are (from the top left, clockwise) a wyvern (half bird, half dragon), a griffin (a winged lion), a unicorn and a lion. The braid border to the picture suggests that it was once mounted on a work-box, while the design may have come from a Bible illustration.[1] When acquired it was in a red tortoiseshell frame.

25 × 37 cm

Provenance: purchased through M. Harris and Sons, 1 March 1918, £44.

References: **1** Apart from the frontal depiction of the couple and the snake twisting round the tree, LL5264 bears little relationship to the Boetius Bolswert engravings of the subject used in the 1633 Edinburgh Bible, which created a storm over its 'Popish pictures', nor does it derive from the print of the couple used as the end plate to Stent's *Therd Booke of Flowers*, published in 1661.

1928 Catalogue no. 84.

LL5264

LL5341 (WHL2690)

## Cavalier and Lady with Floral, Animal and other Motifs

Second half of the seventeenth century

*Satin with couched and threaded, coloured and striped beads. The tree-tops are represented by groups of three or four beads looped and couched down in such a way as to imitate the use of purl.*

All the figures have been rather schematically drawn. Among the animals appear a camel (to the lower left), a relatively common motif, and the more unusual cockerel (above).

37 × 52.2 cm

Provenance: purchased through D.L. Isaacs, 17 December 1915, £40 and first displayed at Thornton Manor.

1928 Catalogue no. 93.

LL5341

LL5342 (WHL3469)

## Abigail Offering Food and Drink to King David(?)

Second half of the seventeenth century

*Satin worked with coloured, clear, dyed(?) and striped beads with some features, padded with leather and wire, wound round with silk, and embroidered with running stitch, split stitch and French knots and trimmed with a blue and yellow cord surround.*

Theresa Macquoid thought LL5342 was probably intended to show the mother and family of the defeated Persian King Darius kneeling before the victorious Alexander the Great. Although Alexander is usually depicted in helmet and armour, the scene is not a commonly embroidered one, and it

24.8 × 31.5 cm

Provenance: purchased through M. Harris and Sons, 24 April 1918, £27.10.0.

1928 Catalogue no. 82.

LL5342

could well be intended to represent the more frequently chosen biblical story of Abigail offering food and drink to King David (I Samuel, 25: 18–36). Interesting methods have been used to colour the beads red, which was the most difficult and expensive colour to achieve in glass beads and so often used sparingly. White beads on the house appear to have been covered in a rust-coloured paste which has subsequently flaked, while some clear beads have been threaded with red silk to give a pinkish-red tinge to David's boot.

LL5343 (X2498)

**Beadwork basket**

## Lady and Gentleman under Floral Arch with Stag and Leopard

Second half of the seventeenth century

*Multicoloured clear and opaque beads strung round a wire frame wrapped in canvas and silk with a base of satin, worked with beads, padded with wool and a small amount of detached buttonhole stitch. The rim and base are worked in squares of white beads in a right-angle weave technique stringing four beads at a time on the thread.*

Beadwork baskets such as this may have been made to commemorate a child's christening, as, with a raised picture on the base, they are similar in shape and style to baskets made in silver repoussé, which were traditionally intended to hold a child's clothes before the christening ceremony.[1] LL5343 must originally have looked similar to two equivalent

54 × 63 cm (including handles)

Provenance: purchased through M. Harris and Sons, 24 April 1918, £40.

Exhibited: Birmingham, *Exhibition of British Embroidery*, 1959, No. 103.

Literature: Therle Hughes, 'Stuart Needlework' in Anthony Howarth, *Treasures of Britain*, Drive Publications, undated, colour illus. fig. 3.

References: **1** See for example the Dutch silver 'layette basket' of 1666 in Boston Art Museum #1982.617. Alexander Globe, *Peter Stent London Printseller c. 1642–1665*, 1985, fig. 24b, pl. 30.

LL5343

baskets in the Rous Lench and Percival Griffiths collections,[2] respectively dated 1663 and *c.* 1675, but LL5343 has lost much of the beaded foliage that may originally have trailed up its sides and all of the beads from its handles, which, as in most beadwork baskets, follow the standard trefoil shape. In 1912 Leverhulme purchased two Stuart beadwork baskets[3] which are no longer in the collection.

**2** Sotheby's London, Rous Lench Collection, vol. 2, 4 July 1986, lot 603 and Sotheby's New York, 24 April 1987, lot 28; 'A Collection of Old English Needlework', *Connoisseur*, vol. 63, 1923, pp. 154, 157 and illus. There are also thirteen beaded 'christening' baskets in United States collections and various others in British collections, including one in Nottingham Museum of Costume and Textiles (no. 48.46) with similar but reversed central figures to those on LL5343. These baskets are being researched by Miss Valerie Hector of the Chicago Bead Society to whom I am most grateful for discussing with me the techniques and bead types used on all the Lady Lever's beadwork items. **3** Purchased from Frank Partridge, 6 May 1912, £55.

1928 Catalogue no. 5.

# Georgian, Regency and Victorian Period

## 1. Techniques and Use

The pictorial embroideries of the eighteenth century differed from those of the seventeenth both in subject-matter and in a more restricted range of techniques, at least until the latter part of the century, when a wider range of themes was introduced and workmanship flowered to show a greater variety of embroidery skills. Until the last few decades of the eighteenth century most pictorial panels, whether intended as pictures or for furniture, were worked on fine linen canvas in a combination of tent stitch (*petit point*) and the larger related stitches, gobelin and cross stitch. These types of stitches were chosen for their hard-wearing properties, rather than to imitate tapestry weave as before, for both tent stitch and cross stitch helped reinforce the linen canvas which was the usual ground fabric. Large numbers of pieces produced by both professional and domestic embroiderers were intended for use on, or as items of, furniture. They would have covered chairs, sofas, and furniture suites with series of related scenes (e.g. LL5373–7, pp. 120–5) or acted as fire-screens (LL5378, p. 112) or as larger folding screens such as that produced by K. Howard in 1735–6 (LL5447, p. 221). The practical nature of such items is emphasized in the latter case by the re-use of seventeenth-century embroidered slips and raised-work motifs on the screen. The screen also shows that, although raised-work was no longer fashionable, its skills and techniques were still admired and appreciated enough to be incorporated into a design worked in the following century. But the needlewoman in the reign of Queen Anne (1702–14) no longer had need of glittering mica and jewels to create a luxurious effect. Fashion was moving from the rich effects of the seventeenth century to the restrained elegance of the eighteenth and wealthy women in particular were able to confirm their leisured status by producing extensive suites of embroidered furnishings. Purely pictorial embroideries still continued to be produced, sometimes on a large scale (LL5346, p. 110), as cheaper home-made alternatives to paintings, especially of classical or Arcadian landscapes. Occasionally an embroideress like Elizabeth Tole (LL5251, p. 128) reverted to the smooth satin ground of the previous century, which was so effective if one wanted to create a shimmering effect of silks and had the skill in embroidery and use of colour to show them off, as she obviously had. She was so proud of the result that she signed her name in silks twice. By the second half of the century needlework had reached a level of skill rarely surpassed since. As it became more fashionable to cover furniture with tapestry covers from French factories, watered silks, patterned woven fabrics and painted textiles, domestic embroiderers sought to display their talents again in ornamental needlework pictures and personal items such as pocket-books and purses. By the end of the century embroiderers had reverted to the production of decorative pictures for which hard-wearing linen canvas was not appropriate. Instead, the usual background to such pictures became painted silk, embroidered in fine shining silks, thick wools and fluffy chenille, usually leaving the faces, hands and limbs unworked. The painted silk-work picture enabled a lady to demonstrate two desirable female accomplishments at the same time – drawing in watercolour and embroidery, both of which were confirmed as fashionable feminine pursuits. Those who preferred could buy ready-made painted silk to embroider. The variety of threads used enabled the expert embroiderer to show off her skills (LL5316, p. 156) and provide pictures tastefully suitable for any boudoir's light turn-of-the-century décor. The taste for painted-silk pictures continued through the Regency and up until the Victorian period, by which time Berlin woolwork, with its graph paper patterns, uniform stitch and use of brightly dyed wools, had begun to dominate the embroidery scene. That domination was not broken until the Arts and Crafts revival movement towards the end of the nineteenth century. In 1872 the Royal School of Art Needlework was established with the aim of raising the status of embroidery design by studying the best examples of 'ancient needlework' and commissioning contemporary artists, including William Morris and Walter Crane, to provide designs. Art needlework took many forms. The Lady Lever's only example of the type (LL5443, p. 223) shows sunflowers and peacocks replacing the overblown blooms of mid-Victorian Berlin woolwork and the uniform cross stitch was replaced by a variety of straight stitches and knots derived from the study of seventeenth-century crewel-work. The vogue for this technique and style continued into the first decades of the twentieth century.

## 2. Popular Themes

Elizabeth Tole's picture, dated 1741, also demonstrates the change in subject matter which had occurred. Throughout the first half of the eighteenth century pastoral, Arcadian and bucolic themes were preferred, sometimes with a hint of the classical in the form of ruinous architecture (LL5346, p. 110). The biblical themes of the previous century became very rare. When they did appear New Testament scenes, such as *Christ Meeting Mary Magdalene* (LL5365, p. 106), were favoured over those from the Old Testament, although *The Finding of Moses* was still popular. The taste for pictures of shepherdesses accompanied by their swains in a general way reflected the artistic, literary and musical taste of the period, in particular the pastoral poetry of Alexander Pope (1688–1744) and Ambrose Philips (1675(?)–1749) and the operas of Handel, which promoted admiration for the innocence and simplicity of an aristocratic and leisured view of rural life (LL5346, LL5383, pp. 110–11). Occasionally an embroideress used motifs which related to specific scenes from pastoral poetry, such as those from the classical age of Virgil's *Eclogues* and *Georgics* which were used by Lady Julia Claverley in the embroidered wall panels which line a room at Wallington Hall, Northumberland, or the *IX Pastoral* of Virgil which provided the *Hunters* on an early eighteenth-century embroidery, formerly in the Lever collection, but now in the Metropolitan Museum, New York (see Appendix AG1, lot 552). Such a specific use of an illustrated version of a classical author was unusual. More commonly the needleworks shared similar themes to those used by contemporary porcelain designers in England and abroad. Often the embroidered pictures were so generalized, merely depicting a couple or a single shepherd or shepherdess in a landscape, that it is impossible to specify original print sources for the designs. They were in some ways a continuation of the 'engagement' pictures of the seventeenth century, scenes in which the elegantly dressed genteel 'shepherdess' was waited on and courted by an equally well-mannered 'shepherd'. Thus the typical chair or sofa cover of the first half of the century consisted of a central pastoral or mythological subject worked in fine tent-stitch, over one canvas thread, while the surrounding floral and geometric border was worked in larger stitches over two threads. French influence was dominant here as elsewhere in the decorative arts. Certainly many of the embroidered chair and sofa coverings and fire-screens which make up a large part of the embroidered textiles of the first half of the eighteenth century show evidence of the French taste for dark brown or black grounds to the floral borders surrounding the vignettes of rural life. Later, the detailed engraved copperplate designs produced for the French printed cottons of Jouy may also have provided motifs for needlework pictures, such as the *Coastal Scene* (LL5389, p. 131), and other painted-silk pictures may also have been after French paintings or engravings (see LL5316, p. 156).

By the final decades of the century embroidery had returned to a pictorial art, drawing on a wider range of themes than before. Print series and paintings of the period also emphasized the healthy 'moral' qualities and feminine virtues which had come to be associated with the art of embroidery – virtues imparted, by implication, to all those who practised the art. The series by Morland relating the downfall and eventual reconciliation of the young country girl *Laetitia* illustrates the scene of *Domestic Happiness* with the mother and daughter embroidering while father reads from the Bible. By 1789 when the series was published in print form this sentiment was common (and contrasted markedly with the zealot-dominated seventeenth century, when those stitching for their own satisfaction might be accused of the sins of vanity and pride). It is not surprising, therefore, to find that the favoured themes often emphasized the 'virtuous' qualities associated with the the art itself, so that a coloured print after Sir William Beechey's *The Beggar Boy*, which illustrated the wealthy children of an MP giving money to a poor country child, was considered a suitable theme to be embroidered (LL5349, p. 145).

The manufacturers of the painted-silk picture kits, like their colleagues in the ceramics factories, relied for their choice of themes on the vast range of prints then on the market, particularly stipple engravings and etchings. The threads and stitches used on many painted silk needleworks, for example very fine knots, speckling stitches and chenille, are the embroideress's attempt to reproduce in needlework the effects of the stipple engravings popular at the end of the century, such as the Bartolozzi print of *Fame paying homage to Shakespeare* (LL5356, p. 136). Such prints were sometimes illustrated in the ladies' magazines of the late eighteenth and early nineteenth centuries. The *Lady's Magazine or Entertaining Companion for the Fair Sex* was first published in 1770 with the stated aim of providing 'the most elegant patterns for . . . every kind of needlework'. The prints or paintings chosen by manufacturers to be reproduced as embroidery kits relied heavily on scenes with children at play and often on works by artists such as Beechey, Hoppner and Adam Buck, known for their portrayal of children (LL5349, LL5311, pp. 145, 140). On occasions family portraits were reproduced as prints with titles which were possibly meant to attract the embroidery market. Hoppner's portrait of *Lady Lambton and Family* was published with the title *Domestic Happiness* and was probably embroidered for that reason (LL5321, p. 158). Thus embroiderers followed the fashion of contemporary professional painters and other applied artists in celebrating childhood and maternal affection (LL5310, p. 146).

New themes were introduced and old ones developed anew. The pleasures of rural life as expressed in needlework moved away from the aristocratic poetic vision towards the more sentimental coy view provided by prints after Francis Wheatley and Redmore Bigg (LL5312, p. 138). The taste for classical antiquity was reflected in scenes with classically draped figures (LL5316, p. 156), sometimes shown in mourning for a departed author. Shakespeare (LL5356, p. 136), Goethe and his creation, Werther, proved particularly popular. Portraits of people in the guise of theatrical characters (LL5313, p. 139) provided new subjects, others were supplied by the commemoration of contemporary heroes, such as Nelson (LL536-7, pp. 159–60). By the turn of the century biblical scenes once more became popular, having more or less disappeared since the seventeenth century, with an emphasis on themes suitable as models for marriage, such as Ruth and Boaz (LL5323, p. 168) or Isaac and Rebecca (LL5359, p. 169). Finally, a multiplicity of new themes was inspired by Sir Walter Scott's novels and poetry (LL5360, LL5368, LL5386, pp. 173, 166, 172), which proved particularly popular with the manufacturers of the newly introduced Berlin woolwork patterns. By the mid-nineteenth century scenes taken from Scott were so closely associated with needlework that a reviewer in the *Athenaeum* (19 February 1853) criticized a painting of *Ivanhoe and Rowena* as fit only for 'sampler-work or tea-board illustration'.

## 3. Designers and Embroiderers

The eighteenth century saw the professional upholsterer at his most prominent. Upholsterers such as the London and Wakefield firm of Wright and Elwick advertised that they 'drew for all sorts of Needle Work, for carpets, beds, chairs, fire screens' and sold to ladies 'painted patterns and shades of Silk and Worsted for such works in the best and cheapest manner'. Patterns and materials were sold by needlework repositories and haberdashers, as their trade cards show.

In America teachers advertised for sale 'all sorts of beautiful Figures on Canvas for Tent Stick', in other words designs drawn on canvas to be worked over in tent stitch. The involvement of teachers and governesses in the drawing of needlework designs shows that children were still one of the main groups making purely pictorial needleworks. Their mothers, other female relatives and servants were more inclined to show off their versatility with a needle by producing some of the large amount of embroidery required to furnish an eighteenth-century house properly. Mrs Delany, the wife of the Dean of Down in Ireland, and an eminent and indefatigable needlewoman, was constantly at work on a succession of small carpets, seatcovers, bed and window curtains. By the end of the eighteenth century needlework was considered among the highest feminine accomplishments of a young lady. It had again become fashionable for an adult woman to be seen at her needlework frame creating purely decorative fragile pictures to ornament the home along with other forms of feminine 'fancy work', such as felt-work and filigree paper-work pictures and trinket-boxes.

# Canvas-work Pictures

LL5348 (WHL3782)

## The Finding of Moses

Worked in 1702, initialled 'SG[?]' on a tree trunk

*Canvas worked in wool in tent stitch.*

65 × 65 cm

The *Finding of Moses* is a subject that appears more commonly on late seventeenth-century and early eighteenth-century embroidery pictures. Another early eighteenth-century tent-stitch example,[1] equivalent in size and style to LL5348 was in the collection of Sir Frederick Richmond, an embroidery collector similarly attracted to seventeenth- and early eighteenth-century items.[2] LL5348 is not similar in design to the Richmond piece, nor to other embroideries in public

Provenance: purchased through M. Harris and Sons, 28 April 1919, £60; displayed at The Hill, Hampstead.

References: **1** Christie's, 23 June 1987, lot 213, colour pl. 12. **2** A.J.B. Wace, 'Embroidery in the collection of Sir Frederick Richmond, Bt.' parts I and II, *Apollo*, 1933 vol. XVII, p. 207, vol. XVIII, p. 23–8; A.F. Kendrick, 'Embroideries in the Collection of Sir Frederick Richmond, Bt.', *Connoisseur*, May 1935, vol. 95, p. 282–8; for full bibliography see Christie's sale catalogue above. **3** N.M.S. 1945.4546. Ducret, *Keramik und Graphik*, 1973, pl. 49. **4** Giuseppe Fiocco, *Paolo Veronese, 1528–1588*, 1928, pl. LXXI. The embroidery is not, however, based on Veronese's interpretation of this subject in the National Gallery, Washington, The Prado, Madrid or the studio version in the Walker Art Gallery, Liverpool (Inv. 2854) nor is it close to Benedetto Caliari's *Finding of Moses*, in the Uffizi, Florence see Fiocco as above, p. 151.

1928 Catalogue no. 120.

LL5348

collections known to the author, nor to any that have recently passed through the sale rooms. It is not, for example, derived from the print of 1685 by Peter Schut, from which the embroidery in the National Museums of Scotland seems to be derived.[3] The motif of the queen leaning on her maidservant suggests that the design source may have derived from a print after a painting by Veronese or his studio, as this stance features prominently in his interpretation of the scene, and the subject was a studio favourite.[4]

LL5387 (WHL3611)

## Shepherd and Flock outside a House

Initialled and dated 'RB, 1708'

*Canvas worked with silk in tent, cross, chain and stem stitch. The picture had been darned or mended at some time before purchase.*

The careful delineation of the house and its unusual setting, beside a shepherd and his flock, suggest that it may well have been known to the embroiderer and that it is not the stock type often used in seventeenth- and eighteenth-century embroidered pastoral scenes.

20 × 24.5 cm

Provenance: W. Mills Esq., Old Sun House, Cheyne Row, Chelsea;[1] sold Christie's, 18 June 1918, lot 125; bought M. Harris and Sons £19.19.0 the pair.[2]

Literature: illustrated in colour Virginia Glenn Pow, 'A new look in traditional textiles', *Discovering Antiques*, BBC p. 444–5.

References: **1** Mill also owned LL5225, LL5242 and LL5332 (pp. 101, 102, 228) bought by Lever from the same sale lots 126, 124 and 127. **2** The pair to LL5387 on purchase, an oval panel, *c.* 1750, was sold in 1925. See Appendix KFR1, lot 321.

1928 Catalogue no. 95.

LL5387

LL5296 (WHL3133)

## Vase of Flowers

Early eighteenth century

*Tent-stitch motif in silk on canvas, on a ground of some form of drawn-work(?) with an attached scalloped-edged nineteenth-century border of braid.*

The size and type of motif was fairly common in the early eighteenth century, but the large, bold background stitching is unusual, though probably contemporary with the vase of flowers. The embroidery was purchased along with a raised-work picture of a lady (LL5287, p. 34), which was formerly owned by Mrs Rachel Head.

27 × 21.5 cm

Provenance: Mrs Rachel Head(?); purchased through D.L. Isaacs, 8 January 1917, £35 for the pair; first displayed at The Hill, Hampstead.

1928 Catalogue no. 79.

LL5296

LL5225 (WHL3612)

## Sacrifice of Isaac by Abraham

Worked by Elizabeth Suffolk, aged nine or ten, early eighteenth century(?)

*Canvas worked with wool in very coarse tent stitch with a few highlighting stitches in silk.*

LL5225 is an embroidered copy of a type of tapestry square woven by the Sheldon tapestry works during the first two decades of the seventeenth century[1] and usually referred to as a 'cushion cover'. The attempted sacrifice of Isaac by Abraham (Genesis 22) was the key Old Testament scene showing Abraham's faith in God's promise of numerous descendants, and the Promised Land. In the seventeenth century it was the most frequently reproduced and embroidered theme from the life of Abraham and Isaac, and would have had an obvious narrative appeal to a child like Elizabeth Suffolk. She has copied from the original woven panel not only the central scene, of Abraham's attempted sacrifice of his son, which is adapted from a print published by Gerard de Jode (fig. 17),[2] but also the decorative border design of fountains with cherubs, caryatids, garlands of flowers and stag- and fox-hunting scenes. There are only two known Sheldon piece designs showing the Abraham story, both dated after 1603. One, in the collection of the Duke of

64 × 61 cm

Provenance: W. Mill, Old Sun House, 2 Cheyne Row;[5] sold Christie's, 18 June 1918, lot 216; purchased by Lever through M. Harris and Sons, 26 June 1918, £31.10.0; displayed at The Hill, Hampstead.

References: **1** A.J.B. Wace, 'Sheldon Tapestry Cushions in the Collection of Sir William Burrell', *Old Furniture*, vol. V, 1928, p. 80. **2** Gerard de Jode after Martin de Vos used in the *Thesaurus Sacrarum Historiarum Veteris Testamenti*, Antwerp 1585 and reprinted in a pictorial Bible, the 'Piscator Bible', 1643, which was copied from extensively throughout northern Europe. **3** E.H.B. Barnard and A.J.B. Wace, 'The Sheldon Tapestry Weavers and their Work', *Archaeologia*, vol. LXXVIII, 1928, p. 309; pl. XLI, fig. 2. A similar panel, formerly in the collection of Colonel Henry Howard, Kidderminster, is in the Metropolitan Museum of Art, New York, Y. Hackenbroch, *English and other Needlework Tapestries in the Irwin Untermyer Collection*, 1960, p. 15, fig. 33, pl. 21. **4** Barnard and Wace, as above, pl. XLIX, fig. 3. The tapestry panel was then owned by a Mr S.R. Verecker of Hamsterley Hall, Newcastle-Upon-Tyne. Both panels were embroidered with the inscription: HAVE A STRONG FAITH IN GOD ONELY | NOT THIS BUT MY GOOD WILL. **5** Mill would appear to have been a collector of early to mid-eighteenth-century pictorial embroideries in particular. He also owned LL5387, *A Shepherd and Flock outside a House*, dated 1708, LL5332, an early eighteenth-century pictorial sampler showing the *Holy Family; Zacharias, Elizabeth and St John the Baptist*, and LL5242 which Lever bought at the same sale, lots 127, 125 and 124 respectively.

1928 Catalogue no. 123.

Figure 17   The sacrifice of Isaac by Abraham, from a print published by Gerard de Jode, after Martin de Vos, in the *Thesaurus Sacrarum Historiarum Veteris Testamenti*. (*Courtesy of the British Museum*)

LL5225

Rutland,[3] is not similar in its design to LL5225, but the other is almost identical and could have provided the basis for the embroidered copy.[4]

When LL5225 was acquired it was dated to the early eighteenth century. A walnut settee (also in the Lady Lever Art Gallery, LL4234) which has Sheldon tapestry cushion covers re-set into it *c.* 1725, shows that Sheldon designs were still appreciated in the early eighteenth century. There is no evidence that Elizabeth Suffolk's name was added later as suggested by the entry in the 1928 catalogue.

## LL5242 (WHL3610)

### *Moses and Aaron and the Tablets of the Law*

Early eighteenth century, initialled 'BB'

*Silks and wool(?) on canvas in tent stitch, with individual squares of rococo stitch and a variety of cross stitches.*

The figures of Moses, with his rod, and Aaron, holding a censer, are shown as if they were statues in an architectural setting similar to that commonly found at the east end of late seventeenth- and early eighteenth-century churches. The central tablets are the ten commandments housed within a frame formed by marble columns and a broken pediment. To the left of Moses is the Lord's Prayer and to the right of Aaron

48 × 48 cm

Provenance: W. Mill, Old Sun House, 3 Cheyne Row;[4] sold Christie's, 18 June 1918, lot 124, £19, bought from M. Harris and Sons £19.19.0.

References: **1** The title page to a Bible printed in Edinburgh, whose illustrations continued in use into the 1660s, showed Moses, rod over shoulder and Aaron holding a censer in a similar fashion. A.S. Herbert, *Historical Catalogue of Printed Bibles, 1525–1961*, 1968, no. 475. **2** Philippa Lewis & Gillian Darley, *Dictionary of Ornament*, 1990. **3** See Appendix AG1, lot 582, dated to *c.* 1710. **4** Lever also bought from Mill's collection lots 126, 127 and 125, LL5225, LL5332, LL5387 (pp. 101, 228, 99) all of which are datable to the early eighteenth century.

1928 Catalogue no. 87.

LL5242

is the Creed. The embroidery might be meant to depict a particular church or, more likely, could be a design created from a Bible frontispiece.[1] The inclusion of the swastika as part of the design is probably due to the motif's Christian symbolism of resurrected life.[2] The undulating zig-zag pattern forming the background, in shades of pale blue and cream, is reminiscent of marbled paper, and appears most often in tent-stitch pieces at the beginning of the eighteenth century.

Lever owned another sampler with verses from the chapter of Exodus similar in description to LL5242 and LL5239, which was sold from the collection in 1926.[3]

LL5347 (WHL3727)

## Seated Lady and Gentleman with Begging Dog

Early eighteenth century

*Canvas worked in silk and wool(?) in tent stitch.*

30.5 × 35cm

Provenance: purchased through M. Harris and Sons, 5 February 1919 for £40.

1928 Catalogue no. 85.

LL5347

The ill-defined clothes of the couple suggest a date in the early eighteenth century. The man is seated under an oak tree while a spotted dog, sheep and a lion are on the grassy bank in front. The pastoral scene is typical of early eighteenth-century embroidered pictures.

## LL5382 (WHL3138)

### Shepherd and Shepherdess with Dog

Early eighteenth century

*Canvas worked with silk in tent stitch.*

The summary outlining of the leaves and clouds is similar to that found on LL5387 (p. 99) which is dated 1708.

23 × 27 cm

Provenance: purchased through D.L. Isaacs, 12 January 1917, for £15.

Literature: Virginia Glenn Pow, 'A New Look in Traditional Textiles', *Discovering Antiques*, 1970, no. 19, pp. 444–5 colour illus. fig. 3.

1928 Catalogue no. 98.

LL5382

## LL5254 (WHL4309)

### Christ and the Samarian Woman at the Well

First third of the eighteenth century

*Canvas worked with wool and silk in tent stitch with attached pieces of mica and glass beads.*

New Testament scenes are uncommon in the late seventeenth century and even rarer in the following century. Of the few

28.5 × 36.5 cm

Provenance: unknown. At The Hill, Hampstead, by July 1921.

References: **1** See Appendix KFR1, lots 282, 305; C1 lot 35. **2** T.86–1813, G.W. Digby and W. Hefford, *The Tapestry*

*Collection: Medieval and Renaissance*, 1980, no. 71f, pl. 103c; detail from Danish sampler T.59–1914, related to an engraving by F.A. Meloni published in a Bible of 1717. **3** Georg Garde, *Dansk Silkebroderede Laerredsduge*, 1961, p. 262–3. **4** A.S. Herbert, *Historical Catalogue of Printed Bibles 1525–1961*, 1968, No. 475. These illustrations created reactions against the introduction of 'Popish pictures' in Bibles.

1928 Catalogue no. 80.

LL5254

pieces that are known, this scene (John 4:25–6), in which Christ declares himself to be the Messiah for the first time, and to a woman, was the most frequently embroidered. The Lady Lever has another eighteenth-century view of the subject (LL5291) and originally had a further three eighteenth-century versions which were sold on Lever's death.[1] The composition is rather generalized and shows no similarities to other versions found on a Sheldon tapestry cushion cover and a 1751 sampler in the Victoria and Albert Museum.[2] It may be adapted from a print produced by Hans Collaert for Nicholas Visscher's Bible published in the middle of the seventeenth century,[3] but is not similar to a Boetius Bolswert engraving used to illustrate a New Testament published in Edinburgh in 1633.[4]

59.5 × 41 cm

Provenance: purchased through M. Harris and Sons, 5 February 1919, £48.

References: **1** See LL5254. **2** Lanto Synge, *Antique Needlework*, 1982, p. 93, fig. 59, where it was thought probably to derive from a Bible illustration.

1928 Catalogue no. 112.

LL5291 (WHL3726)

## Christ and the Samarian Woman at the Well

First third of the eighteenth century

*Canvas worked with silk and wool in tent stitch, florentine stitch and French knots.*

The subject was one of the more popular embroidered New Testament scenes.[1] Apart from its partially golden setting, LL5291 is very close compositionally to a tent-stitch picture dated *c.* 1730, once in the hands of Mallet and Sons.[2] It is worked in a more detailed manner than the latter and is unusual for the abstract pattern of the golden florentine or flame stitch which covers most of the background.

LL5291

LL5365 (WHL3512)

## Christ Appearing as a Gardener to Mary Magdalene

Early to mid-eighteenth century

*Canvas worked with silk and wool in tent stitch.*

58 × 47.5 cm

The depiction of a New Testament scene, unusual enough in the seventeenth century, was even rarer at the beginning of the next century. Another canvas-work scene similar not in its style, but in depicting the risen Christ appearing to his disciples, is to be found on a firescreen probably worked in 1754 by Henrietta, Duchess of Gordon, a member of a devout Scottish Catholic family.[1] It is possible, therefore, that LL5365 may also have been worked in a Catholic family.

Provenance: purchased through Arthur Edwards, 59 and 61 Wigmore Street, 8 May 1918, £35.

References: **1** In the collection of the Earl of Wermyss and March KT, LLD, Margaret Swain, *Scottish Embroidery*, 1986 p. 75–7. **2** Alexander Globe, *Peter Stent, London Printseller*, Vancouver 1985, p. 239. **3** Illustrated Bartsch *Le Peintre Graveur*, vol. 52 (Cornelis Cort), p. 113.

1928 Catalogue no. 110.

LL5365

It would appear from the detailed depiction of the figures' dress and tunic folds and the attempted modelling of their torsos, that LL5365 has a definite print source but none has so far been identified. It is not for example after the engraving by F. Delaram used by Peter Stent as the title page to his *A Booke of Flowers, Fruits, Beastes* published around 1650,[2] nor is it based on Cornelis Cort's popular print after Giulio Clovio.[3]

LL5304 (WHL3470)

## Lady Seated with Flowers

First third of the eighteenth century

*Canvas worked with silk in tent stitch.*

29 × 33.5 cm

Provenance: purchased through M. Harris and Sons as pair with LL5305, 24 April 1918, £32.6.9.

1928 Catalogue no. 105.

LL5304 was probably meant as a pair to LL5305, *Man Snaring Birds*. Not only are their background landscapes similar but they are the same size and were certainly purchased together. It is possible, therefore, that the lady is meant to represent spring to LL5305's autumn or winter. There would appear to be no particular reason for Macquoid's suggestion that the pair are examples of German work.

LL5304

## LL5305 (WHL3471)

### *Man Snaring Birds*

First third of the eighteenth century

*Canvas worked with silk in tent stitch.*

A pair to LL5304 which may represent autumn or winter, the period in the agricultural year when bird snaring takes place.

29 × 33.5 cm

Provenance: purchased through M. Harris and Sons as pair with LL5304, 24 April 1918, £32.6.9.

1928 Catalogue no. 106.

LL5305

LL5325 (WHL2686)

## Pastoral Scene – Shepherd Piping to a Shepherdess

Worked by Anne Maria Smith, first third of the eighteenth century

*Canvas worked with silk and wool in tent stitch.*

A larger version of the common pastoral theme seen, for example, in LL5393 (p. 114), and slightly more animated with its inclusion of a fox-hunting scene on the left. Its size suggests that it must always have been intended to be displayed as a picture like LL5346.

46 × 66.5 cm

Provenance: purchased through Frank Partridge, 16 December 1915, £35; displayed at Thornton Manor.

1928 Catalogue no. 108.

LL5325

LL5346 (WHL519; H71)

## Pastoral Scene with Classical Ruins

First third of the eighteenth century

*Canvas worked with silk and wool in tent stitch.*

This embroidery may be seen as an attempt to depict (in a more naturalistic manner than in the previous century) gentry couples strolling through their parkland landscaped with ruinous classical tombs. The view is also markedly suffused with the pastoral poetry of Pope and Ambrose Philips,[1] who transposed Virgil's *Eclogues* from classical Greece to Georgian England. Amorous dalliances and grieving shepherds appeared in many guises throughout their poems. The composition of LL5346 could even have been inspired by Philips's *Fifth Pastoral*, which describes the musical competition between the shepherd Colin and a nightingale, which Colin wins and in so doing kills the bird. In order to assuage his grief for her:

> He builds her Tomb beneath a Laurel Shade:
> Then adds a Verse and sets with flowr's the Ground.[2]

80.5 × 116 cm

Provenance: unknown but acquired by January 1907 for £60(?) and displayed at The Hill, Hampstead.

Literature: illustrated in A. Carlyle Tait, 'English Needlework in the Lady Lever Art Gallery – Part II', *Apollo*, July 1947, p. 4.

References: **1** Pope's *Pastorals* were first published in 1709 and edited by E. Audra and A. Williams, Pope's *Pastoral Poetry and An Essay on Criticism*, 1961. **2** Ed. M.G. Segar, *Poems of Ambrose Philips*, Oxford, 1937 p. 31, ll. 112–13.

1928 Catalogue no. 109.

LL5346

Another pastoral scene of a similarly large scale can be seen in LL5381. There seems to be no particular reason to believe that LL5346 is of foreign workmanship, as suggested by Theresa Macquoid.

## LL5381 (WHL2633)

### Pastoral Scene with Shepherdess, Piper and Children

First third of the eighteenth century[1]

*Canvas worked in silk and wool in tent stitch. The colours and threads are much worn and faded.*[2]

The large scale and pastoral theme of LL5381 would suggest that it could have been worked as a pair with LL5346, of a similar size and subject, except that the two do not appear to have been purchased at the same time and there must originally have been many such large pictorial embroideries.

82 × 118 cm

Provenance: purchased through D.L. Isaacs, 20 August 1915 for £65 and kept at Thornton Manor.

References: **1** Macquoid dated the piece *c.* 1730–50. Very few tent-stitch needleworks of this period are dated. One dated 1735 shows a shepherdess figure and trees similar in style to LL5381 (Huish, *Samplers and Tapestry Embroideries*, 1900, pl. LII). **2** LL5381 was cleaned immediately on acquisition.

1928 Catalogue no. 96.

LL5381

## LL5378 (WHL3410)

# *Shepherd Couple Dancing round a Maytree to a Piper's Tune*

First half of the eighteenth century

*Canvas worked with silk and wool in tent stitch.*

81 × 63 cm

The walnut frame of LL5378 was made specially for the embroidery soon after purchase[1] which suggests that it may have been taken from a piece of furniture such as a sofa or a fire screen. The figures, and particularly the stylized floral border, suggest French work,[2] though when purchased it was said to be English.

Provenance: purchased through Frank Partridge, 24 January 1918, when it was dated to 1780, for £145[3] and displayed at The Hill, Hampstead.

References: **1** Invoice for cost of making frame in gallery archives. **2** See G. de Bellaigue, *Waddesdon Manor Furniture, Clocks and Gilt Bronzes*, 1974, vol. II, p. 586, set of French chairs *c.* 1735. **3** This figure is substantially more than for pieces of equivalent quality purchased from M. Harris and Sons and may account for Lever's rare embroidery purchases from Partridge.

1928 Catalogue no. 119.

LL5378

50 × 45 cm

Provenance: purchased through Frank Partridge, 23 March 1917, £40 and displayed at The Hill, Hampstead.

References: **1** In the collection of Mrs A. De Pass according to M.B. Huish, *Sampler & Tapestry Embroideries*, 1900, pl. LII.

1928 Catalogue no. 122.

LL5383 (WHL3175)

## *Shepherdess Standing in a Landscape*

First half of the eighteenth century

*Canvas worked with silk and wool in tent stitch. The picture is backed with a striped, woven textile of a later date.*

The manner in which the oak leaves have been stylized is similar to that found in an embroidered picture of a shepherdess dated 1735.[1] A date of around that period would probably suit LL5383 as well. The shepherdess has been drawn and embroidered in a very sophisticated way so that the outline of her legs can be discerned underneath her lightly swaying skirt. This effect, along with the shepherdess's dominance in the composition and the rare inclusion of items such as the brick water trough, suggest that the embroidery could well have been designed after a particular engraving, perhaps inspired by the pastorals of Alexander Pope or Ambrose Philips, though no appropriate print has been discovered.

LL5383

113

LL5393 (WHL4200)

## *Shepherd Piping to a Shepherdess*

First third of the eighteenth century

*Canvas worked with silk and wool in tent stitch.*

Generalized pastoral scenes in which gentlemen played musical instruments to their ladies while a dog rests nearby, perhaps as a symbol of fidelity, were very popular during the first three decades of the century.[1] Another example similar in character is the pair of scenes dated to *c.* 1720, formerly in the collection of Percy Griffiths.[2] LL5393 was purchased as a pair with LL5394.

41.5 × 51.5 cm

Provenance: purchased as a pair through Frank Partridge, 25 May 1920, £140.

References: **1** LL5394, LL5325. **2** Eugenie Gibson, 'Mr Percival D. Griffiths' Collection of Old English Needlework (Conclusion)', *Connoisseur*, vol. 63, 1922 p. 149.

1928 Catalogue no. 104.

LL5393

LL5394 (WHL4201)

## Lady and Gentleman Seated with Sheep and Deer

First third of the eighteenth century

*Canvas worked with silk and wool in tent stitch.*

41.5 × 51.5 cm

Provenance: purchased with LL5393 through Frank Partridge, 25 May 1920, £140 the pair.

References: **1** Some of the many attributes of which a deer was considered symbolic were fertility and sexual love; Guy de Tervarent, *Attributs et Symboles dans l'Art Profane*, 1958, vol. I, pp. 66–7.

1928 Catalogue no. 107.

The embroiderer of LL5394 did not follow the design as drawn on the canvas. Immediately above the couple's heads one can see the outline of further bush-covered hillocks and an oak tree branch, which were ignored when the design was worked. The lady's gesture towards the deer (or stag?) may have some symbolic significance with regard to this companionate image.[1]

LL5394

115

LL5308 (WHL3682)

## Shepherd Piping to Sheep

First third of the eighteenth century[1]

*Canvas worked in silk in fine tent stitch.*

The peculiarly shaped central section, which has been attached to another piece of embroidered landscape to form a rectangle, may originally have been mounted as a hand-held fire-screen, of the sort popular in the eighteenth century.[2]

32.5 × 24.5 cm

Provenance: purchased through M. Harris and Sons, with its pair LL5309, about 16 October 1918 for £45 each and kept at The Hill, Hampstead.

References: **1** The first inventory dated it 1780. **2** For examples see 'Percival Griffiths Collection of Old English Needlework (Conclusion)', *Connoisseur*, vol. 63, 1922, p. 152, pl. V, VI. LL5308 and 5309 may have been the embroideries referred to in a telegram sent by Harris to Lord Leverhulme on 19 October 1918 stating that they were 'genuine but repaired'.

1928 Catalogue no. 102.

LL5308

Plate 1   *The Defeat of the Armada and the Gunpowder Plot* (LL5292, pp. 18–20), a canvas-work picture based on a 1621 engraving by Samuel Ward

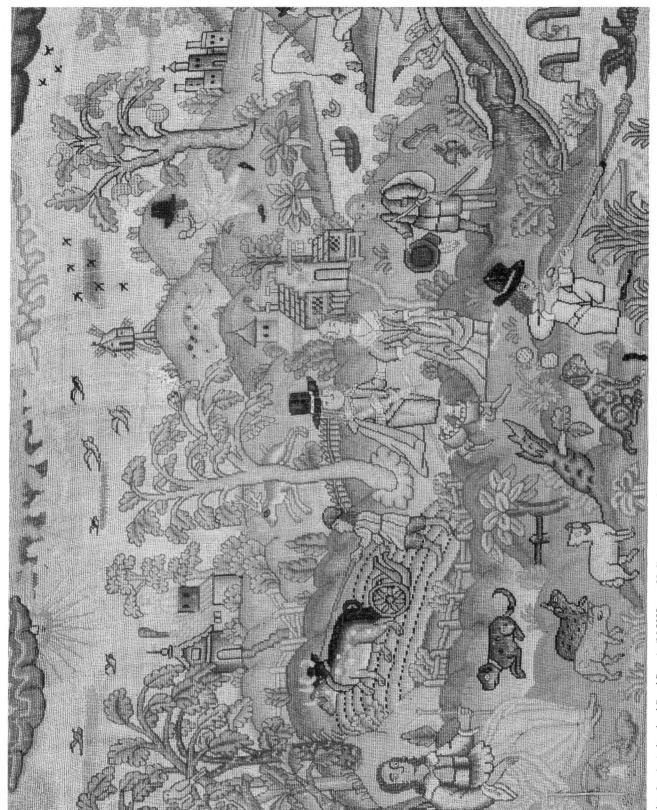

Plate 2  *Agricultural and Rural Pursuits* (LL5255, pp. 28–9), a canvas-work picture embroidered during the mid-seventeenth century incorporating a number of popular motifs

Plate 3  *Jacob, Rachel, Leah and Laban* (LL5233, pp. 36–7), a silk-work embroidered picture of the late seventeenth century surrounding narrative elements from the Genesis story of Jacob and Rachel with spot motifs of flowers, birds and animals

Plate 4 *The Expulsion of Hagar and Ishmael by Abraham* (LL5241, pp. 42–3), a silk-work picture of a very popular subject, embroidered during the second half of the seventeenth century and adapted from an engraving published by Gerard de Jode of a sixteenth-century painting by Martin de Vos

Plate 5 *Landscape with the Meeting of Jacob and Esau* (LL5249, pp. 50–1), a Flemish silk-work embroidery of the seventeenth century, based upon an engraving by Boetius Bolswert after a painting by Gillis van Coninxloo

Plate 6   *The Story of David and Bathsheba* (LL5270, pp. 57–9), a raised-work picture dated 1665 which uses silk, metal thread and silk-covered wooden moulds to depict the Old Testament story of David and Bathsheba in five scenes adapted from engravings published by Gerard de Jode

Plate 7  *The Drowning of the Pharaoh in the Red Sea* (LL5229, pp. 59–61), a raised-work picture probably embroidered by Damaris Pearse (1659–79) of Ermington, Devon, when under sixteen years of age

Plate 8   *Paris and Pallas (Athene) with the Four Continents* (LL5260, pp. 66–7), another example of raised-work from the second half of the seventeenth century. Pallas (Athene), the goddess of all the arts, and Paris, the Trojan prince and shepherd, occupy the central panels, while in the corner roundels are depicted (clockwise from top left) the continents of America, Europe, Asia and Africa. It is likely that the sections were originally intended to be divided up to form a mirror frame

Plate 9 *Apollo(?) and Minerva(?) Surrounded by Cherub Heads* (LL5267, pp. 67–8), a raised-work picture from the third quarter of the seventeenth century depicting the gods of the creative and domestic arts respectively. The figures could alternatively represent Mercury and Paris

Plate 10    *Adoration of the Holy Family and the Holy Trinity by St Elizabeth, the Infant St John and St Peter(?) as Pope* (LL5101, pp. 84–5), worked in high relief in central Europe during the second half of the seventeenth century, with heads, limbs and torsos seemingly having been carved from wood and plaster and covered in silk before having their features painted

Plate 11   *Shepherd Piping to a Shepherdess* (LL5251, pp. 128–9), a pastoral scene worked in silk by Elizabeth Tole in 1741

Plate 12 *Seated Shepherdess within a Flowered Border* (LL5380, pp. 140–1), a late eighteenth-century painted silk picture perhaps depicting the heroine Leonora from Isaac Bickerstaffe's popular comedy, *The Padlock*, first performed in 1768

Plate 13  *Couple in Classical Dress with a Man Writing in the Sand* (LL5316, pp. 156–7), a painted silk picture of the early nineteenth century based on an engraving by the French artist, Pierre-Michel Alix (1762–1817)

Plate 14  *The Sacrifice of Isaac with Three Scenes from the Story of Isaac and Rebecca* (LL5256, pp. 179–81), an embroidered casket worked in 1667 and initialled 'HP'. The canvas-work picture on the lid depicts the sacrifice of Isaac adapted from an engraving published by Gerard de Jode; the raised-work on the front depicts Eliezer's encounter at the well with Rebecca, that on the left side, Isaac greeting Eliezer and Rebecca on their return to Canaan

Plate 15   Detail from *The Sacrifice of Isaac with Three Scenes from the Story of Isaac and Rebecca* (LL5256, pp. 179–81), showing the raised-work picture on the right side of the casket of Eliezer taking leave of Abraham to go in search of a bride for Isaac

Plate 16  *King and Queen with Leopard, Lion, Kingfisher and Eagle* (LL5216, p. 190), a raised-work mirror frame from the second half of the seventeenth century

Plate 17  *The Coronation of Athaliah and the Usurpation of Joash* (LL5226, pp. 203–4) and *The Coronation of Joash and the Execution of Athaliah* (LL5227, pp. 204–5), two canvas-work valances from the late sixteenth or early seventeenth century depicting the deposition and restoration of King Joash and the House of David

Plate 18 Detail from an early eighteenth-century coverlet (LL5294, pp. 213–15), showing the three differently embroidered sections. The spot motifs in the outer section (at the bottom of the plate) include a huntsman attacking a lion with a club who may perhaps represent either Samson or Hercules

Plate 19 *Joseph and his Brothers with Surrounding Scrolling Foliage and Parrots* (LL5442, pp. 216–17), an eighteenth-century coverlet possibly embroidered in Portugal

Plate 20 Detail from a late nineteenth-century coverlet or table cover (LL5443, p. 223). The peacocks, sunflower and rising sun are motifs typically associated with Arts and Crafts textiles

Plate 21    Sampler: *Triple-towered House, Flying Union Jack, Vases of Flowers, Bowls of Fruit, Animal Motifs and Verse* (LL5335, p. 238), embroidered in a variety of stitches by Naomi Harrison, aged ten, in the early nineteenth century

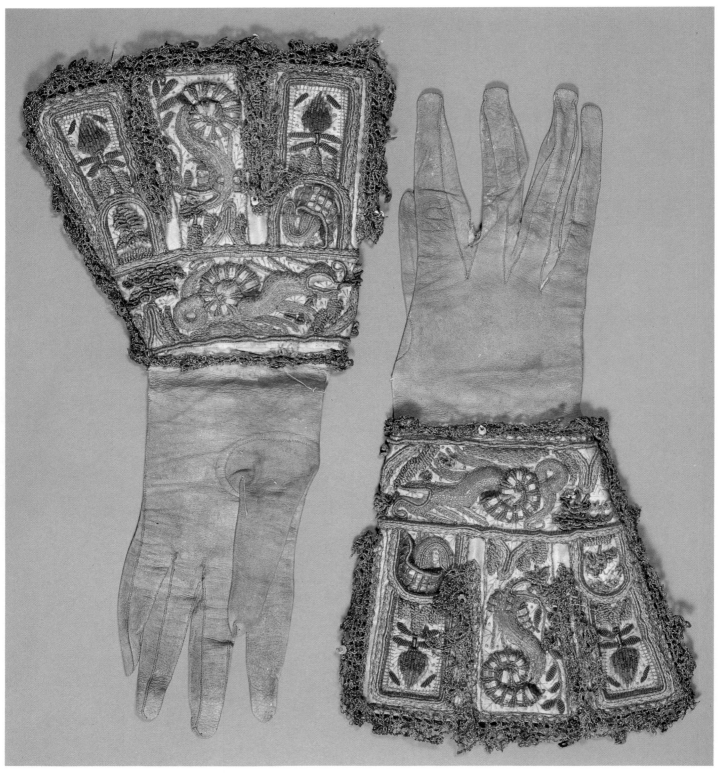

**Plate 22** A pair of early seventeenth-century buff-leather gloves with embroidered gauntlets (LL5415, pp. 250–1), alternately depicting on each of the six tabs a fruit (perhaps a strawberry) and what appears to be a salamander or snail-like reptile

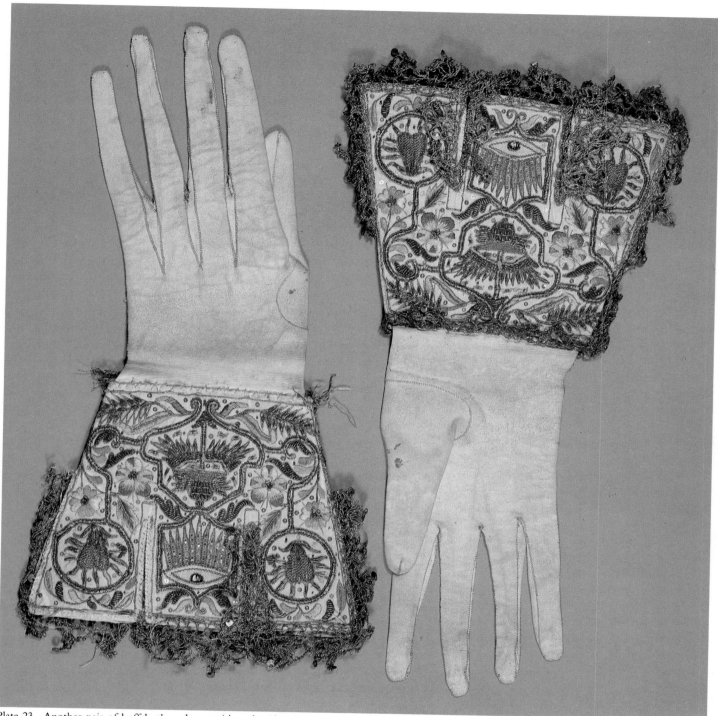

Plate 23   Another pair of buff-leather gloves with embroidered gauntlets of *c.* 1610–30 (LL5416, pp. 251–2), of such an elaborate design that they are unlikely to have been used other than as a love token or *momento mori*, as the motifs of flaming hearts, a winged crown, an eye weeping tears, and pansies also indicate

Plate 24  *Cupids at Archery Practice* and *Aurora Pulled through the Sky by Cupids* (LL5397, pp. 257–8), a beadwork wallet, probably produced in a French workshop, from the second quarter of the eighteenth century. It is likely that it was given as a betrothal gift

LL5309 (WHL3683)

## Seated Shepherdess

First third of the eighteenth century

*Canvas worked in silk in fine tent stitch.*

Theresa Macquoid suggested that this fragment was part of a woman's dress, but like its pair, LL5308 (p. 116), it is most likely to have been originally a hand-screen.

32.5 × 24 cm

Provenance: as LL5308.

1928 Catalogue no. 99.

LL5309

LL5318 (WHL4187)

## *Eliezer and Rebecca at the Well within a Floral Border*

First third of the eighteenth century

*Canvas worked with wool and silk in tent stitch and cross stitch. Many of the dark threads have rotted.*

This piece was probably originally intended, like its pair (LL5319), to cover a chairback, or form a firescreen. The composition is unlike other versions of the subject found on seventeenth- and nineteenth-century embroideries in the collection.[1]

65 × 50 cm

Provenance: Sir Edward Hopkinson Holden, Bart;[2] sold Christie's, 24 March 1920, as part of lot 12; purchased through M. Harris and Sons, 30 March 1920, along with LL5319 for £99.15.0.

References: **1** See casket LL5256 and a painted silk picture LL5359 (p. 169). **2** Sir Hopkinson Holden was the Chairman of the London Joint City and Midland Bank. Other purchases made from his collection include a mirror (LL5224, p. 198) and a settee covered with Sheldon Tapestry panels (LL4234).

1928 Catalogue no. 121.

LL5318

LL5319 (WHL4188)

## Lady and Gentleman as Shepherd and Shepherdess

First third of the eighteenth century

*Canvas worked with wool and a small amount of silk in tent stitch and cross stitch.*

The flowers in the border and around the eight-sided cartouche are slightly different than those on its pair (LL5318), but it was obviously made to form a set with it, perhaps for a suite of furniture.

64.5 × 49.5 cm

Provenance: as LL5318.

Literature: A. Carlyle Tait, 'English Needleworks in the Lady Lever Art Gallery – Part II', *Apollo*, July 1947, p. 5, illus.

1928 Catalogue no. 111.

LL5319

## LL5373 (WHL2681)

### Multi-lobed canvas-work panel

## *The Goddess Diana Hunting Boar*

French, first third of the eighteenth century

*Canvas worked with wool and silk in tent stitch and cross stitch.*

LL5373 is one of a set of five panels all with the same black background and a formalized border of strapwork combined with flowers (LL5373–7). They would appear to have originally been intended as chair (or sofa) backs. The octafoil mount was made to follow the contour of the pictorial embroidery. The set is probably French and the figure and border style bears similarities to a French canvas-work chair dated *c.* 1735 at Waddesdon Manor.[1] Both Macquoid and Tait suggested

55.5 × 68 cm

Provenance: purchased through D.L. Isaacs, 12 May 1915, no. 18, £60 for the set.

Literature: A. Carlyle Tait, 'English Needlework in the Lady Lever Art Gallery – Part II', *Apollo*, July 1947, pp. 5–6.

References: **1** Pamela Clabburn, *The National Trust Book of Textile Furnishings*, 1988, illus. p. 158. **2** Tait, ibid, July 1947 pp. 5–6.

1928 Catalogue no. 118.

LL5373

that the large dragonfly insect conspicuously embroidered into the design of all the panels may be the worker's signature.[2] Tait further stated that the condition of the panels is such that they were obviously never used. This would appear to the author to be unlikely, as the top part of the uppermost quatrefoil of LL5374 had rotted or worn so badly that the pattern was reconstructed with paint so as to fill the mount. The whole set was probably cut out of damaged panels.

## LL5374 (WHL2682)

### Quatrefoil canvas-work panel

## The Goddess Ceres and a Man Digging

French, first third of the eighteenth century

*Canvas worked with wool and silk in tent stitch and cross stitch and paint on board.*

LL5374 is one of a set of five panels, for which see LL5373. The combination of Ceres, goddess of the harvest, with a man digging, may be meant to represent agriculture as a complement to the companion hunting scene (LL5373). The uppermost part of the top quatrefoil has had the design painted in to fit the mount, presumably when the panel was framed. The pagodas and other such buildings in the background of several panels, including LL5374, provide a chinoiserie mood to the set as a whole.

55.5 × 68 cm

Provenance: purchased through D.L. Isaacs, 12 May 1915, no. 18, £60 for the set.

Literature: A. Carlyle Tait, 'English Needlework in the Lady Lever Art Gallery – Part II', *Apollo*, July 1947, pp. 5–6.

1928 Catalogue no. 114.

LL5374

LL5375 (WHL2683)

**Multi-lobed canvas-work panel**

## Page in Court Dress

French, first third of the eighteenth century

*Canvas worked with wool and silk in tent stitch and cross stitch.*

50.5 × 38 cm

LL5375 is one of a set of five panels, for which see LL5373. As an upright panel it could have been intended to be placed on a narrow upright chair or to the side of one of the larger oval shaped panels (LL5373 and LL5374) on a sofa back, possibly to the right of L5374 as both these panels feature a pagoda in the background design.

Provenance: purchased through D.L. Isaacs, 12 May 1915, no. 18, £60 for the set.

1928 Catalogue no. 113.

LL5375

122

LL5376 (WHL2684)

**Multi-lobed canvas-work panel**

## *Lady with Basket of Flowers* (Flora?)

French, first third of the eighteenth century

*Canvas worked with wool and silk in tent stitch and cross stitch.*

LL5376 is one of a set of five panels, for which see LL5373. As an upright panel LL5376 could have been intended to be placed to the left of *The Goddess Diana Hunting Boar* (LL5373) as it shares a similar architectural background scheme with it and LL5377.

50.5 × 38 cm

Provenance: purchased through D.L. Isaacs, 12 May 1915, no. 18, £60 for the set.

1928 Catalogue no. 115.

LL5376

LL5377 (WHL2685)

**Multi-lobed canvas-work panel**

## Shepherdess

French, first third of the eighteenth century

*Canvas worked with wool and silk in tent stitch and cross stitch.*

LL5377 is one of a set of five panels for which see LL5373. LL5377 may have been intended to be placed on the right of *The Goddess Diana Hunting Boar* (LL5373) as it shares a similar architectural background scheme with it and LL5376.

50.5 × 38 cm

Provenance: purchased through D.L. Isaacs, 12 May 1915, no. 18, £60 for the set.

1928 Catalogue no. 117.

LL5377

LL5384 (WHL3208)

## Landscape with Cattle and Castle Surrounded by a Red Floral Border

Mid-eighteenth century(?)

*Canvas worked with silk and wool in tent stitch and cross stitch.*

LL5384 may originally have been intended to cover a fire-screen.

79.5 × 72 cm

Provenance: purchased through M. Harris and Sons, 28 June 1917, £35, and kept at The Hill, Hampstead.

1928 Catalogue no. 116.

LL5384

LL5385 (WHL3326)

## Landscape with Church and House

Mid-eighteenth century(?)

*Fine gauze worked with silk in very fine tent stitch.*

8 × 9 cm

Theresa Macquoid dated this small embroidery, which appears to be a complete picture and not a fragment, to *c.* 1700 but it is closer in style to work produced much later in the century.[1]

Provenance: purchased through M. Harris and Sons, 27 July 1917 for £25 and kept at The Hill, Hampstead.

References: **1** The original gallery inventory dated it to *c.* 1750.

1928 Catalogue no. 42.

LL5385

LL5303 (WHL4208)

## Bust Portrait of Robert, Earl of Leicester

Eighteenth or nineteenth century(?)[1]

*Canvas worked with wools and silks in tent stitch in an octagonal frame.*

15.2 × 11.5 cm

Provenance: purchased through F. Partridge, 29 May 1920, £28 and kept at The Hill, Hampstead.

References: **1** Theresa Macquoid dated LL5303 to *c.* 1710 while the original invoice dated it to 1680. **2** R. Strong, *National Portrait Gallery, Tudor and Jacobean Portraits*, 1969, I, p. 195 pl. 378, 380. **3** Wallace Collection P534.

1928 Catalogue no. 48.

The embroidered portrait does not appear to be based on any major painted portrait of the Earl of Leicester (1532(?)–88), although as Sir Roy Strong points out 'more different types of him exist than for any other 16th century English celebrity'.[2] However, the jewelled pendant worn by the figure appears to be an attempt to show the drop of pearls and garnets from which the badge of the Garter is suspended in Steven van der Meulen's portrait of Leicester (*c.* 1560–5) in the Wallace Collection.[3]

LL5303

127

# Silk-work Pictures

LL5251 (WHL4054)

## Shepherd Piping to a Shepherdess

Worked by 'Eliz Tole' in 1741

*Satin worked with silk in a wide variety of very fine straight stitches including satin, split, stem, long and short and brick stitch laid in patterns with French knots and silk bullion knots and applied seed pearls.*

An almost identical version of this scene (apart from there being three swans not four), worked in a very similar manner with fancy stitches and knots, is in the Fitzwilliam Museum, Cambridge.[1] The pastoral scene in which ladies and gentlemen dressed as shepherds sat or walked sedately amidst a verdant parkland was the main theme for picture embroideries throughout the first half of the eighteenth century. LL5251 and some other Lady Lever pastoral scenes in which a shepherd pipes to a shepherdess may be meant to represent Orpheus and Eurydice or Daphnis and Chloe. The tale of bucolic romance and marriage between Daphnis and his sweetheart Chloe (which was translated into English in 1657), had great appeal for the first two-thirds of the century, when 'bergeries' were fashionable in many areas of the fine and decorative arts.[2] The shepherd couple were also embroidered in the late seventeenth century but it was not as predominant a theme as it became in the eighteenth century when Old Testament scenes fell from favour.

Elizabeth Tole was obviously proud of her fine work on the picture as she signed it twice, once in the sky and a second time on the tree trunk to the right. Tole appears to be a common Bedfordshire name and it is possible that Eliz Tole may be the Eliz Tole who married Thomas Hart in Blunham on 13 October 1757.[3]

35 × 49 cm

Provenance: purchased through M. Harris and Sons, 8 August 1919, £75; displayed at The Hill, Hampstead.

References: **1** T.134–1938. **2** Entry under Longus in N.G.L. Hammond and H.H. Scullard, *The Oxford Classical Dictionary*, 2nd edition, 1970, p. 619. **3** An Elizabeth Toll was christened in Pavenham on 24 December 1732 and other Elizabeth Tole/Tolls are found in the International Genealogical Index for the first half of the eighteenth century in further Bedfordshire villages.

1928 Catalogue no. 97.

LL5251 (see also colour plate 11)

50 × 43 cm

Provenance: B.C. Creasy, Linden Cottage, Springfield, Chelmsford; sold Christie's, 28 January 1919, lot 105;[1] purchased through M. Harris and Sons, 12 February 1919, £4.14.6.

References: **1** Also purchased from B.C. Creasy at this sale were LL5361 and LL5362 *The Rest on the Flight* and *Justice* (pp. 165–6) and a feltwork collage LL5391 (p. 174).

1928 Catalogue no. 165.

LL5379 (WHL3737)

## Basket of Flowers

Late eighteenth century

*Silk worked with silk in fine satin, long and short and stem stitch. The silk backing has split around the edge of the frame.*

The flowers shown include, honeysuckle, roses, daffodils and cornflowers. The oval shape suggests LL5379 might have been intended for a pole screen although it could equally well have hung on an eighteenth-century drawing-room wall.

LL5379

LL5389 (WHL3725)

## Coastal Scene with Fishermen Unloading Nets

Last quarter of the eighteenth century

*Very fine canvas(?) entirely covered with silk in fine long and short stitch and a variety of straight stitches.*

The picture, with its rock arch to the right and ruined tower in the background, would appear to be based on one of the very many coastal scenes by the painter, Claude-Joseph Vernet (1714–89). It is, for example, similar (but in reverse) to Vernet's oval *Mediterranean Coastal Scene: Night*, which he painted in 1751 for Uppark House, Sussex.[1] Theresa Macquoid assumed in the 1928 catalogue that the embroideress was foreign and it is the case that motifs adapted from Vernet's paintings were used by French manufacturers of printed cottons between 1783–1811.[2] But as Vernet's work was very popular among aristocratic British Grand Tourists of the second half of the eighteenth century and prints were engraved after his paintings, one cannot assume that the embroiderer was French. In the last few decades of the eighteenth century British needlewomen were stimulated, by the fame and success of embroideresses such as Mary Linwood (1755–1845), to show off their skills by reproducing paintings with needle and thread. It is possible that LL5389 dates from about this period.

30 × 41.5 cm

Provenance: purchased through M. Harris and Sons, 5 February 1919, £15.

References: **1** Kenwood, London, *Claude-Joseph Vernet* June–September 1976, Cat. no. 28, pl. 28. The same elements of rock arch, fishermen with nets, sailing ship in the centre background and distant tower are also found in the Louvre's *Coastal Sunset*, see F. Ingersoll-Smouse, *Joseph Vernet: Peintre des Marine* 1926, no. 444, pl. XXXX. **2** Nancy Graves Cabot, 'Some Pattern Sources of 18th and 19th Century Printed Cottons', *Bulletin of the Needle and Bobbin Club*, 1949, vol. 33, p. 5, pl. IV for designs used on textiles produced at Jouy.

1928 Catalogue no. 168.

LL5389

LL5395 (WHL4206)

## Landscape with Washerwomen in front of a Bridge and Castle

Late eighteenth to early nineteenth century

*Silk worked with silk in very fine long and short, thorn and satin stitch and French knots[1] mounted within a paper frame.*

This very fine silk-work picture and its pair (LL5396) appear similar in technique, size and pure landscape subject matter to a picture in the Copenhagen, Kunstindustrimuseet, which is signed and dated, Petrine Christensen, 24 August 1833.[2] LL5395 and LL5396 may be embroidered copies of a pair of related landscape paintings.

18 × 23 cm

Provenance: purchased through F. Partridge as a pair with LL5396, 29 May 1920 for £20 and kept at The Hill, Hampstead.

References: 1 According to the original invoice the picture was supposed to be partly straw-work. There is no evidence that this was ever the case. 2 Charlotte Paludan, *Alverdens Broderier i Kunstindustrimuseet*, 1983, pp. 47, 48, cat. no. 131.

1928 Catalogue no. 162.

LL5395

LL5396 (WHL4207)

## Landscape with Washerwoman in front of Cottage

Late eighteenth century to early nineteenth century

*Silk worked with silk in fine long and short and thorn stitch and French knots.*[1]

Paired in style and theme with LL5395.

17.5 × 22.5 cm

Provenance: as LL5395.

References: **1** Like its pair this picture was stated to have been partly worked in straw but this would seem not to have been the case.

1928 Catalogue no. 183.

LL5396

# Painted Silk Pictures

## LL5246 (WHL3773a)

### St Paschal Baylon's Vision of the Host

Italian, second half of the eighteenth century

*Painted silk worked with silk and cord laid on and stuck to the support with gum or wax(?), with applied coloured tinsel(?)*

The saint can be identified as the Spanish Franciscan, Paschal Baylon (canonized in 1690), who experienced visions of angels presenting the Eucharist to him in a monstrance. LL5246 was said to be Italian when it was bought and other collectors who owned related 'embroideries' with similar religious (Counter-Reformation) subject matter, also considered them to be Italian.[1] An *Assumption of the Virgin*, in the Victoria and Albert Museum, made by the same technique is thought to be Venetian.[2] At the time of purchase Lever already owned eight other 'adhesive embroideries' of 'heathen mythology', which were by Gaetano Pati of Rome and dated 1763.[3] The technique used to create LL5246 may be that outlined in an article in the *Connoisseur*, which describes how a layer of half-melted wax was laid over an engraving and silk threads were then laid back and forwards and secured to the surface by pressing, leaving only the hands and faces to be coloured by paint.[4]

25 × 18.3 cm

Provenance: Mrs Nigel Heathcote Cohen, The Lodge, Burnham Norton, Norfolk; sold Christie's, 8 April 1919, as part of lot 189;[5] purchased through M. Harris and Sons, 11 April 1919, 7 guineas.

References: **1** Mrs Lilla Hailstone had four such pictures, including one depicting *Ignatius Loyola receiving the rules of his order*, which she described as 'not strictly needlework but silk threads laid on surface . . . adhering to satin by means of gum and wax with hands and faces painted. They are from Rome and dated to *c.* 1600', *Illustrated catalogue of ancient framed needlework pictures in possession of Mrs S.H. Lilla Hailstone*, privately printed, 1897 pl. XI; Mr Talbot Hughes had an Italian laid silk picture of *The Death of St Francis of Assisi*, 1725–1750, G.S. Seligman and T. Hughes, *Domestic Embroidery*, 1926, pl. 79c. **2** T.13 – 1954. **3** These were purchased from the Whitehead Sale, Christie's, 11 August 1915, lot 789 and described in an inventory of The Bungalow, Rivington. See Appendix AG1, lot 63 and AG2, lot 305? **4** Miss A.F. Morris, 'Needlework Pictures: their pedigree and place in Art', *Connoisseur*, June 1906, pp. 98, 100. **5** LL5246 was purchased along with LL5407, a seventeenth century purse and a small seventeenth century panel of *Susannah and the Elders* sold in 1926, Appendix C1, lot 316.

1928 Catalogue no. 145.

LL5246

LL5356 (WHL3329)

## Fame Scattering Flowers over Shakespeare's Tomb

1782 to early nineteenth century

*Painted silk worked with silk in long and short stitch, satin and stem stitch.*

The engraved source for LL5356 is a print by Francesco Bartolozzi, after a drawing by Angelica Kauffmann, published by A. Paggi in August 1782 (fig. 18).[1] The print was accompanied by a verse about Shakespeare's tomb by Gilbert Cooper Dodsley.[2] Other known embroidered examples of this subject, in the Victoria and Albert Museum[3] and Leicestershire Museums,[4] are also oval in shape and follow the Kauffmann design.

21 × 16.5 cm

Provenance: purchased through M. Harris and Sons, 27 July 1917, as a pair with LL5355 for £13.

References: **1** *100 Examples of Engravings by Francesco Bartolozzi; Selected from Rare Examples in the Department of Prints and Drawings*, British Museum, 1885, vol. II, pl. XLV. A colour print of exactly the same design was engraved by Thomas Burke, Lady V. Manners and G.C. Williamson, *Angelica Kauffmann*, 1924. **2** Selwyn Brinton, *Bartolozzi and his Pupils in England*, 1903, p. 33, provides an alternative title of *Fancy Scattering Flowers over Shakespeare's Tomb* derived from Dodsley's poem. **3** V&A T.39–1874. **4** Exhibited at *The Subversive Stitch; Embroidery in Women's Lives 1300–1900*, Whitworth Art Gallery, Manchester, 27 May–29 August 1988, cat. no. 75 as *Lady Scattering Flowers on a Tomb*.

1928 Catalogue no. 144.

LL5356

Figure 18  Francesco Bartolozzi's engraving of *Fame Scattering Flowers on Shakespeare's Tomb*, after a drawing by Angelica Kauffmann, published by A. Paggi in August 1782. (*Courtesy of the British Museum*)

LL5355 (WHL3328)

## Una and the Lion

1783 to early nineteenth century

*Painted silk worked with silk in long and short and stem stitch.*

One of a pair of oval embroidered pictures of the same size and frames and very similar workmanship purchased together by Lever. Like its pair (LL5356) *Una and the Lion* may be after a design by Angelica Kauffmann, engraved as an oval by Thomas Burke and published in 1783 (fig. 19).[1] The same design appears as a painted oval on two pieces of furniture from the same period in the Lady Lever collection, a long sideboard commode (LL4323) and a large cabinet and stand ornamented with rolled paper 'filigree' work (LL4224).[2] The Una legend appears to have been popular, as in 1780 Reynolds had painted his well-known portrait of Mary, eldest daughter of Lady Diana Beauclerk, as Una. The popularity of the subject, drawn from Spenser's *Faerie Queene*, Book I, may be ascribed to its combination of delicate sentiment and patriotism, as Una typifying true religion meets and is protected by the Lion of England. As a print *Una* was paired with *Abra* also by Burke after Kauffmann[3] but its embroidered pair in the Lady Lever collection was the equally patriotic *Fame Scattering Flowers over Shakespeare's Tomb* (LL5356).

21 × 16.5 cm

Provenance: purchased through M. Harris and Sons, 27 July 1917, as a pair with LL5356, £13.

References: **1** Lady V. Manners and Dr G.C. Williamson, *Angelica Kauffmann, R.A., Her Life and Works*, 1924, p. 229. **2** In 1868 Mrs Hailstone also owned an oval painted-silk example of the theme, EE17, in her collection *Catalogue of a Collection of Lace and Needlework*, 1868. **3** Julia Frankau, *Eighteenth-century Colour Prints*, 1900, p. 77.

1928 Catalogue no. 170.

Figure 19 *Una and the Lion*, after a design by Angelica Kauffmann, engraved as an oval by Thomas Burke and published in 1783

LL5355

137

LL5312 (WHL3740)

## The Harvest Girl

1787 to early nineteenth century

*Painted silk worked with silk in long and short stitch, speckling stitch and French knots.*

An embroidered copy of an oval painting by William Redmore Bigg (1755–1828), *The Harvest Girl*, which was engraved by Ogborne and published in 1787 (fig. 20). Bigg's paintings were also used for designs by the Pontypool japanned tray manufacturers.[1] The embroidery is paired with a *Leonora*(?) *Lady with a Bird-cage* (LL5313), in place of Bigg's painted pair of a lady angler.

24 × 16.5 cm

Provenance: Professor F. Gade, Clifford's Inn; sold Christie's, 28 January 1919 for £14.14.0 the pair; purchased through M. Harris and Sons, 12 February 1919, for £14.14.0 the pair and kept at The Hill, Hampstead.

References: **1** Ian Mackenzie, *British Prints: Dictionary and Price Guide*, 1987.

1928 Catalogue no. 147.

LL5312

Figure 20 *The Harvest Girl* by William Redmore Bigg, engraved by M. Ogborne and published in 1787. (*Courtesy of the Witt Library at the Courtauld Institute of Art*)

LL5313 (WHL3741)

## *Leonora(?) from* The Padlock

Late eighteenth century

*Painted silk worked with silk mainly in long and short, satin, and stem stitches, French knots and speckling stitch.*

The lady, who stands in a parkland setting with a classical temple in the woods behind her, has just released a bird from its cage. She probably represents the character Leonora from Isaac Bickerstaffe's musical comedy *The Padlock*, as she is represented in a similar way, with a freed bird on her finger and an empty birdcage hanging from a tree behind her, in two theatrical prints for the play published in 1770.[1] The play was first performed by David Garrick's company in the 1768–9 season and was a popular 'musical entertainment' for at least the next decade.[2] LL5380 is another embroidery which may represent Leonora.

24 × 16 cm

Provenance: as LL5312.

References: **1** Theatre Museum, Production File for *The Padlock*, Covent Garden, 23 October 1770, GE.513, GE.514. **2** G.W. Stone Jr, *The London Stage* 1962, part IV, pp. 1348, 1356.

1928 Catalogue no. 167.

LL5313

LL5380 (WHL3778)

## Seated Shepherdess (Leonora?) within a Flowered Border

Final third of the eighteenth century

*Painted silk worked with silk in long and short, satin, and stem stitches, French knots and speckling stitches.*

LL5380 may depict Leonora from Isaac Bickerstaffe's popular comedy *The Padlock*, first performed at Drury Lane in 1768.[1] For another embroidery with Leonora as subject see LL5313. Leonora, the play's female protagonist, bewails the prospect of an unhappy marriage to an older but wealthier man. In the play's first act she enters with a pet robin on her finger and exits with the following refrain:

> Was I a shepherd's maid to keep
> On yonder plains a flock of sheep:
> Well pleased I'd watch the live-long day,
> My ewes at feed, my lambs at play:
> Or would some bird that pity brings,
> But for a moment lend its wings,
> My parents then might rave and scold,
> My guardian strive my will to hold:
> Their words are harsh, his walls are high,
> But spite of all away I'd fly.[2]

Leonora provided the motif for Sir Joshua Reynolds's portrait of the actress Miss Harriet Powell, later Countess of Seaforth painted in 1769 and engraved in 1770. However, LL5380 does not appear to be based on a mezzotint of the Reynolds painting[3] nor does it display an empty birdcage, the key motif in other representations of the scene.[4] The fine embroidery of LL5380 is particularly evident in the unusually elaborate floral border. The picture may have been intended for a polescreen, although there is no evidence of attachment to the back of the frame.

45 × 39.5 cm

Provenance: purchased through M. Harris and Sons, 28 April 1919, £12 and displayed at The Hill, Hampstead.

References: 1 Stephen Jones ed., *Biographia Dramatica*, 1811, vol. 1, part 1, p. 40, vol. III, p. 114. (The plot was taken from one of Cervantes' *Exemplary Novels*, 'The Jealous Husband'.) 2 Mrs Inchbald, *A Collection of Farces*, 1815, vol. IV, pp. 178. 180. 3 Edward Hamilton, *Catalogue Raisonné of the Engraved Works of Sir Joshua Reynolds, P.R.A., from 1755 to 1820*, 1874, pp. 95–6. 4 Theatre Museum file on the performance of *The Padlock*, Covent Garden, 23 October 1770, GE513, GE514. But LL5380 does show the bird perched on the lady's finger as do the two Theatre Museum prints.

1928 Catalogue no. 150.

LL5311 (WHL3687)

## Children Playing at Ghosts

1791 to early nineteenth century

*Painted silk worked with chenille in long and short stitch and French knots.*

The subject is based on a mezzotint engraving by Luigi Schiavonetti after Richard Westall's *The Ghost (L'Apparition)*,

33 × 42 cm

Provenance: purchased through M. Harris and Sons, 19 November 1918, £15; displayed at The Hill, Hampstead.

LL5380 (see also colour plate 12)

which was first published in 1791 (fig. 21).[1] A coloured print of the same subject by Schiavonetti finished by Bonnefoy was published in 1798.[2] The latter depicts the figures reversed and in a vaguely interior setting, rather than the landscape of LL5311, which enables the embroiderer to show off her abilities with chenille. The *Ghost* was probably a fairly popular print as it was intended as a well-known companion to *The Mask*, after Reynolds' portrait of the two young daughters of the 3rd Duke of Marlborough, Ladies Charlotte and Anne Spencer.[3] LL5311 would appear to be in its original painted oval glass mount and gilt frame.

References: **1** Julia Frankau, *Eighteenth-century Colour Prints*, 1900, p. 98. The print is not illustrated. **2** Illustrated in *Connoisseur*, vol. XI, March 1905, p. 163. **3** See Frankau, p. 98.

1928 Catalogue no. 163.

LL5311

## LL5352 (WHL3195)

## *English Peasants*

1791 to early nineteenth century

*Painted silk worked with wool and silk in long and short, stem, and chain stitches and some French knots. There are some splits in the painted silk background.*

LL5352 is an embroidered copy of a painting by Richard Westall (1766–1836) which was engraved by I. Bortignoni under the title *English Peasants* and by Antoine Cardon (1772–1813) under the title *L'Enfant en Nourrice*, when it was published in Paris in June 1807 (fig. 22).[1] Westall exhibited a painting called *English Peasants* at the Royal Academy in 1791 (no. 518). The French coloured print was part of a series after Westall paintings entitled *The Unhappy Separation* and the pair to this embroidery (LL5353) is copied from another print in the series.

32.5 × 37.5 cm

Provenance: purchased with LL5353 through M. Harris and Sons, 31 May 1917, £35 and first kept at The Hill, Hampstead.

References: **1** Witt Library Files, n18, nr202.

1928 Catalogue no. 184.

LL5352

Figure 22  I. Bortignoni's engraving, after Richard Westall, of *English Peasants*. (*Courtesy of the Witt Library at the Courtauld Institute of Art*)

LL5353 (WHL3196)

## The Unhappy Separation: the Goatherd's Family

Early nineteenth century

*Painted silk worked mainly in wool with some silk in long and short stitch, and stem stitch.*

Like its pair (LL5352) this embroidery copies a Richard Westall painting which was engraved by Cardon and published in 1807 under the French title *La Séparation Douloureuse* (The Unhappy Separation) (fig. 23).[1]

32.5 × 37.5 cm

Provenance: as LL5352.

References: **1** Witt Library Files.

1928 Catalogue no. 155.

LL5353

Figure 23   Cardon's engraving of a Richard Westall painting, published in 1807 under the French title, *La Séparation Douloureuse*. (*Courtesy of the Witt Library at the Courtauld Institute of Art*)

46 × 39 cm

Provenance: purchased by Lever through M. Harris and Sons, 22 March 1917, £35; displayed at The Hill, Hampstead.

References: 1 Julia Frankau, *Eighteenth-century Colour Prints*, 1900, p. 110. 2 William Roberts, *Sir W. Beechey*, 1907, pp. 40–1, 265; Sotheby's, New York, 10 January 1991, lot 101a. 3 *Connoisseur*, vol. XVI, November 1906, p. 164. 4 Miss A.F. Morris, 'Needlework Pictures: their pedigree and place in art', *Connoisseur*, vol. XVI, June 1906, p. 100 illus. p. 96. 5 Noted on purchase invoice.

1928 Catalogue no. 161.

Figure 24 Charles Wilkin's print, after Sir William Beechey's *Portrait of Sir Francis Ford's Children Giving a Coin to a Beggar Boy*

LL5349 (WHL 3173)

## Children Giving Alms to a Beggar Boy

1793 to early nineteenth century

*Painted silk worked with silk and wool in long and short stitch, stem stitch and a number of other fine straight stitches.*

LL5349 is a version in needlework of a well-known print by Charles Wilkin after Sir William Beechey's *Portrait of Sir Francis Ford's Children Giving a Coin to a Beggar Boy* (fig. 24).[1] The painting was shown to great critical acclaim at the Royal Academy in 1793 and the engraving was dedicated to Queen Charlotte and provided with the title *Here Poor Boy without a Hat, Take this Ha'penny*.[2] The present title was provided for the print when it was reproduced in the 1906 volume of the *Connoisseur*.[3] An oval embroidered version of the same print, but referred to as *The Blind Beggar* after Morland, was in Lord Sackville's collection at Knole in 1906.[4] The theme was obviously thought a suitable one, likely to arouse a sympathetic response from any child or young lady. LL5349 is not in its original frame and may have been removed while it was being repaired by the Decorative Needlework Society of Sloane Street, London.[5]

LL5349

LL5310 (WHL3673)

## Mother with Child Frightened by a Dog

Late eighteenth to early nineteenth century

*Painted silk worked with silk in long and short stitch, stem stitch and French knots.*

The Embroiderer's Guild collection has a picture with the same composition, although lacking the trees.[1] LL5310 is typical in its subject matter of the embroidered pictures produced in the last decade of the eighteenth century. In common with other visual arts, they stressed an affectionate and companionate ideal of motherhood, an ideal similarly reflected in other embroidered pictures of the period in the collection (LL5363). Macquoid considered that it might be French, though there is no reason not to ascribe it to British hands. The frame and decorated glass mount are probably original to the needlework and are similar to many of the collection's other embroidered pictures from this period.[2]

27 × 20 cm

Provenance: purchased through M. Harris and Sons, 16 October 1918, £12 and displayed at The Hill, Hampstead.

References: **1** EG235 1983. **2** See also EG235 1983.

1928 Catalogue no. 169.

LL5310

39.5 × 31.5 cm

Provenance: purchased through M. Harris and Sons, 28 April 1919, £12 and displayed at The Hill, Hampstead.

Exhibited: Whitworth Art Gallery, Manchester, *The Subversive Stitch: Embroidery in Women's Lives 1300–1900*, 27 May– 29 August 1988, cat. no. 68, illus. p. 17.

1928 Catalogue no. 152.

LL5363 (WHL3779)

## Seated Lady Playing with a Small Boy

Late eighteenth to early nineteenth century

*Painted silk worked with silk, wool and chenille in long and short stitch and French knots.*

The frame and oval glass mount decorated with painted gold leaves in its corners is probably original to the embroidery as is a stylistically similar frame around LL5310.

LL5363

LL5300 (WHL3436)

## The Flight into Egypt

Late eighteenth to early nineteenth century

*Silk painted in watercolour and worked predominantly in wools with some silks in long and short, and split stitch, and French knots.*

Like most painted silk embroideries the faces, hands and feet have not been embroidered over. The black and gilt glass mount which provides the oval frame for the picture is commonly found on this type of painted silk embroidery at the beginning of the nineteenth century. They were probably mass-manufactured specifically for such embroideries. LL5300 was acquired along with its pair *The Finding of Moses* (LL5320).

34 × 41.5 cm

Provenance: Miss E.J. Abbott of Leightonstone [*sic*]; sold Christie's, 12 March 1918, lot 267 as pair with LL5320; purchased through M. Harris and Sons, 15 March 1918, £21 and kept at The Hill, Hampstead.

1928 Catalogue no. 164.

LL5300

## LL5320 (WHL3437)

## *The Finding of Moses*

Late eighteenth to early nineteenth century

*Silk painted in watercolour and worked predominantly in wools with some silks in long and short stitch, satin stitch and French knots.*

A similar oval painted silk embroidery of *The Finding of Moses* is in the Victoria and Albert Museum and is dated to the last quarter of the eighteenth century, its design is, however, not similar to that of LL5320.[1] LL5320 is framed in a similar manner to its pair LL5300.

34 × 42 cm

Provenance: as LL5300.

Literature: A. Carlyle Tait, 'English Needleworks in the Lady Lever Art Gallery – Part II', *Apollo*, July 1947, illus. p. 4.

References: **1** V&A T.118 – 1963; Liverpool Museum has a silk picture the same as LL5320 but showing only the central figures (56.53.2). For another eighteenth-century depiction of the scene see LL5392.

1928 Catalogue no. 149.

LL5320

40 × 51 cm

Provenance: purchased through M. Harris and Sons, 25 March 1919, £22; displayed at The Hill, Hampstead.

References: **1** V&A T.118 – 1963. For a canvas-work picture of the same subject dated 1702 see LL5348 (p. 98).

1928 Catalogue no. 158.

LL5392 (WHL3749)

## The Finding of Moses

Late eighteenth to early nineteenth century

*Silk painted with watercolour and worked in wools and silks in long and short stitch, satin stitch and French knots.*

This oblong picture is similar in composition to an oval late eighteenth-century embroidery in the Victoria and Albert Museum.[1] The quality of work on LL5392 is better than that found on LL5320.

LL5392

LL5314 (WHL4018)

## Bo-peep and Boy Blue(?)

Late eighteenth to early nineteenth century

*Painted silk worked with silk and wool(?) in fine long and short and satin stitch and French knots.*

The finely embroidered picture showing a young woman with a flock of sheep and a seated boy playing a pipe may have represented the nursery-rhyme characters of Bo-peep and Boy Blue, although the male figure does not wear blue. By the beginning of the nineteenth century Boy Blue had featured in several song books and Bo-peep had made her appearance in verse.[1] LL5314 was bought along with its pair LL5315, showing two women outside a cottage.

46.5 × 39.5 cm

Provenance: purchased along with LL5315 through M. Harris and Sons, 24 June 1919, £45 and kept at The Hill, Hampstead.

References: **1** Iona and Peter Opie, *The Oxford Dictionary of Nursery Rhymes*, 1951, pp. 93–4 no. 66, pp. 98–9 no. 74.

1928 Catalogue no. 148.

LL5314

LL5315 (WHL4019)

## Two Women outside a Cottage

Late eighteenth to early nineteenth century

*Painted silk worked with silk and wool in very fine long and short, satin and split stitches and French knots.*

The picture shows a young girl returning from the fields with an apron full of corn which she displays to an older woman seated beside a spinning wheel. As Theresa Macquoid commented the scene looks similar to many painted by George Morland (1762/3–1804), the master of such anecdotal scenes from rural life, which were much engraved after 1780.

46.5 × 39.5 cm

Provenance: as LL5314.

1928 Catalogue no. 166.

LL5315

LL5354 (WHL3186)

## Two Girls Carrying Flower Baskets

Late eighteenth or early nineteenth century[1]

*Painted silk worked with wool in long and short, and split stitch and French knots.*

38.5 × 34 cm

Provenance: purchased through M. Harris and Sons, 30 May 1917, £12 and kept at The Hill, Hampstead.

References: **1** The first inventory dated it to *c.* 1780.

1928 Catalogue no. 174.

The monastic(?) ruins in the background of the picture are an unusual element, but one which would have fitted in with eighteenth- and early nineteenth-century interests in the Gothic revival.

LL5354

LL5388 (WHL3671)

## Couple in a Cornfield

Early nineteenth century

*Painted silk worked with silk in satin, long and short and thorn stitch and French knots.*

Although the subject of young girls gleaning was a popular one with painters at the turn of the eighteenth century, LL5388 may depict the Old Testament story of Ruth and Boaz updated to the Regency period.[1] The sympathetic and somewhat romantic tale of the young, widowed Ruth who was allowed to glean the corn in the fields of her wealthy kinsman Boaz and eventually married him (Ruth 2–3) would have been popular, particularly among young women, and

25.5 × 30 cm

Provenance: purchased through M. Harris and Sons, 23 October 1918, £12 and kept at The Hill, Hampstead.

Literature: A. Carlyle Tait, 'English Needleworks in the Lady Lever Art Gallery – Part II', *Apollo*, vol. 45, 1947, p. 6.

References: **1** See also LL5390 for another possible Ruth and Boaz scene.

1928 Catalogue no. 146.

LL5388

also appealed to artists. In 1835 Richard Westall exhibited at the Royal Academy a *Ruth Gleaning in the Fields of Boaz* with the subtitle 'Then said Boaz to Ruth, Hearest thou not, my daughter, go not to glean in another field'.

LL5390 (WHL3728)

## Lovers and Reapers

Late eighteenth to early nineteenth century

*Painted silk worked with silk and chenille in long and short, satin, chain and split stitch and French knots with applied gauze on the figures' clothes. The silk ground has entirely rotted away to reveal a canvas backing in the upper left-hand corner.*

Harvesting scenes were a commonly painted and embroidered theme at the end of the eighteenth century[1] but this picture may, like LL5388, be intended as an updated version of the Ruth and Boaz story.

54 × 59 cm

Provenance: purchased through M. Harris and Sons, 5 February 1919, £16.

References: **1** See for example William Redmore Bigg's *The Harvest Girl*, LL5312 (p. 138).

1928 Catalogue no. 139.

LL5390

LL5317 (WHL3783)

## Countrywoman and Family Leaving Home

Late eighteenth or early nineteenth century

*Painted silk worked with wool mainly in long and short stitch with other straight stitches in basket weave and fern patterns with French knots. The painted silk has been torn, repaired and glued at some time in the past.*

Theresa Macquoid suggested that LL5317 was after a scene by George Morland (1762/3–1804). LL5317 also looks similar in painted style and theme to a pair of embroideries (LL5352, LL5353, pp. 142–4) after a series of paintings by Richard Westall entitled *The Unhappy Separation*.

48 × 65 cm

Provenance: purchased through M. Harris and Sons, 28 April 1919, £22 along with five other mainly painted-silk pictures.[1] First kept at The Hill, Hampstead.

References: **1** Finding of Moses (LL5348); Lady of the Lake (LL5368); Boy writing (LL5364); Woman and Child (LL5363); Seated Shepherdess within a flowered border *Leonora*(?) (LL5380, pp. 98, 166, 171, 140).

1928 Catalogue no. 157.

LL5317

LL5316 (WHL3750)

## Couple in Classical Dress with a Man Writing in the Sand

Early nineteenth century

*Painted silk worked with silk and chenille in fine long and short stitch, satin, stem and straight stitch.*

The names of the engraver, Alix, and the original painter(?) of the scene (now indecipherable), have been written on the silk in ink under the frame. Alix can be identified as the French artist Pierre-Michel Alix (1762–1817), who occasionally produced stipple engravings of scenes from ancient Greek myth

30.5 × 35 cm

Provenance: purchased through M. Harris and Sons, 25 March 1919, £22; kept at The Hill, Hampstead.

Literature: Bridgeman and Drury ed., *Needlework: an Illustrated History*, colour pl. 20.

1928 Catalogue no. 181.

and history. Alix's neo-classical scenes were often reproductions of paintings or drawings by Louis Lafitte (1770–1828). The man and woman in classical dress may be meant to represent the Trojan prince, Paris; and his first love Oenone, the water spirit. They are often shown dallying in the shade of trees, but Paris usually declares his love for her by carving her name in the bark rather than on the sand.

LL5316 (see also colour plate 13)

LL5321 (WHL3406)

## *Lady Anne Lambton and Children: Domestic Happiness*

Inscribed on the glass mount 'Eliza Tunno, 1802'

*Painted silk worked with wool in fine long and short, and stem stitches and French knots.*

An embroidered copy of a portrait by John Hoppner of Lady Lambton (second daughter of the 4th Earl of Jersey) and her three sons and one daughter. A mezzotint of the painting was engraved by John Young and published in April 1799 under the title *Domestic Happiness.*[1] It was probably in this form that Eliza Tunno knew and embroidered it.

60.5 × 44 cm

Provenance: purchased through M. Harris and Sons, 24 January 1918, £22.

Exhibited: Birmingham Art Gallery, *Exhibition of British Embroidery*, 1959, cat. no. 201.

References: **1** *Connoisseur*, vol. LI, July 1918, illus. p. 93.

1928 Catalogue no. 143.

LL5321

LL5366 (WHL3379)

## Memorial Portrait of Lord Nelson

1806

44 × 49 cm

Provenance: purchased through M. Harris and Sons, 12 December 1917, along with LL5367 for £75, and kept at The Hill, Hampstead.

References: **1** British Museum, *Catalogue of Engraved British Portraits*, 1912, vol. III, p. 314 Nelson no. 2, p. 317 no. 52; Oliver Millar, *Later Georgian Pictures in the Collection of Her Majesty the Queen*, 1969, cat. no. 849. **2** See LL5367. Lever also owned a further one or two Nelson needleworks which were sold in 1926, Appendix C1, lot 29. For printed souvenir handkerchiefs see Mary Schoeser, *Printed Handkerchiefs*, Museum of London, 1988, no. 28; and Coalport China plate see V&A C.67–1984.

Not previously catalogued.

*Painted silk worked with silk and chenille in satin, long and short, stem and chain stitch. The painted silk sky is torn and stained.*

The embroidery is probably adapted from the well-known portrait of Nelson by L.F. Abbott (*c.* 1760–1802), dedicated to Lady Nelson, and engraved as a mezzotint by W. Barnard in 1799 (fig. 25). However, the painted portrait shows both a naval engagement in the background and a building ablaze. The latter is not included in LL5366, whose shoreline setting and sea battle appears closer to that found in John Hoppner's Nelson portrait for the Royal Collection, which was engraved in several versions from 1805 onwards.[1] The embroidered motto 'England expects' shows that the needlework design must have been published after Nelson's death at the battle of Trafalgar in October 1805. As one might expect the death of a national hero like Nelson led to the production, in the months that elapsed between his death and state funeral, of a multitude of souvenirs, including embroidered pictures, which even in Lever's day still commanded premium prices because of their Nelson connection.[2]

Figure 25   Portrait of Nelson, by L. F. Abbot, engraved as a mezzotint by W. Barnard in 1799. (*Courtesy of the British Museum*)

LL5366

159

LL5367 (WHL3380)

## Nelson's Armorial Bearings with Sailor and Lion Supporters

1806

*Painted silk worked with silk and chenille in long and short and stem stitch. The satin backing is torn in several places.*

LL5367 shows a coat of arms, including a shield, a plumed helmet crest, flags and supporters in front of a tree, around

47 × 49 cm

Provenance: as LL5366.

References: **1** J.P. Brooke-Little ed., *Boutell's Heraldry*, ed. 1978, p. 127–8; C.R. Bean, 'Heraldry', *Connoisseur*, vol. 99,

LL5367

April 1937, p. 232. **2** Mary Schoeser, *Printed Handkerchiefs*, Museum of London, 1988, no. 28, and the motto was used on the tickets for Nelson's funeral procession.

Not previously catalogued.

42.5 × 37.5 cm

Provenance: purchased through M. Harris and Sons, 19 November 1918, with its pair LL5358 for £20 the pair and kept at The Hill, Hampstead.

References: **1** W.G. Strickland, *Dictionary of Irish Artists*, 1913, pp. 117–23.

1928 Catalogue no. 151.

Figure 26 *The Father's Darling*, by Adam Buck, engraved and published by J.C. Stadler in 1807

which a ribbon is draped with Nelson's motto, 'PALMAM QUI MERUIT FERAT' ('May he who has earned it take the palm'). The upper third of the shield with its ship, palm tree and battery was added to Nelson's coat of arms after the Battle of the Nile in 1801.[1] The rest of the shield has not been embroidered with his arms but has been left blank. Like its pair, LL5366, the picture was probably worked very shortly after Nelson's death. A handkerchief printed in 1806 to commemorate the funeral shows a very similar oak tree with the mourning figures of a lion and Britannia sitting amongst flags and drums.[2]

LL5357 (WHL3688)

## The Father's Darling

Early nineteenth century after 1807

*Painted silk worked with wool in long and short, stem, and split stitches.*

This picture is an embroidered copy of a work by Adam Buck which was engraved and published by J.C. Stadler in 1807 under the title *The Father's Darling* (fig. 26). Buck's figure subjects were frequently reproduced as stipple engravings and published in magazines such as *The Lady's Monthly Mirror*. His work was also used for furniture decoration.[1] The embroiderer has attempted to reproduce in thread the visual effect of stipple engraving.

LL5357

LL5358 (WHL3689)

## The Mother's Hope

Early nineteenth century, after 1807

*Painted silk worked with wool in satin and stem stitch.*

Like its pair (LL5357) this picture is after a composition by Buck engraved by Freeman and Stadler and published in 1807 under the title *The Mother's Hope* (fig. 27). Both compositions by Buck were originally rectangular and were embroidered within a rectangular pencil-drawn frame but mounted under an oval glass frame.

42.5 × 37.5 cm

Provenance: as LL5357.

1928 Catalogue no. 160.

Figure 27 *The Mother's Hope*, by Adam Buck, engraved by Freeman and Stadler and published in 1807

LL5358

LL5350 (WHL3193)

## Girl Holding a Basket of Flowers

Early nineteenth century

*Painted silk worked with wool, some silk and chenille in long and*

40.5 × 36 cm

Provenance: purchased with its pair LL5351 through M. Harris and Sons, 30 May 1917, £12 and kept at The Hill, Hampstead.

References: **1** See LL5357 (p. 161).

1928 Catalogue no. 154.

*short, satin, and split stitches and French knots, with wool thread couched with silk. The silk ground is split in several places.*

This type of picture with a solitary curly headed child standing against a landscape is typical of the miniatures and watercolours produced by Adam Buck (1759–1833). The figure is obviously based on Buck's *Father's Darling*[1] although the background differs. Like its pair, LL5351, it was meant to have an oval frame.

LL5350

LL5351 (WHL3194)

## Child Holding a Hat in Parkland Setting

Early nineteenth century

*Painted silk worked in wool and some silk and chenille in long and short, and split stitches and French knots.*

Like its pair, LL5350, this picture is after Adam Buck. The figure of the child is the same as that in Buck's *A Mother's Hope*.[1]

40.5 × 36 cm

Provenance: as LL5350.

References: **1** See LL5358.

Not previously catalogued.

LL5351

36.5 × 28 cm

Provenance: B.C. Creasy, Linden Cottage, Springfield, Chelmsford;[2] sold Christie's, 28 January 1919, lot 102, along with LL5362 for 10 guineas the pair; purchased through M. Harris and Sons, 12 February 1919, along with LL5362 and kept at The Hill, Hampstead.

References: **1** This inscription was not found when the picture was deframed. **2** Also purchased from B.C. Creasy at this sale was an eighteenth-century *Basket of Flowers* LL5379 and a feltwork collage LL5391 (pp. 129, 174).

1928 Catalogue no. 140.

LL5361 (WHL3735)

## The Holy Family at Rest on the Flight into Egypt

Early nineteenth century, after 1811(?)

*Painted silk worked in silk in long and short and satin stitch.*

According to an early inventory of the gallery this picture has inscribed on its back, 'Begun May 11th 1811 ended August 23 1811.'[1] Artists such as Richard Westall exhibited paintings of the Holy Family at the Royal Academy from 1799 including one in 1808.

LL5361

LL5362 (WHL3736)

## Figure of Justice

Early nineteenth century

*Painted silk worked with silk in long and short and stem stitch and knotted silks.*

39.5 × 33.5 cm

Provenance: as LL5361, *Rest on the Flight into Egypt.*

1928 Catalogue no. 156.

LL5362

LL5368 (WHL3781)

## The Lady of the Lake

Second decade(?) of the nineteenth century

*Painted silk worked with silk and applied gilt paper in long and short, satin, and split stitch and French knots. The silk ground has split in several places.*

62.5 × 66 cm

LL5368

Provenance: purchased through M. Harris and Sons, 28 April 1919, £12 and kept at The Hill, Hampstead.

References: **1** Witt Library Files. **2** Richard Altick, *Paintings from Books*, 1985, pp. 426, 429. **3** For example Elizabeth Gillard's embroidery *The Resurrection* dated 1834 with watercoloured faces cut from coloured engravings and sewn on to backing (Manchester, Cornerhouse, *Art of the People* exhibited 23/11/1985–5/1/1986) and LL5360 (p. 173).

1928 Catalogue no. 153.

Sir Walter Scott's very popular poem with a Scottish Highland setting, *The Lady of the Lake*, was first published in 1810. The embroidery is possibly based on Richard Westall's illustration to Canto I Stanza XVII of the poem:

> In listening mood she seemed to stand,
> The Guardian Naiad of the strand

which was engraved by Charles Heath in 1811 (fig. 28).[1] Westall's illustration, however, does not include the huntsman (Sir Roderick Dhu?) and his dogs. In 1811 alone there were four other paintings based on the narrative poem which continued to be illustrated until about 1819.[2] Glued-on paper continued to be used in some embroideries' design up to the middle of the century.[3]

Figure 28   Richard Westall's illustration of *The Lady of the Lake*, engraved by Charles Heath in 1811. (*Courtesy of the Witt Library at the Courtauld Insitute of Art*)

LL5323 (WHL4386)

## The Meeting of Ruth and Boaz[1]

Attributed to Eliza Lever *c*. 1829

*Painted silk worked with silk, chenille, wool and metal thread and metal beads in long and short stitch, and French knots.*

The picture is said to have been embroidered by Lever's mother and is dated from a note in the gallery's files.

45.5 × 65.5 cm

Provenance: presented by the Misses Lever, Hesketh Grange, 19 September 1922.

Literature: A. Carlyle Tait, 'English Needlework in the Lady Lever Art Gallery – Part II', *Apollo*, July 1947, p. 6.

References: **1** A late eighteenth-century 'Boaz and Ruth' in the collection was sold in 1926, Appendix C1, lot 33. The story of Ruth, Naomi and Boaz was chosen as one of the scenes on the memorial stained-glass window in honour of Lady Lever, Lever's wife, in Christchurch, Port Sunlight.

1928 Catalogue no. 74.

LL5323

69 × 53 cm

Provenance: purchased through M. Harris and Sons, 12 December 1918, £12 and kept at The Hill, Hampstead.

References: **1** The collection of Sir Frederick Richmond also contained an early nineteenth-century version of this theme. Lot 223, Christie's, 23 June 1987.

1928 Catalogue no. 172.

LL5359 (WHL3706)

## Rebecca and Eliezer at the Well[1]

Early nineteenth century

*Painted silk worked with silk and wool in long and short, satin and stem stitch with couched threads and French knots.*

The embroidery shows Rebecca drawing water for Abraham's servant Eliezer after his journey to find a bride for his master's son, Isaac (Genesis 24:15–21). By 1800 British artists such as Richard Westall were exhibiting oils of the Nativity and other Gospel stories and by the early 1830s they were reviving the same Old Testament stories so popular with embroiderers over a century before. The painted features and sky are similar to those found on the *Rest on the Flight to Egypt* (LL5361) which may have been worked in 1811 and to *Ruth and Boaz* (LL5323) dated to about 1829.

LL5359

LL5364 (WHL3780)

## Young Man Writing in a Parkland Setting

Early nineteenth century

*Painted silk worked with silk and chenille in long and short stitch and French knots.*

The young man is dressed in a blue costume and plumed hat which appears to be in the 'Van Dyck' style of seventeenth-century dress. The embroidery may be based on a portrait of some noble family's child (see for example LL5321 *Lady Lambton and Children*, p. 158), as it was fashionable to be painted in the 'Van Dyck' style from the 1730s to the 1780s,[1] or it could be after an historical genre painting of the type popular in both France and England at the beginning of the nineteenth century. The figure may be intended to represent a poet or lover.

29.5 × 35.5 cm

Provenance: purchased through M. Harris and Sons, 28 April 1919, £13 and kept at The Hill, Hampstead.

References: **1** Buck, *Dress in Eighteenth-century England*, p. 40.

1928 Catalogue no. 175.

LL5364

LL5245 (WHL3739)

## Elijah and the Raven

Early nineteenth century

*Painted silk worked with wool in long and short stitch and French knots.*

Lever owned another example of this scene, a late eighteenth-century oval (28 × 25.5 cm), which was sold along with its pair, *Moses and the Burning Bush*, after Lever's death.[1]

28 × 25.5 cm

Provenance: Mrs Renwick, Jubilee House, Bradmore Lane, Hammersmith; sold along with another painted silk-work embroidery, Christie's, 28 January 1919, lot 107, 3 guineas; bought through M. Harris and Sons, 13 February 1919, £1.10.

References: **1** Appendix C1, lot 38.

1928 Catalogue no. 159.

LL5245

LL5386 (WHL3551)

## Young Couple Listening to a Bagpiper

First third of the nineteenth century

*Painted silk worked with silk in long and short, satin stitch, stem and speckling stitches with French knots and a ribbed, knotted(?) stitch.*

The Scottish Highland setting of LL5386 would suggest that it might illustrate a scene from one of Sir Walter Scott's

57 × 59 cm

Provenance: purchased through M. Harris and Sons, 29 May 1918, £22.

References: **1** Portfolios of separate engravings were also published from the 1820s through to the 1840s. Altick, *Paintings from Books*, 1985, p. 427. Poor paintings of Scott scenes were criticized as being only suitable for reproduction as 'sampler-work', Altick, as above, p. 199. For other possible 'Scott' embroideries in the collection see LL5360 and LL5368 (p. 166) and G.S. Seligman and T. Hughes, *Domestic Embroidery*, 1926, pl. 85a.

1928 Catalogue no. 177.

(1771–1832) popular novels, collections of which were frequently published with engraved illustrations and were a common source of needlework designs.[1]

LL5386

46.5 × 57.5 cm

Provenance: purchased through M. Harris and Sons, 5 February 1919, £12.

References: **1** C. Heath, *The Waverley Gallery of the Principal Female Characters in Scott's Romances*, 1841, pl. 35. LL5360 could also represent a scene from *The Fair Maid of Perth*, published 1828, in which the heroine Catherine Glover accompanied by her friend Louise feed a prisoner in a castle dungeon by passing to him morsels of food wedged in the top of a long willow stick. For other embroidered versions of Scott material see LL5368 *Lady of the Lake* (p. 166).

1928 Catalogue no. 171.

LL5360 (WHL3729)

**Embroidered and collage picture**

## *Two Female Pilgrims(?) Standing outside a Guarded Castle*

Early nineteenth century

*Linen base covered in woollen felt worked with wool and chenille in coarse long and short and split stitch with French knots and attached painted card for the features and limbs. In its original oval glass mount.*

This unusual subject may represent a scene taken from a popular novel of the period, perhaps by Sir Walter Scott. In Scott's *Castle Dangerous*, published in 1832, the heroine Lady Augusta Berkeley is shown wearing a cloak with a hood, a scallop shell on her shoulder and a broad-brimmed hat hanging from her waist.[1] The glass mount to LL5360 has stylized shell motifs in the corner.

LL5360

## LL5391 (WHL3734)

### Feltwork collage picture

## *Tavern Interior with Seated Huntsmen*

First third of the nineteenth century

*Felt ground with crudely drawn felt pieces attached with thread and glue(?) and stitched over with straight stitches and long and short stitch.*

This type of felt-work collage picture was manufactured by certain commercial firms in the first half of the nineteenth century to be made up at home.[1] LL5391 may have been a copy of an eighteenth-century inn scene.

44.5 × 64 cm

Provenance: B.C. Creasy, Linden Cottage, Springfield, Chelmsford; sold Christie's, 28 January 1919, lot 103; purchased through M. Harris and Sons, 12 February 1919, £8.18.6 and kept at The Hill, Hampstead.

References: 1 Rous Lench Collection sale, Sotheby's, 4 July 1988, lot 627, a 'George Smart Collage Picture' *c.* 1830; Jane Toller, *Regency and Victorian Crafts*, 1969, chapter 5.

1928 Catalogue no. 142.

LL5391

# EMBROIDERED FURNISHINGS

Detail from a mirror frame showing *The Prodigal Son* (LL5215, p. 189)

Most embroidered textiles in a seventeenth- or eighteenth-century house would have been intended to cover furniture. The bed was the most important and expensive piece of furniture and would have been lavishly adorned with sumptuous materials and trimmings. A well-dressed bed required between two and six curtains, although four was the most common number; three lower and three upper valances, which were hung outside the bed frame and bedposts, either as a continuous run or as three individual panels (see LL5226–8, pp. 203–5); hangings (bonegraces and cantoons) (see LL5429–30, p. 206) to place around the bedposts and so close the gap between the curtains; a coverlet or counterpane (see LL5294, p. 213); and any number of pillows. All of these could be embroidered. Counterpanes and upper valances were often the most elaborately decorated bed furnishings. Items such as the valances were normally produced by professional workshops, like most large-scale furnishing schemes. On the other hand seventeenth-century mirrors and caskets were the *pièce de résistance* of the youthful amateur embroideress and displayed her skills.

In the eighteenth century upholsterers acted as interior decorators, supplying fabrics as well as furniture. Chippendale, for example, is known to have provided patterns and seat-covers embroidered for a set of the Earl of Bute's chairs. Some upholsterers were skilled with the needle, and embroidered bed curtains themselves; others had professional embroidery workshops producing furnishings to their design which were made to shape to cover particular suites of furniture. Workshops often had yards of material already made up in different techniques, such as chain stitch or quilting, and with various designs, and advertised for sale already 'wrought' beds. But a good deal of furnishing embroidery was also produced by the ladies of the house, everything from small rugs and suites of chair-seats to screens which varied in scale from eight-fold screens, acting as draught excluders, through the smaller two-fold screen worked by K. Howard (LL5447, p. 221) to dainty hand-held screens which protected the complexion from the fire. Some major furnishing projects were also well within the capabilities of an eighteenth-century lady and her household, as Mrs Delany's letters about her own activities and those of her friends make clear. Sometimes there were economic reasons for working them oneself, as Mrs Delany admitted to her sister when she wrote in 1743: 'I have bought your worsted and silk for my brother's chair that you are to work; I could not meet with any workwoman that would do it under two guineas and a half.' But aristocratic women, such as Lady Julia Claverley at Wallington, worked on large-scale home-furnishing schemes not only to make their homes comfortable at an affordable price, but also as a way of emphasizing that they were ladies of leisure.

LL5256 (detail from casket front)

# Caskets and Boxes

35.6 × 29.9 × 20.5 cm

Provenance: unknown. At The Hill, Hampstead by January 1907.

Exhibited: Birmingham, 'Exhibition of British Embroidery', 1959, no. 102.

References: **1** T.9–1945. **2** For example Burrell Collection, Glasgow, needlework picture (29/50). **3** Martin de Vos's design shows Eliezer prominently bending his knee, while the fountain is adorned with a reclining river god. **4** T.23–1928. **5** Martha Edlin's casket dated 1672 in the V&A (T.432–1990) is also lined with a coloured print of David holding Goliath's head, but it is not the same as that in LL5256.

1928 Catalogue no. 4.

LL5256 (H12)

## *The Sacrifice of Isaac with Three Scenes from the Story of Isaac and Rebecca*

Worked in 1667, initialled 'HP'

*Casket top faced with canvas worked with silk in tent, cross, rococo, and encroaching gobelin stitches and couched threads; casket sides faced with satin worked in silk, purl, metal thread, cut silk pile and seed pearls in surface stitches, including long and short, satin, and brick stitches, with couched threads and French knots and a wide variety of padded lace stitches and detached buttonhole stitch and braided silk, trimmed with metal thread braid. Some stitches have perished, showing the wool padding of the raised work. The back panel is worked entirely in couched and laid-work on card and many threads have perished. The whole casket is raised on silver ball feet.*

The three scenes from the life of Isaac shown on the casket sides are: the servant Eliezer taking leave of Abraham to go in

Figure 29 The sacrifice of Isaac by Abraham, from a print published by Gerard de Jode, after Martin de Vos, in the *Thesaurus Sacrarum Historiarum Veteris Testamenti*. (*Courtesy of the British Museum*)

179

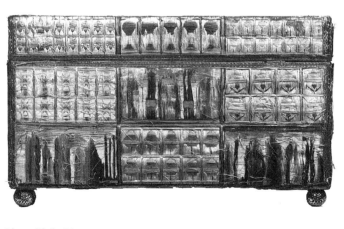

LL5256. Clockwise from the top of page : casket top, front, back, right side and left side (see also colour plates 14 and 15)

search of a bride for Isaac; Eliezer's encounter at the well with Rebecca, and Isaac greeting Eliezer and Rebecca on their return to Canaan (Genesis 24). The combination of Isaac's sacrifice with scenes from the lives of Rebecca and Isaac also occurs on a casket in the Fitzwilliam collection, Cambridge.[1] A different mix of scenes from the life of Isaac and Abraham can be seen on another casket in the Lady Lever collection (LL5258). *The Sacrifice of Isaac* on the casket lid was one of the most frequently worked scenes in the seventeenth century and like other such examples[2] it derived from the popular print published by Gerard de Jode (1521–91) after Martin de Vos (fig. 29). This engraving was not only published by de Jode in his *Thesaurus Sacrarum Historiarum Veteris Testamenti* in 1585 but it was also used by Nicolaas Visscher in his 'Piscator' Bible, which was extensively copied from, and in his *Historiae Sacrae Veteris et Novi Testamenti* of 1660. Another Martin de Vos design was used in the 'Piscator' Bible to illustrate the meeting of Eliezer and Rebecca but this did not form the basis for the scene on the casket's drop front,[3] which has more in common with a panel mounted on a casket in the Victoria and Albert Museum.[4] The back of LL5256 is covered in oblong panels of laid and couched silks on card, which may originally have depicted geometrical shapes and flowers, but the silks have deteriorated to such an extent that the original pattern is impossible to decipher. The casket's front drops to show small drawers covered in salmon-pink velvet while its lid rises to reveal an interior with the usual fitments of mirror, compartment, pin cushion and bottles. It is lined with salmon-pink silk. The central well is fitted with silver balusters and mirror glass which reflects what is probably an early seventeenth century coloured print of *David slaying Goliath*.[5]

LL5256 details of interior

LL5258 (X2491)

## The Meeting of Rebecca and Eliezer with Scenes from the Lives of Abraham, Isaac and Jacob

Second half of the seventeenth century

*Canvas worked with silk in long and short, split and stem stitches and French knots with couched thread and trimmed with silver braid. Although the lid is beautifully worked, some threads along the sides have rotted to show the canvas underneath and many are very loose. The inner side of the doors is lined with pink silk stamped with crowns and the drawers covered in velvet of the same colour.*

The central figures on the lid of Eliezer drinking from the jar of well water offered to him by Rebecca (Genesis 24:15–21) are lifted from the prints published by Gerard de Jode after Martin de Vos in his *Thesaurus Sacrarum Historiarum Veteris Testamenti* of 1585,[1] (fig. 30) which provided a popular composition format for this theme.[2] The *Thesaurus* also provided the design for Abraham offering Isaac for sacrifice (Genesis 22) on the casket's left side[3] while another Martin de Vos drawing, of the early 1580s, (fig. 31 – an engraving after which was published by Gerard de Jode[4]) is closely followed in the scene of Jacob's dream (Genesis 28:12), on the right-hand side. The Jacob print was reissued in C.J. Visscher's *Theatrum Biblicum*, 1674. However, the episode of Abraham's meeting with the three angels (Genesis 18:1–19), shown on the casket's front doors, at which they announce the future birth of Isaac to the previously barren Sarah, does not appear to derive from the *Thesaurus*, which often provided the source for this theme in other embroideries. On the back of the casket a mermaid is shown staring into a mirror and combing her hair. She is similar to one shown in *A New Book of all Sorts of Beasts*, pl. 27, published by Peter Stent as an engraved version of a horn book, subtitled *Or a Pleasant Way to Teach Young Children to Reade almost as soone as Speake*.[5] The portrayal of mermaids, lions, unicorns and other animals in reading books such as this must account for their overwhelming popularity as motifs in young girls' embroideries of this period.

26 × 35 × 17 cm

Provenance: purchased from Frank Partridge, 16 April 1918, £130 and first displayed at The Hill, Hampstead.

Literature: illustrated in colour, Therle Hughes, 'Stuart Needlework', fig. 6, p. 104 in *Treasures of Britain*, Drive Publications, undated.

References: **1** See also LL5256. **2** See for example the mid-seventeenth-century panel in the Untermyer collection, Y. Hackenbroch fig. 76 pl. 71 which provides a closer parallel to LL5258 than V&A caskets T.308 and T.23–1928 all of which take their figures from the same design. **3** See LL5256. **4** The

Figure 30   Eliezer drinking from the jar of well water offered to him by Rebecca, after Martin de Vos, in Gerard de Jode's *Thesaurus Sacrarum Historiarum Veteris Testamenti*. (*Courtesy of the British Museum*)

Figure 31   Jacob's dream published by Gerard de Jode after a drawing by Martin de Vos. (*Courtesy of the Courtauld Institute of Art*)

drawing (Courtauld Institute, Witt Collection, inv. 2257) was engraved anonymously and not published by de Jode in the *Thesaurus* series but as the third of a set of four episodes from Jacob's life. *The Age of Brueghel: Netherlandish Drawings in the Sixteenth Century*, National Gallery of Art, Washington 1986–7, no. 120. Martin de Vos made many drawings specifically for reproduction as engravings or book illustrations.
**5** Advertised for sale in 1662 and by John Overton in 1673. Alexander Globe, *Peter Stent, London Printseller*, 1985, cat. no. 526, p. 142. Another analogous hornbook illustrated with animals was being sold by John Garrett *c.* 1675. A whole page of illustrations of mermaids and men was published in Randle Holme's *Academy of Armory* in 1688.

1928 Catalogue no. 2.

LL5258

LL5262 (X571)

## Shepherd and Shepherdess with Four Senses

Worked in 1668, initialled 'EP'

*Satin worked with silk and metal thread in long and short, and running stitches with applied canvas motifs in tent and rococo stitch, and padded detached buttonhole and lace stitches with purl and raised, couched and looped metal thread and cut silk pile and attached seed pearls, trimmed with a border of metal thread braid.*

The central arcadian scene on the casket lid showing the shepherd handing a fruit to the shepherdess may represent the princely shepherd, Paris, awarding the golden apple to Venus, depicted as a half-naked shepherdess. A related scene of a shepherd passing an apple to a lady on the lid of a casket owned by Marcus Huish was referred to as the Judgement of Paris.[1] The five seated ladies on the casket sides represent the senses: Hearing, two ladies playing the lute (one of whom has lost part of her instrument); Taste with a fruit basket; Touch, whose hand is being pecked by a bird; and Smell, holding a flower. They are shown in the usual way for embroideries of this period[2] though the fact that they are seated, not standing, differentiates them from the collection's other representation of the senses, LL5239 (p. 40). Four animals are depicted on the lid's corners; they are (from left clockwise) a peacock, a wyvern, a unicorn and a lion. The returns to the lid are worked in the form of a frieze of farmsteads, a windmill and labourer, a hound chasing a hare and flowers, foliage and birds. The figures on the lid and sides are surrounded by plant motifs some of which can be identified as tulips, vines, oak trees, crown imperial lilies, roses, carnations, cornflowers and strawberry plants. The casket's interior is lined with padded salmon-pink silk and is fitted with a mirror, pin cushion and variously sized compartments, some of which are lined with marbled paper, which may originally have housed glass bottles.

39 × 52 × 15.9 cm

Provenance: Jeffrey Whitehead;[3] sold Christie's, 11 August 1915, lot 790; purchased through Frank Partridge, £60.18.0 and displayed at Thornton Manor.

References: **1** M.B. Huish, *Sampler and Tapestry Embroideries*, 1900, pl. XLIII. Marcus Huish was an early collector of historical needlework. **2** See for example the late seventeenth-century embroidery formerly in Sir Frederick Richmond's collection, Christie's, 23 June 1987, lot 152. **3** Lever purchased several items from the sale of Jeffrey Whitehead of The Mayes, East Grinstead, most of which were purses and other small clothing accessories, LL5400, LL5401 (pp. 260, 262).

1928 Catalogue no. 1.

LL5262 interior

LL5262. From top of page : left side – Smell, front – Hearing, right side – Taste, back – Touch, lid – Shepherd and Shepherdess

LL5410 (H?739)

## Trinket box

First half of the seventeenth century

*Small squared oval wooden box covered in linen(?) and worked entirely with green and gilt purl, and gilt spangles in a design of intertwined leaves and flowers. Trimmed with silver braid and strips and lined with blue silk.*

6.5 × 10 × 4 cm

Provenance: Viscountess Wolseley; sold through Puttick and Simpson, 12 July 1906, lot 150; bought M. Harris for £4.4.0. Kept at The Hill, Hampstead, in a recess of the Stuart Room along with LL5399 (p. 254).

Not previously catalogued.

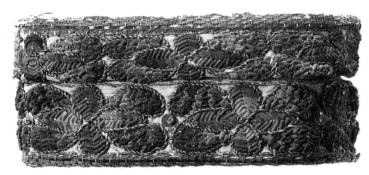

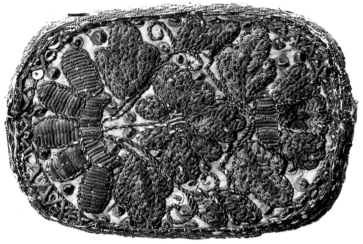

LL5410

LL5448 (X3057)

## Small quadrant-angled casket

Mid-eighteenth century

16.5 × 14.5 × 10 cm

Provenance: purchased through Frank Partridge, 9 January 1919, £22.

Not previously catalogued.

*Silk over pasteboard worked with silks in long and short stitch, satin, stem and couching stitches, trimmed with yellow and white silk cord and lined with pink silk. The lid is hinged at one side.*

The box is very finely worked and may have been made abroad. When Lever purchased it, LL5448 was described as a 'jewel box' of the Queen Anne period and it may well have acted as some kind of trinket box for a dressing-room table.

# Mirrors

LL5214 (X2458)

## *Lady and Gentleman with Animal and Floral Motifs*

Second half of the seventeenth century

*Satin worked entirely with applied canvas motifs in tent and rococo stitch and some basket stitch filling with applied spangles with a painted-glass mirror surround.*

The canvas-work slips, which are now very faded and in bad condition, with the spangles either tarnished or missing, are all typical of the third quarter of the seventeenth century and include, on either side of the mirror, a cavalier doffing his hat to a lady carrying a basket. However, the mirror and its painted glass surround certainly post dates the needlework and covers up several of the embroidered motifs.

63 × 53 cm, mirror size: 28 × 23 cm

Provenance: purchased through M. Harris and Sons, 12 March 1918, £80.

1928 Catalogue no. 70.

LL5214

73.5 × 66 cm, mirror size: 35.2 × 27 cm

Provenance: sold Christie's, 14 June 1916, lot 268 for £81.18.0; purchased through D.L. Isaacs, 19 June 1916.

References: **1** G. Wingfield Digby and W. Hefford, *The Victoria and Albert Museum Tapestry Collection*, 1980, cat. no. 62, pls. 90A–F. The Flemish series was copied by the Sheldon tapestry works, cat. no. 71a. **2** Illustrated in Y. Hackenbroch, *English and other Needlework in the Irwin Untermyer Collection*, 1960, p. xix. **3** T.H. Darlow and H.F. Moule, *Historical Catalogue of the Printed Edition of Holy Scripture in the the Library of the British and Foreign Bible Society*, 1903, p. 211 ff. 506.

1928 Catalogue no. 9.

Figure 32  The prodigal son and swine, from an engraving by Peter de Jode, after Adrian van Nylant. (*Courtesy of the Elisha Whittelsbey Collection, the Metropolitan Museum of Art, New York*)

LL5215 (WHL4364)

## The Prodigal Son

Second half of the seventeenth century

*Satin worked with silk in satin, long and short, running and brick filling stitch and trellis-pattern couching with raised-work motifs in purl, detached buttonhole and needle-lace stitches and French knots, with applied seed pearls, cut-silk pile and mica.*

The story as embroidered around the mirror does not appear to have been designed after any known engraved or woven series. Although the scene of the prodigal son and swine (in the lower right-hand corner) is not unlike that found on one of six Flemish tapestry cushion covers in the Victoria and Albert Museum, the figures on the rest of the set bear little resemblance to those on the mirror frame.[1] The swine episode appears somewhat closer to an undated engraving by Peter de Jode after Adrian van Nylant[2] (fig. 32). It may also be relevant that three of the four embroidered scenes – riotous living, feeding with the swine and the son's return, were the same scenes chosen to illustrate the story in the 1655 Stationers' Company Bible with engravings by Jacob Fl. van Langeren.[3]

LL5215

LL5216 (WHL4440)

## King and Queen with Leopard, Lion, Kingfisher and Eagle

Second half of the seventeenth century

*Satin worked in raised-work in a variety of detached buttonhole and padded lace stitches, purl, French knots, chain stitch, couching and padded canvas slips with tent, satin, long and short, and stem stitch with applied beads, pieces of mica, couched silver thread, strips, and braid couched over each other, and cut-silk pile in a tortoiseshell frame. The back is covered with salmon-pink velvet.*

The embroidery is of high quality and particularly well preserved. Overall the design is very similar to LL5217 even down to the seahorse fountain, though the kingfisher and exotic bird (probably an eagle) have switched sides. The four animals depicted within roundels are often used alongside representations of monarchs, although sometimes a stag (see LL5218) or unicorn are substituted. The royal couple, standing on a distinctive chequer-board paving, may well have derived from prints representing Charles II and Catherine of Braganza.

49.5 × 45.5 cm, mirror size: 25 × 20 cm

Provenance: purchased through M. Harris & Sons, 18 January 1923, £120.

1928 Catalogue no. 23.

LL5216 (see also colour plate 16)

LL5217 (WHL507)

## King and Queen with Leopard, Lion, Exotic Bird and Parrot

Second half of the seventeenth century

70 × 54 cm, mirror size: 35.5 × 27 cm

Provenance: unknown. Acquired by sometime between July 1906 and June 1907 and kept at The Hill, Hampstead.

1928 Catalogue no. 36.

*Satin worked predominantly with silk in satin and long and short stitch, brick and basket filling stitch, and couching stitches with raised-work figures padded with wool and worked in detached buttonhole and needle-lace stitches, purl, French knots, and applied embroidered cloth for the Queen's dress, black glass beads, silk wound wire? in the upper roundels and cut-silk pile.*

Apart from the domed top to the border the design is very similar to that on LL5216, though the quality of needlework is slightly lower. The leopard and lion have often in the past been related symbolically to the coat of arms and standards of Charles II and Queen Catherine of Braganza, but both these animals were used frequently in a non–symbolic way throughout Elizabethan and Stuart embroidery.

LL5217

191

LL5218 (WHL4356; X3864)

## *King and Queen with Parrot, Exotic Bird, Stag and Lion*

Second half of the seventeenth century

*Satin worked predominantly with silk in stem stitch, long and short and satin, and some raised-work in couched metal thread, strips, rouleau and purl.*

The embroidery is of high quality although the metal thread is now badly tarnished, so the mirror has lost much of the sumptuous and imposing effect it would once have had. The fountain is of the same seahorse design found in many of the embroidered mirror frames (see LL5216, LL5217). The king's features suggest that he could be meant to represent Charles I, unlike the anonymous purely symbolic royal figures found on other embroideries in the collection.

77 × 57 cm, mirror size: 36 × 27 cm

Provenance: purchased through M. Harris and Sons, 7 May 1920, £120.

1928 Catalogue no. 62.

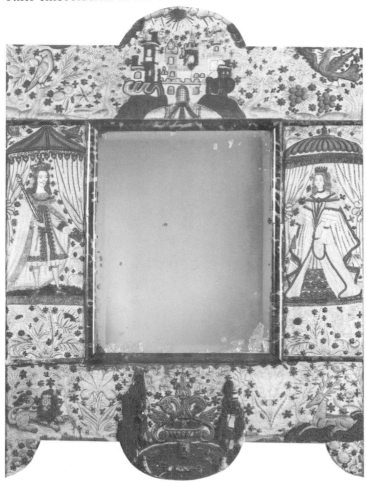

LL5218

LL5219 (WHL4330)

## The Four Continents with Oval Landscape Cartouche and Horse, Lion, Leopard and Camel

Second half of the seventeenth century

*Satin worked with silk in long and short, satin, split, and running stitches and a variety of chain and couching stitches and applied canvas motifs in tent and rococo stitches, with applied spangles, purl, French knots and some cut-silk pile, and raised figures padded with dyed wool and covered in detached buttonhole stitch.*

The figures of the four continents (clockwise from lower left) Europe, Africa, the Americas and Asia could be derived from the prints of these allegorical figures, etched by Withers and published by William Marshall (1617–50).[1] The Withers

68.5 × 48 cm, octagonal mirror size: 36.5 × 25 cm

Provenance: Percival D. Griffiths; sold Christie's, 28 June 1917, lot 111; bought through D.L. Isaacs, 3 July 1917, £56.14; displayed at The Hill, Hampstead.

References: **1** British Museum, Prints and Drawings Dept. 166c. 1. Whatever the original design source the four continents on LL5260 (p. 66) could be based on it also. **2** Alexander Globe, *Peter Stent, London Printseller*, 1985, no. 484. **3** A.J.B. Wace 'Exhibition of Early English Needlework', *Old Furniture*, vol. III, April 1928 p. 233 and Christie's, 23 June 1987, lot 168. **4** Verbally Margaret Swain 16 February 1989; 'John Nelham's needlework panel', *Bulletin of the Needle and Bobbin Club*, 1982, pp. 3–16.

1928 Catalogue no. 49.

LL5219

prints were later reissued by Stent.[2] The horse and camel, respectively placed above the heads of Europe and Asia, presumably act as their familiars, as they are also embroidered alongside the same allegorical figures on a casket lid formerly in the collection of Sir Frederick Richmond Bart.[3] The purl oval cartouche at the top of the mirror is similar to one found on an embroidered picture at Blair Castle, Scotland, which is signed by the professional embroiderer John Nelham (died 1684) and datable to between 1654 and 1666.[4]

LL5220 (WHL502)

## Lady and Gentleman with Woman Lutanist, Lion and Stag

Second half of the seventeenth century

*A scalloped-edge looking-glass frame in predominantly flat silk embroidery on satin ground in satin, long and short and running stitches, with purl, cross stitch, chenille, French knots and a variety of detached buttonhole and chain stitches and applied mica and seed pearls. The raised faces of the lady and gentleman have their features painted onto the silk.*

The composition showing, a lady offering a flower to a bareheaded cavalier with a female lutanist seated between two palatial buildings, is almost the same as that found on a looking-glass frame in the Irwin Untermyer Collection, Metropolitan Museum of Art and dated to the third quarter of the seventeenth century.[1] The design, of figures viewing each other across the mirror, recalls contemporary title pages to books, with a mirror as substitute for the script.[2] The scalloped shape is similar to LL5221 and would be identical to that of a mirror in Percival Griffiths's collection[3] had the joiner or upholsterer who finished off the frame for LL5220 followed the original hemispherical design for the top, which can still be seen, drawn on the silk.

53 × 45 cm, mirror size: *c.* 27 × 21 cm

Provenance: unknown. Acquired by between July 1906 and June 1907, appearing in a photograph of W.H. Lever's collection at The Hill, Hampstead published between 1906 and 1910.[4]

References: **1** Y. Hackenbroch, *English and Other Needlework Tapestries and Textiles from the Irwin Untermyer Collection*, 1960 fig. 102 illus. pl. 68. This was formerly in Viscount Wolseley's collection from which Lever purchased various Stuart items at auction in July 1906, see LL5397, LL5398, LL5420, LL5421 (pp. 257–9, 269, 271). **2** As suggested by Hackenbroch, above. **3** Illus. G.S. Seligman and T. Hughes, *Domestic Embroidery* pl. XXIX. **4** Illus. G.M. Ellwood, *English Furniture and Decoration* (Batsford, n.d.) p. ll.

1928 Catalogue no. 55.

LL5221 (WHL504)

## Truth, Wisdom, Temperance and Justice with Leopard, Exotic Bird, Parrot and Lion

Second half of the seventeenth century

*Satin with raised work in lace and detached buttonhole stitch, French knots, cut-silk pile, twisted-silk pile, purl, couched threads and a*

48 × 40 cm, mirror size: 22 × 18 cm

LL5220

variety of chain stitches padded with wool and parchment, applied embroidered fabric and tent stitch canvas slips with flat silk embroidery in satin and running stitch. The frame is bordered with metal thread and strip braid, typically used to mount embroidery by cabinet makers and joiners.

The original wool padding to Wisdom's face and its silk facing have fallen away to reveal the high quality ink underdrawing on the satin ground. Some of the silk threads of the clouds above Wisdom's head have also perished revealing further drawing. The design for the parrot in the upper right-hand corner could be derived from a parrot shown on one of the plates from John Overton's *A New Book of all Sorts of Beasts*, published in 1671[1] (fig. 33). The shape of the embroidered frame is similar to that of LL5220.

Provenance: unknown. Acquired sometime between July 1906 and June 1907. It appears in a photograph of W.H. Lever's collection at The Hill, Hampstead, published between 1906 and 1910.[2]

References: **1** John Overton, *A New Book of all Sorts of Beasts*, 1671, pl. 53. **2** Illustrated in G.M. Ellwood, *English Furniture and Decoration*, (Batsford n.d.) p. 11.

1928 Catalogue no. 56.

Figure 33 A plate from John Overton's *A New Book of all Sorts of Beasts*, published in 1671 showing a parrot in the lower left corner. (*Courtesy of the British Museum*)

LL5221

56 × 52 cm, mirror size: 25 × 20 cm

Provenance: purchased through D.L. Isaacs, 17 December 1915, £40.

References: **1** Compare with T.142–1931. **2** Mary Schoeser, *Printed Handkerchiefs*, Museum of London 1988, pp. 3–4, figs. 5, 6.

1928 Catalogue no. 51.

LL5222 (WHL2691)

## Lady and Gentleman with the Four Seasons

Second half of the seventeenth century

*Satin ground with predominantly flat silk embroidery in satin, long and short and running stitch and French knots with detached buttonhole stitch and couched padded metal thread. The satin is very badly perished and may have undergone some restoration and rebacking earlier this century.*

The main figures are probably meant to represent an Arcadian shepherd and shepherdess as the gentleman holds a shepherd's spud, used to throw stones to frighten away animals from flocks of sheep. More specifically, they could represent Paris and Venus, as do two similar figures on an unfinished looking glass frame in the Victoria and Albert Museum.[1] The representations of Spring, Autumn and Winter are similar to those found on the raised-work panel LL5259 (p. 64). From the medieval period onwards Winter has typically been shown as an old man beside a fire, but apart from this figure neither of the embroideries derive their designs from Hollar's engravings of the months, used on a silk handkerchief *c.* 1675–80 in the Museum of London.[2]

LL5222

LL5223 (WHL4339; X2428)

## Charity, Hope, Truth and (?)Faith

Second half of the seventeenth century

*Canvas worked with raised coloured and clear beads with couched silk thread, satin, tent and chain stitches. In a few areas small patches of beads have fallen from their ground and the frame is in poor condition overall.*

The giant size of many of the motifs used here is unlike that found on other late seventeenth century beadwork mirror frames with similar subject matter.[1] The quality of work was probably never very high on this piece.

76 × 67.5 cm, mirror size: 47 × 40 cm

Provenance: purchased through M. Harris and Sons, 1 March 1918, £100 and kept at The Hill, Hampstead.

References: **1** See a mid-seventeenth century beadwork mirror with figures of Faith and Hope sold Sotheby's, 15 June 1984, lot 2, from Irwin Untermyer's collection.

1928 Catalogue no. 30.

LL5223

LL5224 (WHL4351)

## King and Queen with Lady and Gentleman, Lion, Wyvern, Camel, Leopard and Stag

Mid- to late seventeenth century

*Separate satin panels, some padded with squares of thick parchment, stitched together to form a raised-work mirror frame in a wide variety*

88 × 60 cm, mirror size: 45 × 28 cm

Provenance: Sir Edward Hopkinson Holden, Bart;[1] sold Christie's, 24 March 1920, lot 9, £131.5.0; purchased from M. Harris and Sons, 30 March 1920, £137.16.0.

References: **1** Lever also acquired LL5318, LL5319 and LL4234 (pp. 118, 119) (a settee covered with Sheldon Tapestry panels) from the sale of the deceased Sir Hopkinson Holden, (the former chairman and managing director of London Joint City and Midland Bank) of 19 New Cavendish Street. Lever also bought four other pieces from the sale, most of which were seventeenth-century pieces, Appendix AG1, lots 161, 204, 449 and 514.

1928 Catalogue no. 64.

*of detached and surface stitches including buttonhole, needle-lace, brick, long and short and satin stitches with couched metal thread and cord and purl in a herring-bone pattern, and applied pieces of cloth including brocade, with attached stem motifs cut out of parchment or card, metal thread and rouleau and seed pearls on the King's sceptre and the royal couple's crowns.*

The mirror frame is made up of panels taken from a seventeenth-century casket (possibly in the nineteenth century). The panel with the royal couple, probably originally forming the casket lid, was cut in half and placed on either side of the mirror. This section of embroidery is still in relatively good condition, and includes a painted enamel medallion, worn round the king's neck, of St George fighting the dragon. The enamel is stylistically similar to ones found on a large seventeenth-century beaded urn in the Lever collection (LL4234). The small square embroidered panels, such as the topmost one of the pelican 'in piety' pecking itself and others depicting individual animals or geometrical flower motifs, were originally probably fronts to work-casket

LL5224

199

drawers and doors, later used to create a mirror frame by filling in gaps around the larger casket panels. The perished thread in some of the raised figures shows that unspun wool was used as padding and that several of the single motifs were embroidered on card. Among the many flowers carefully embroidered in surface and raised stitches is a snake's head fritillary, shown in the lower right-hand corner.

## LL5273 (WHL4345; X2932)

## Orpheus and a Shepherdess with the Four Elements, a King, a Queen and Animal Motifs

Third quarter of the seventeenth century

*Satin worked with silk in long and short, tent, and rococo stitch, French knots, and couched threads, and raised figures padded with dyed wool and parchment, worked with detached buttonhole, and knitted fabric(?) with applied purl, cut- and coiled-silk pile and applied tassels.*

The figure of the queen appears to have lost her entire skirt and stuffing, revealing the original under-drawing of the design on the silk. Other areas in which the under-drawing shows are Orpheus's face, the pineapple motif on the fountain in front of the shepherdess and the cannons in front of the castle. The possibility that LL5273 was never finished is less likely as such a large proportion of it has been embroidered. The frame is made up of four silk strips, and the stitched seams are still visible beneath the flower and insect motifs embroidered over them.

   The original description of the four corner figures as the four seasons is now changed to the four elements, (from top left clockwise) Fire, Air, with her attribute the chameleon (which according to Pliny lived solely on air), Water and Earth. The combination of the four elements with Orpheus, the tamer of nature, is also to be found on an embroidered casket in the Fitzwilliam Museum.[1] The shepherdess figure may be meant to represent Eurydice, the wood nymph and wife of Orpheus. Prints of Orpheus charming the animals were advertised by Peter Stent and John Overton throughout the 1650s and 1660s and into the next decade,[2] but the etching they sold, by Gaywood after Francis Barlow, was not the design source for LL5273.

92.5 × 85.5 cm, mirror size: 51 × 43 cm

Provenance: purchased through M. Harris and Sons, 8 October 1918, £152.10.0.

References: **1** T.8–1945. Orpheus is shown on the back of the casket surrounded by animals, including a seated camel, while the four elements are on the inside of the casket's doors and lid. **2** Alexander Globe, *Peter Stent, London Printseller*, 1985, p. 119 pl. 315. The print was advertised for sale in 1658, 1662, 1663 and 1673. **3** Adrian Collaert print after Adam van Noort which forms the basis for a panel at the V&A (T.85–1959), is also not the source for LL5273 although two of the more unusual embroidered animal motifs, a high-stepping horse and a camel, appear in the print.

1928 Catalogue no. 18.

LL5273

## LL5213 (X1728)

Second quarter of the eighteenth century

*Satin worked with silk and couched metal thread in satin, long and short, running, split and stem stitch.*

The embroidered design of trailing flowers (possibly lotus blossom?), and strawberries was not originally made to frame a mirror. The satin appears to be all of one piece, the divisions around the frame merely hiding breaks in the glass, and it is possible that it was originally one of a set of pillows with embroidered borders. In the 1928 catalogue it was thought to be of Italian origin, but LL5213 could equally well have been embroidered in England.

62.5 × 51.5 cm, mirror size: 37.5 × 27 cm

Provenance: bought through D.L. Isaacs, 18 September 1916, £18.

1928 Catalogue no. 176.

LL5213

# Bed Furnishings

LL5226 (WHL3455)

**Valance**

*The Coronation of Athaliah and the Usurpation of Joash*

Late sixteenth or early seventeenth century

*Canvas worked with wool in tent stitch and silk to highlight details in a variety of stitches including stem and raised satin stitch.*

Valances of this type, showing a crowd of elaborately dressed 'courtier' figures, have in the past been thought to be from professional French workshops, as the figures usually wear fashionable French costume of the last decades of the sixteenth century, as they do in LL5226.[1] They have been linked to the Scottish court, through Mary, Queen of Scots. However, as Margaret Swain has pointed out, this figure style was a pan-European one, and there is not yet any evidence that the professional workshops were located in France.[2] In fact the Scottish collections from which many of these valances come suggest that they might have been made in Scotland.[3]

LL5226 is one of two valances (see LL5227) which relate the Old Testament story of Athaliah and the boy king Joash (or Jehoash) (2 Kings 11 and 2 Chronicles 22–3). In the centre Athaliah, the supposed daughter of Ahab and Jezebel and the

49 × 187 cm

Provenance: S.E. Kennedy Esq. of Upper Brooke Street, London; sold as one of a pair Christie's, 18 March 1918, lot 613; purchased as pair through M. Harris and Sons, 28 March 1918, £1, 151.11.9.

Literature: A. Carlyle Tait, 'English Needleworks in the Lady Lever Art Gallery – Part I', *Apollo*, vol. 45, 1947, p. 113; L.F. Salzman, *England in Tudor Times*, 1926, illus. only pl. IX.

References: **1** Apart from those mentioned by Margaret Swain in 'Engravings and Needlework of the Sixteenth Century', *Burlington Magazine*, May 1977, vol. 118, pp. 343–4 and in her *Scottish Embroidery*, 1986, pp. 28–31, these include a *Scene from the Story of Esther*, Untermyer Collection, Museum of Metropolitan Art New York, 64.101.1369; *Story of Jacob*, 3 panels, Christie's, 9 July 1931, lot 57; *Unknown Scene*, Christie's, 23 June 1987, lot 32, formerly Sir Frederick Richmond Collection; *Biblical Scene with Four Virtues*, Sotheby's, 11 December 1987, lot 176. **2** M. Swain, *Scottish Embroidery*, p. 28;

LL5226 (see also colour plate 17)

only queen to hold the throne, is shown seizing the throne, with the help of her troops. In order to secure her position on the throne she ordered the slaying of all the male members of the House of David, an action depicted in the background to the left, while in the foreground Joash escapes death by hiding in the Temple with the help of Jehosheba, the chief priest's wife. The second valance (LL5227) depicts the restoration of Joash (and the House of David) to the throne after six years. The episode is one of the most dramatically described in the Hebrew history of the Old Testament, but not many prints or print series depicting it appear to survive. A series of four prints after Martin van Heemskerk by Herman Muller[4] illustrated the story showing: Athaliah destroying the male line of the House of David; Joash, being presented to the army and captains of the guard by the chief priest Jehoiada after hiding for six years; Jehoiada anointing Joash, Athaliah tearing her clothes and being killed; the destruction of the temple to the god Baal. It is possible that a Heemskerk print was used for the design of the two valances, as another professionally worked valance similar in style to LL5226–7 did make use of such a print,[5] but neither appears to be closely derived from the Heemskerk set of prints.

Of other panels the closest to LL5226 and LL5227 in size, costume, style and, most importantly, subject matter was a set, now destroyed, depicting the *History of Reheboam*.[6] It is intriguing to note that towards the end of the sixteenth and the beginning of the seventeenth century both these, now somewhat obscure, themes would have had strong political resonances in England and Scotland, for the Athaliah series related the story of the overthrow of the only queen to sit on the throne of the House of David by its rightful claimant, and the Reheboam series depicted the secession of the northern tribes of Israel from Reheboam, son of King Solomon, because of his refusal to lift tax burdens.

M. Swain, as above, p. 28–9. **3** Three other 'Elizabethan valances' owned by Lever and sold in 1926 were from the Scottish collection of the Earl of Kinnoull, Balhousie Castle, Perthshire, Appendix AG1, lot 579. **4** Kerrich, *Catalogue of Martin van Heemskerk*, 1829, pp. 26–7. **5** M. Swain, 'Engravings and Needlework of the Sixteenth Century', *Burlington Magazine* as above. An engraving after Heemskerk taken from the series *Bel the Dragon* was used for the design on a valance of *Daniel Rescued from the Lions' Den*, Duke of Buccleuch, Drumlanrig Castle. **6** R. Scott Moncrieff, *Proceedings of the Society of Antiquaries of Scotland*, 11 February 1918, pp. 72–81. The series was owned by Mr Scott Moncrieff but it was destroyed according to M. Swain, *Historical Needlework: a Study of Influences in Scotland and Northern England*, 1970, p. 28. Other long panels, noticeably similar in style and subject, include the pair depicting the *Story of Philomela* in the Untermyer Collection of the Metropolitan Museum, Hackenbroch, *English and other Needlework*, 1960, p. 13, fig. 27, pl. 16.

1928 Catalogue no. 53.

## LL5227 (WHL3456)

**Valance**

## *The Coronation of Joash and the Execution of Athaliah*

Late sixteenth or early seventeenth century

*Canvas worked with wool in tent stitch and with a little silk to highlight details in a variety of stitches including stem and raised satin stitch.*

One of two valances (see LL5226) which relate the Old Testament story of Athaliah and the boy king Joash (2 Kings 11 and 2 Chronicles 22–3). In the centre Joash is being

49 × 189.5 cm

Provenance: S.E. Kennedy Esq. of Upper Brook Street, London; sold as one of a pair Christie's, 18 March 1918, lot 613; purchased as pair through M. Harris and Sons, 28 March 1918, £1,151.11.9.

Literature: A. Carlyle Tait 'English Needleworks in the Lady

Lever Art Gallery – Part I', *Apollo*, vol. 45, 1947, p. 113. L.F. Salzman, *England in Tudor Times*, 1926, illus. only pl. LX.

References: **1** Base valances, which hung down between the legs of the bed, were usually plain rather than elaborately embroidered. Peter Thornton, *Seventeenth-century Interior Decoration in England, France and Holland*, 1978, p. 175, fig. 118.

1928 Catalogue no. 60.

proclaimed King of Judah by the high priest Jehoiada while on the left the unlawful Queen Athaliah tears her bodice in fury at the trumpeting and rejoicing of the troops and people. On the right Athaliah is put to death by the troops outside the Temple. Erhard Schoen in his illustration for the Lyons Bible, published throughout the sixteenth century, combines the two scenes of Athaliah tearing her clothes and her execution into one. This relatively simple woodcut is not the design source for this elaborate item of bed furnishing. Originally there would have been a third valance to complete the set, which would probably have been hung around the upper part of the bed-frame.[1]

LL5227 (see also colour plate 17)

LL5228 (WHL4296)

## Valance

### *Susanna and the Elders*

Late sixteenth to early seventeenth century

*Canvas worked with wool and and a little silk in tent stitch.*

41 × 203 cm

Provenance: purchased through Frank Partridge, New York, 23 November 1920, £175, supposedly an heirloom of a United States family, who settled there in the seventeenth century.[6]

Exhibited: Gemeente Museum, The Hague, *The Age of Shakespeare*, January–April 1958, no. 290.

Susanna was one of the twelve exemplary women of the Old Testament; the 'chaste and lovely woman slandered with lies yet saved by God' as an inscription above one sixteenth-century print describes her.[1] The story was also frequently illustrated on sixteenth-century Italian wedding chests.[2] It is,

LL5228

therefore, not surprising that a large number of embroidered versions of her story survive using a wide variety of design sources. Although these vary in format, almost all show a naked or half draped figure being harassed by the two church elders[3] and thus they differ substantially from the fully-dressed figure in LL5228.[4] Although no other design similar to LL5228 has been found, certain elements of the valance, particularly the borders at either end, the fruit trees and the way in which water is depicted are similar to those found on an English or French valance dated *c.* 1600 depicting a musical entertainment.[5] LL5228 might have been one of a set of three valances to be hung around the top of a four-poster bed.

References: **1** An engraving by A. de Bruyn cited by Georg Garde, *Silkebroderede Laerredsduge fra 16 og 17 århundrede*, National Museet, Copenhagen, 1962, p. 10. **2** Cristelle Baskins, 'La Festa di Susanna: Virtue on Trial in Renaissance Sacred Drama and Painted Wedding Chests', *Art History*, 1991, vol. 14, no. 3, p. 330. **3** All those depicted in Y. Hackenbroch, *English and other Needlework, Tapestries and Textiles in the Irwin Untermyer Collection*, 1960, figs. 42, 65, 83, 122. **4** Two pieces, one raised-work embroidery and one Sheldon tapestry, which do depict a clothed Susanna bear no relationship in format to LL5228, 'Antique needlework (Mr Frank Ward's Collection)', *Old Furniture*, vol. IV, 1928, p. 67, col. pl.; A.J.B. Wace, 'Sheldon Tapestry Cushions in the Collection of Sir William Burrell', *Old Furniture*, ibid, p. 79. **5** Y. Hackenbroch, as above, p. 13–14, pl. 16, fig. 28. **6** A. Carlyle Tait, 'English Needleworks in the Lady Lever Art Gallery – Part I', *Apollo*, vol. 45, 1947, p. 114.

1928 Catalogue no. 25.

LL5429 (WHL2256)
LL5430 (WHL2257)

**Pair of bed-hangings**

## *Oriental Figures, Beasts and Birds on a Black Background*

First third of the eighteenth century

*Canvas embroidered in wools and silk(?) in tent and cross stitch.*

These hangings were probably bonegraces or cantoons (from the French bonnegraces and cantonniére), which were considered essential to any well-dressed bed at the beginning of the eighteenth century. They were hung around the corners of the bed to cover the posts from view and close up the gaps between the main curtains. Technically cantoons hung around the posts at the foot of the bed while bonegraces were placed at the head, but the terms were somewhat interchangeable.[1] Their chinoiserie design includes oriental figures dancing with tambourines, playing bassoon-like instruments, and enthroned with a soldier standing guard, all of whom are surrounded by fabulous beasts and birds such as the Chinese crane, phoenix and ho-ho bird. By the beginning of the eighteenth century the taste for chinoiserie was popular across Europe.[2] The style of the hangings and the accompanying valance (LL5446) suggests that they were made in France where a dark ground was commonly used for furnishing fabrics.[3] However, a black ground, derived from lacquered furniture, was also used by the Soho tapestry works in London for the chinoiseries they began weaving in 1699.[4] The figures on the Soho tapestries, which continued to be woven until about 1730, were a mixture of motifs of Chinese and

Each 291 × 81.5 cm

Provenance: unknown. According to a previous inventory LL5429–30 were found at The Hill, Hampstead in 1914.

Literature: A. Carlyle Tait, 'English Needleworks in the Lady Lever Art Gallery – Part II', *Apollo*, July 1947, p. 5 illus.

References: **1** Peter Thornton, *Seventeenth-Century Interior Decoration in England, France and Holland*, 1978, p. 165, fig. 118. **2** Examples of the fashion include an embroidered chair-cover *c.* 1700 in Rosenborg Castle, Copenhagen. **3** They could also have been worked by Huguenot immigrants from France, as was a set of chairs and bed-hangings with a black ground ordered by the Duchess of Norfolk in 1700. Margaret Swain, 'Covered with Care', *Country Life*, 14 March 1991, p. 51. **4** Hugh Honour, *Chinoiserie: The Vision of Cathay*, 1960, p. 252, pl. 27; H. Marillier, *English Tapestries of the Eighteenth Century*, 1930, pp. 34–5. **5** These were originally in the Untermyer Collection, Y. Hackenbroch, *Catalogue of English Needlework . . .*, 1960, pl. 152, 153 but were given to the Baltimore Museum of Art, *BMA News*, June – Summer, 1953, pp. 1–3. **6** POL/F/64a, b, POL/F/32a–c.

1928 Catalogue no. 125.

Indian derivation somewhat comparable to those found on LL5429–30 and LL5446. A pair of bed curtains and several valances, thought to be French and dated to the first half of the century, share the same fantastic oriental style with that found on LL5429–30, though they are 'peopled' entirely with birds and beasts.[5] Several chairs at Polesden Lacey also show similarly robed courtiers in activities, such as playing a harp.[6] The scalloped edges to LL5429–30 are not original to the hangings, but cut later.

As an old photograph in the files was taken for A.H. Lee and Sons, the Birkenhead tapestry and embroidery works, it is possible that the design was copied by them for manufacture in their factory, a practice which they followed with several other needleworks in the Lady Lever.

Detail from LL5429

LL5429 and LL5430

207

LL5446 (WHL2250)

**Valance**

## Oriental Figures, Beasts and Birds on a Black Background

First third of the eighteenth century

*Canvas embroidered in wools and silk(?) in tent stitch and cross stitch.*

Like the pair of bed-hangings (LL5429–30) with which it is *en suite*, the valance is full of fantastic birds, beasts and dragons perched on stylized rock or cloud-like formations. The human element is provided by a number of robed courtiers making slight obeisance to a Buddha-like figure of a child seated on a low platform. Such a figure seated cross-legged on a pillar became an essential ingredient of chinoiserie designs later in the century and probably had its prototype in the painting entitled *Divinité Chinoise*, which the French artist Watteau designed for the Chateau de la Muette in about 1707 and which was later engraved.[1] A drawing after the Watteau painting shows a pagoda-hatted cross-legged man seated with folded arms on a round stepped podium.[2] As with LL5429–30 the scalloped edge was not part of the original design.

43.1 × 201.3 cm

Provenance: as LL5429–30. What would appear to be five other valances or hangings with the same oriental design were sold from the collection, Appendix KFR2, lots 52–53, 81–83.

References: **1** Oliver Impey, *Chinoiserie: The Impact of Oriental Styles on Western Art and Decoration*, 1977, p. 80. **2** Hugh Honour, *Chinoiserie: The Vision of Cathay*, 1960, p. 88, pl. 35.

1928 Catalogue no. 125.

LL5446

LL5431–5 (X789, X790/90a, X791)

**Set of curtains**

Second quarter of the eighteenth century

*Linen(?) worked with wool in fine satin and long and short stitch.*

The curtains originally formed a set of three, two of which were cut up into strips of three, each 17 inches wide, while the remaining one was divided in two. As window curtains were seldom embroidered in the eighteenth century, these curtains

Each curtain 243.8 × 43.2 or 243.8 × 61 cm

Provenance: Lady Dorchester; purchased through D.L. Isaacs, 18 August 1915, for £35 and kept at Thornton Manor.

Literature: Virginia Glenn Pow, 'A new look in traditional textiles', *Discovering Antiques*, 1970, no. 19, p. 443 colour illus.

References: **1** Pamela Clabburn, *The National Trust Handbook of Furnishing Textiles*, 1988, p. 133. **2** Information in letter of Stephen Lee 23/5/1988.

1928 Catalogue no. 71.

were probably originally intended as bed furnishings,[1] though they could later have been reused in windows. The design consists of borders of scrolling garlands of honeysuckle, rushes, ribbons, grapes and corn sheaves, which run around the bottom and sides of the curtain and divide the centre into three panels, which are dotted with isolated sprays of cornflowers, roses, peonies, and other flowers. The emphasis of the motifs on fruitfulness suggest that the

LL5431

curtains might have been worked to celebrate a marriage. The curtains came from Hamlet Lodge, Cowes, owned in the early twentieth century by Charlotte, Lady Dorchester, widow of Dudley Wilmot Carleton, 4th Baron Dorchester. The curtains were also probably those used to create a crewel embroidery design offered for sale, under the title the 'Lady Lever' design, by Lee Fabrics of Birkenhead, from about the 1930s onwards.[2]

LL5433–5

LL5439–41 (X813)

## Pelmets

Late seventeenth–century motifs applied to a later fabric

*Linen worked with wool in long and short stitch, French knots and three-dimensional fabric rosettes made from woollen braid and clumps of dyed wool attached to a green woollen border.*

Each 35.5 × 122 cm

Provenance: purchased through D.L. Isaacs, 16 September 1915, for £25 and kept at Thornton Manor.

Literature: A. Carlyle Tait, 'English Needleworks in the Lady Lever Art Gallery', *Apollo*, July, 1947, p. 5.

References: **1** T.94–1971.

Not previously catalogued.

This type of needlework using double ply 'crewel' wool in deep blues, greens and browns, to create patterns of coiling stems and leaves, distantly derived from the far eastern Tree of Life design found on chintzes imported from India, was

LL5439–41

very popular in the reigns of William and Mary, and Anne. The embroidered motifs of leaves and stems appear to have been attached to a nineteenth-century(?) linen ground, perhaps having been cannibalized from some seventeenth- or early eighteenth-century curtains. A note in the gallery files states that the pelmets were made from a long bed valance. Although this is not impossible, if it was a continuous valance hung outside the bedposts, the note could also mean that the motifs were salvaged from a valance. The applied rosettes relate to some in detached buttonhole stitch on an embroidered hanging of *c*. 1700 in the Victoria and Albert Museum.[1]

LL5445 (WHL2261)

### Canvas-work panel

Early to mid-eighteenth century

*Canvas worked with wool in tent stitch.*

The design of fruit and leaves is in red, yellow, and light and dark brown on a black ground. Teresa Macquoid considered the piece (along with the two other panels catalogued with it (LL5452–3)) to be French, presumably because of the black background (which is often thought to indicate French manufacture), but the bold design is closer to English work.

67.3 × 81.2 cm

Provenance: found at The Hill, Hampstead, in 1914.

1928 Catalogue no. 126.

LL5445

LL5452–3 (WHL2245–6)

**Bed-hangings**

Early to mid–eighteenth century

*Canvas worked with wool in tent stitch.*

112 × 24.5 cm, 122 × 26 cm

Provenance: found at The Hill, Hampstead, in 1914.

1928 Catalogue no. 126.

Theresa Macquoid described the pair as 'lambrequins', to be hung vertically from a mantelpiece, but they are more likely to be bonegraces or cantoons (see LL5429–30, p. 206) and intended to be hung at the sides of bed posts. They were catalogued along with a square panel (LL5445), although their design, of red flowers on a blue ground cartouche set against a black ground with a border of a red scroll spiralling around a green pole, is not the same.

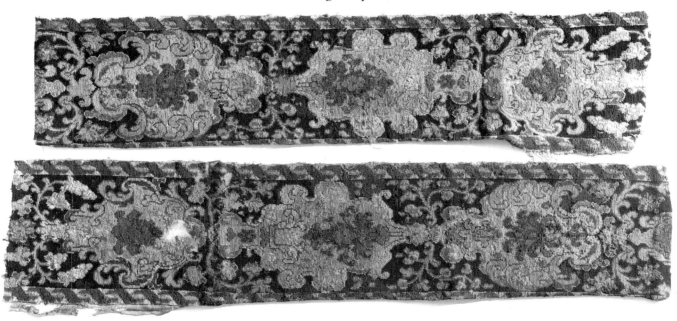

LL5452–3

LL5294 (WHL2784, X792)

**Coverlet**

First third of the eighteenth century

*Linen ground 'falsely quilted' with yellow silk in back stitch and worked with coloured silk in satin, chain, stem, long and short and straight stitch in a lattice pattern and running stitch and French knots.*

183 × 185.5 cm

Provenance: purchased through D.L. Isaacs, 1 September 1915, £42 and first displayed at Thornton Manor.

References: **1** Pamela Clabburn, *The National Trust Book of Furnishing Textiles*, 1988, p. 124. **2** Lanto Synge, *Antique Needlework*, 1982, pp. 99–101 fig. 63 pl. 3b; Christie's,

LL5294 was possibly made as a coverlet, or counterpane as it would have been referred to at the time,[1] but appears to have been displayed as a hanging after Lever acquired it. The coverlet has been made from three different 'falsely quilted' sections joined together, each of which has been embroidered over by a different hand using a different combination of stitches. In false quilts such as this the stitches are not used to help bind layers of material together, instead the pattern is stitched for its own decorative effect. The inner section with a 'quilted' pattern of wavy lines is elaborately embroidered in coloured silks, in a wide range of stitches, with a flowered border surrounding a central design of flowers and ferns. The next section is worked almost entirely in fine chain stitch, with regularly placed sprigs of flowers, including formalized tulips and forget-me-nots, on diaper-patterned 'quilting'. The outer border is 'quilted' in a complex geometric flowered pattern and, in coarser chain stitch and French knots, has worked on it at either end a large number of spot motifs including milkmaids and men with churns, a man leading his horse, kings and queens, a dog, and a huntsman attacking a lion with a club, possibly representing either Samson or Hercules. LL5294 is similar in type to a number of coverlets and blankets produced in the Queen Anne and George I periods which may have been professionally made.[2] A whitework quilt in the Victoria and Albert Museum, embroidered with a comparable floral design to that of LL5294, is dated 1703 and another coverlet dated 1728 with a similar sort of mixture of floral sprigs, figures and animals is in Toronto.[3] The central section of the Lady Lever coverlet is of an accomplished design, fashionable in the first part of the eighteenth century, but the motifs on the outer part are rather old-fashioned and haphazardly placed. It was probably the archaic nature of these figures that led to the original dating of the embroidery as Elizabethan or early Stuart.[4]

23 June 1987 (Sir Frederick Richmond's collection), lot 208, pl. 12; Gawthorpe Hall inv. 1959/1 QE10, Pauline Gittins, *A Brief Survey of the Shuttleworth Collections*, Museums Diploma thesis 1984, pl. 11. **3** T.1564–1902. Other similar falsely quilted and embroidered coverlets in the V&A collections are T.20–1943 and T.287–1910. None of these, however, have figure motifs like those, on LL5294. Katherine Brett, *English Embroidery in the Royal Ontario Museum*, 1972, no. 48 illus. Acc. no. 970.128. **4** The ground was believed to be pieced together from dresses *c.* 1590 and the embroidery to be *c.* 1630.

Not previously catalogued.

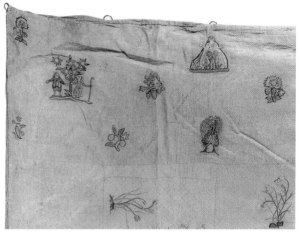

Detail from LL5294

LL5294 (see also colour plate 18)

LL5442 (X1216, WHL2801)

**Coverlet**

## Joseph and his Brothers with Surrounding Scrolling Foliage, Flowers and Parrots

Portuguese(?), eighteenth century[1]

*Linen canvas worked with silks in florentine(?), small and large tent stitch, and a form of drawn-work technique.*

The coverlet may have been embroidered in Portugal. It is worked in very bright acidic colours, yellow acting as a ground to reds, blues and greens. The prominence of the yellow itself suggests a Portuguese origin, as they developed its use after their contacts with China, where it was the imperial colour. The bold swirling design also appears to be a more westernized version of that found on several late seventeenth- and early eighteenth-century Indo-Portuguese and Chinese quilts.[2]

213.5 × 183 cm

Provenance: purchased through M. Harris and Sons, 2 June 1916, £135.[3] Kept at The Hill, Hampstead.

References: **1** According to a note in Gallery files it was said to be late seventeenth-century when purchased. **2** *Exhibition of Embroidered Quilts from the Museu Nacional de Arte Antiga*, Kensington Palace, November 1978. See especially Cat. no. 25 with a central medallion showing Aurora, dated 1768. **3** A month before on 2 May 1916 the important embroidery collector, Percival Griffiths, from whose collection Lever acquired a number of pieces, sold a 'coverlet of Portuguese embroidery, worked with birds, animals and flowers, in coloured silks on linen' (Christie's, lot 36). However, it was not purchased by Harris and Sons.

1928 Catalogue no. 72.

Detail of centre from LL5442

216

LL5442 (see also colour plate 19)

# Rugs and Carpets

LL5097 (X2566)

First quarter of the eighteenth century

*Linen canvas worked with wool in various forms of cross stitch.*

An unusual design consisting of early Georgian male costumed figures surrounded by birds, formalized flowerheads and parrots and a mermaid in each of the corners set against a pale green ground with a pinky-brown border of stylized birds. The concentric circles of birds and flowers are similar to those found on eighteenth-century table carpets from the Portuguese town of Arraiolos.[1] It is possible that this might be a Portuguese carpet.

224 × 133.4 cm

Provenance: purchased through Arthur Edwards, 8 May 1918, for £115.

Literature: M.J. Mayorcas, *English Needlework Carpets Sixteenth to Nineteenth Centuries*, 1963, p. 40, pl. 31.

References: **1** See Mayorcas, as above.

Not previously catalogued.

LL5097

302 × 211 cm

Provenance: purchased from the dealer Frank Partridge, 13 October 1920, £175.

References: **1** Comment made by Mr Stephen Lee on visit to the Gallery 1988.

Not previously catalogued.

## LL5444 (X4063)

Second quarter of the eighteenth century

*Linen canvas embroidered with wool in cross stitch.*

The formal floral pattern is set within borders of different widths and differing colours, blues and scarlets. The outermost borders have faded but the centre retains some of its strength of colour. In 1936 it was photographed by A.H. Lee and Sons of Birkenhead, who might have reproduced its design as they did a needlework carpet lent to them by the Marquess of Salisbury.[1]

LL5444

# Miscellaneous Furnishings

LL5286 (WHL3805)

**Altar hanging?**

## Four Scenes from the Nativity Story

Swiss, early seventeenth century

*Linen worked with silk mainly in long and short and stem stitch with couched metal thread and purl. A pale-green embroidered silk border is stitched to the hanging all the way around.*

The four depicted scenes are (from left to right): the Nativity, the Adoration of the Kings, the Visitation, and the Annunciation. The scenes are on separate pieces of linen which have been stitched together to form the larger hanging, whose lower edge has rounded corners. When purchased it was said to be early sixteenth century and German.[1] However, the border of spiralling tendrils and plant forms, the scrolling, flowery bowers over the narrative scenes and the red-cheeked figures all feature on linen covers embroidered in Switzerland from *c.* 1550 through to the mid-seventeenth century.[2] LL5286 may originally have been an altar panel(?) which was later cut up with the narrative scenes stitched back together in an arbitrary way to form a square.[3] The border is datable, stylistically, to the early seventeenth century, but need not have been part of the original altar panel. Designs for figures on Swiss embroideries were often drawn from prints by Holbein the Younger, Tobias Stimmer, and Virgil Solis's *Biblische Figuren* as well as other German engravers published by German firms such as Feyerabend of Frankfurt.[4] The figures on LL5286 are also similar to those found on a group of late sixteenth-, early seventeenth-century Swiss or German narrative and devotional embroidered scenes formerly in the collection of Sir Frederick Richmond.[5]

77.5 × 84 cm

Provenance: Miss Falche, Dover Street, Piccadilly; sold Christie's, 20 May 1919, lot 118; purchased through M. Harris and Sons, 26 May 1919, £33.1.6.

References: **1** An early inventory description in the Gallery files dates it to 1530 and added that it had originally been removed from an Italian church. **2** See particularly Verena Trudel, *Schweizerische Leinenstichereien*, 1954, pl. XVI and XXX both mid-sixteenth century; Bridgeman and Drury, *Needlework an Illustrated History* 1978, p. 229–30; letter from Dr Irmgard Peter, Historisches Museum, Basel, 9/1/1990. **3** A suggestion made by Dr Peter. **4** Georg Garde, *Dansk Silkebroderede*, 1961, p. 264. **5** Christie's, 23 June 1987, lots 38, 51, 52.

1928 Catalogue no. 69.

LL5286

149.8 × 132 cm

Provenance: unknown. Acquired by sometime between July 1906 and June 1907 when it appears in an inventory of The Hill, Hampstead.

LL5447 (H26)

**Embroidered screen**

Worked by 'K. Howard', 1735–6

*Canvas worked with wool in cross stitch with applied sixteenth- or seventeenth-century motifs on canvas, some padded with dyed wool in tent, long and short, rococo, and detached buttonhole stitch, with applied metal thread and purl.*

The applied slips are datable to the sixteenth or seventeenth centuries and include many that are similar to those found on Elizabethan and Jacobean fabrics. The design of several, such as the pomegranate, large stooping bird and sprigs of fruiting branches and flowers, including carnations and honeysuckle, could easily have derived from sixteenth-century botanical illustrations, natural histories and herbals.[1] The carnations and honeysuckle are somewhat similar to those found in a book put together by Thomas Trevelyon, a copyist and writing master, and completed in 1616.[2] The motifs were presumably saved from another piece of furniture or furnishing, possibly of religious use, as one of the slips is a raised metal-thread cross. The reuse of embroidered fabrics for furnishing materials was fairly common, but LL5447 also shows an interesting appreciation in the eighteenth century of the techniques and embroidery style of the previous century.[3] The dates, embroidered in roman and ordinary numerals, indicate the years in which the screen was begun and finished.

LL5447

Exhibited: Birmingham, *Exhibition of British Embroidery*, 1959 no. 158.

Literature: illustrated E. Foley, *Decorative Furniture*, 1910, vol. I, p. 419, col. pl. L; illustrated Therle Hughes, 'English Furniture Needlework', *Country Life Annual*, 1955, p. 162.

References: **1** An unused canvas slip of a fruiting lemon branch in the Victoria and Albert Museum (T.48–1972) datable to 1596 is similar in style to the orange(?) branch and blossom in the centre of the right-hand panel of LL5447. The applied slips are also not unlike those worked by Mary, Queen of Scots, and applied to a set of red velvet hangings at Scone Palace (M. Swain, *Scottish Embroidery*, 1986, p. 60 illus. 40). **2** J.L. Nevinson, 'The Embroidery Patterns of Thomas Trevelyon', *The Walpole Society*, vol. 41, 1968, pp. 2, 9, pl. 34 C187,188. **3** A similar but more extravagantly displayed eighteenth-century appreciation for historic textiles can be seen in a *c.* 1723–4 walnut settee in the Lady Lever collection (LL4234), which incorporates three Sheldon tapestry pieces of the early seventeenth century in its seat and back.

1928 Catalogue no. 75.

208.2 × 156.5 cm

Provenance: Jeffrey Whitehead, East Grinstead;[3] purchased by August 1915, £5.11.0.

References: **1** Information kindly provided by Linda Parry, letter 19 May 1989. **2** The same verse also appears on a sampler dated 1816 in the Fitzwilliam, Cambridge, T.171–1928. **3** According to a note in Gallery files, but the coverlet was not sold at the Christie's Whitehead sale on 4, 5, 9–11 August 1915.

Not previously catalogued.

LL5443 (X606, WHL2783)

## Coverlet or table cover

Late nineteenth century

*Linen worked in wools in satin, long and short and laid and couched stitches and a form of raised darning stitch.*

The border motifs of rising and setting suns and trellised fruit trees, are very typical of those on Arts and Crafts textiles, as are the sunflowers in the centre. Peacocks were another favourite motif in the last decades of the century and the design for the ones on this coverlet seem to have been derived from early eighteenth-century embroidered quilts in the Victoria and Albert Museum's collection.[1] The motto running around the border, 'Awake my soul and with the sun thy daily stage of duty run', is the first two lines of hymn no. 3 from *Hymns Ancient and Modern*. The hymn was written as part of an anthology in 1695 and became very popular when it was published on its own in 1862.[2] LL5443 was obviously worked in imitation of seventeenth-century crewel work techniques, but much more clumsily than would have been the case on a piece of that period.

LL5443 (see also colour plate 20)

# SAMPLERS

Detail from sampler by Mary Hales of Navenby, aged thirteen (LL5333, p. 230)

In the past a child's needlework education was instilled particularly through the working of samplers. In the seventeenth century these were still 'practice sheets' including groups of 'examples' of a wide range of stitches and patterns, but by the mid-eighteenth century the familiar modern type of sampler, in which a combination of stylized motifs, letters of the alphabet and numbers with simple verses, was being worked predominantly in cross stitch. Their production was thought to have other benefits in the raising of young girls apart from instilling regularity, diligence and neatness, qualities approved of in themselves. As the eighteenth century progressed the inclusion on samplers of passages from the Bible and verses from hymns and psalms, increased in popularity. Samplers provided moral training, with religious or pious verses which stressed the basics of Christian morality, obedience to God and family (LL5334, p. 233), or the brevity of life from which death was considered a sweet release (LL5331, p. 232). Such a concern with death was felt across all the arts in the latter half of the century and resulted in specially embroidered mourning pictures, but its appearance on samplers stemmed more from the ethos behind poems such as *Solemn Thoughts on God and Death* by the nonconformist minister and hymn-writer, Dr Isaac Watts (1674–1748). His *Divine and Moral Songs for Children*, first published in 1716 and a best seller into the nineteenth century, provided the basis for several common sampler verses. The key to the popularity of his moral and religious verses lay in his preface, addressed to 'all that are concerned in the education of a child', whose principle of learning truths, virtues and duties in verse (for 'what is learned in verse is longer retained in the memory and sooner recollected') was soon wholeheartedly adopted by schoolmistresses teaching needlework; the labour involved in stitching them probably made the verses even more unforgettable. During the last three decades of the century, samplers in the form of maps (LL5423–24, pp. 242–3) worked in simple outline stitches, were also used to reinforce school lessons. From about the 1780s printed outlines of maps could be bought for oversewing. The working of samplers was itself considered to produce well-managed households and ordered thoughts – the female equivalent of a young gentleman's Latin.

LL5332 (WHL3613)

## The Holy Family; Zacharias, Elizabeth and St John the Baptist

Worked by Martha Buckel, early eighteenth century

*Linen worked with silk in fine tent stitch, cross stitch and split stitch with an applied painted paper print of a parrot.*[1]

LL5332, which shows Zacharias holding out a flower to Elizabeth who sits under a pear or apple(?) tree (symbolizing the Fall of Man), almost certainly derives from a particular design source, probably from northern Europe. However, no engraved source has been discovered. The verses underneath the picture are from Luke 1:76 and Luke 1:80 and refer to John the Baptist. At auction LL5332 was dated to the eighteenth century and referred to as a sampler.

41.5 × 31.5 cm

Provenance: W. Mill, Old Swan House, 2 Cheyne Row, Chelsea;[2] sold Christie's, 18 June 1918, lot. 127, £10; purchased through M. Harris and Sons, 26 June 1918, for 10 guineas.

References: **1** The parrot appears to have been made from painted paper or card and applied to the ground in order perhaps to cover a hole in the fabric. **2** Mill also owned LL5225, LL5242 and LL5387 (pp. 101, 102, 99) bought by Lever from the same sale lots 126, 124, and 125 most of which were eighteenth-century pieces.

1928 Catalogue no. 135.

LL5332

LL5329 (WHL3520)

## The Ten Commandments and Lord's Prayer with Moses and Aaron

Worked by Sarah Broadway, aged ten, 1763

*Woollen canvas worked with silk in cross, satin, long and short and stem stitch.*

The Commandments are in the form of those in Exodus 20 rather than in the verse form popularized by Isaac Watts, *Divine Songs*,[1] which appears to have been commonly used on early eighteenth-century samplers.[2] Lever owned another sampler dated to *c.* 1710 with verses from Exodus set within an arcade and two 'saints', which was sold on his death.[3]

45 × 33 cm

Provenance: purchased through Arthur Edwards, 8 May 1918, £12.10.0.

References: **1** Isaac Watts, *Divine Songs: Attempted in Easy Language for the Use of Children* 1715, p. 39. **2** Averil Colby, *Samplers Yesterday and Today* 1964, pp. 170–1, fig. 103. **3** Appendix AG1, lot 582.

1928 Catalogue no. 137.

LL5333 (WHL3707)

## Alphabet, Numbers and Motifs within a Stylized Floral Border

Worked by Mary Hales, aged thirteen, 17 August 1788, Navenby, Lincolnshire

*Woollen canvas worked with silk in cross stitch with drawn thread work.*

Among the more unusual motifs employed are (from left to right, from top downwards): the figure of Justice; flying angels with candelabra or monstrances(?) rather than the more commonly held sword or trumpet;[1] a double-gabled building with large doors, perhaps representing a barn; a ship with figures on board;[2] and a building which may represent Solomon's Temple.[3] None of these motifs appear on a strawberry border sampler of roughly the same size worked by Ann Hales (Mary's niece) in 1828 while at Navenby School.[4]

Mary Hales of Navenby, just south of Lincoln, was the daughter of John Hales and Anne (Hannah) Lamb, christened 18 October 1775 and died in 1793.[5] The Hales family had

52.5 × 42 cm

Provenance: purchased through M. Harris and Sons, 12 December 1918, £8; displayed at The Hill, Hampstead.

References: **1** Averil Colby, *Samplers*, 1964, p. 67. **2** Colby as above, p. 70 suggests that the sailing ship pattern used in the later eighteenth century may be meant to indicate the father's or some other relative's occupation. **3** The design is close to that in an English sampler dated 1754 in Dr Glaisher's collection. Leigh Ashton, *Samplers*, 1926, fig. 47. **4** Private collection. **5** *Lincolnshire Parish Registers* ed. W.P.W. Phillimore, 1907–21, vol. VIII; letter from Mrs A.M. Hales 1/10/1991. Mary Hales' mother was illiterate, letter Dr G.A. Knight, Principal Archivist, Lincolnshire Archives Office 21/12/1988. **6** Letter from Mrs A.M. Hales 16/2/1991.

1928 Catalogue no. 130.

Figure 34 Sampler worked by Ann Hales of Navenby School in 1828

LL5333

farmed in the area since 1715.[6] Mary's embroidery, unlike that of her niece, must have been worked at home as there was no school in Navenby in 1788. This makes it more likely that the unusual motifs on LL5333 may have a personal significance compared to the 'institutional' ones found on the sampler worked by Ann Hales (fig. 34).

LL5327 (WHL3330)

## Verses on Religion and Hope with Motifs within a Stylized Floral Border

Worked by Elizabeth Beale, 1799

*Woollen canvas worked with silk in cross stitch.*

The motifs include fleurs-de-lis and parrot-like birds with lifted claws.

39 × 30 cm

Provenance: purchased through M. Harris and Sons, 27 July 1917.

1928 Catalogue no. 128.

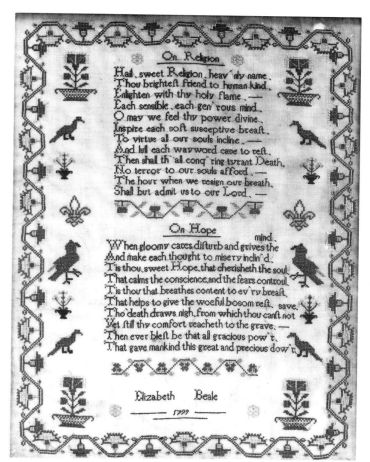

LL5327

LL5331 (WHL3588)

## Verses: 'On Life', 'On Death'

Worked by Elizabeth Dolling, late eighteenth century

*Woollen canvas worked with silk in satin, long and short, stem, and split stitch.*

The verses 'On Life' and 'On Death' have not been identified. The greater freedom and naturalism of the coiling tendrils and flowers suggests that LL5331 may be an eighteenth- rather than a nineteenth-century piece when flowers usually were more stylized. A date in the eighteenth century is also suggested by the format of verses in the centre and scrolling foliage and flowers around the edge.

43 × 33 cm

Provenance: purchased through M. Harris and Sons, 13 June 1918, £5 and displayed at The Hill, Hampstead.

1928 Catalogue no. 138.

LL5331

LL5334 (WHL3775)

## Fisherman in Landscape with Moral Verse

Worked by Diana Whitehouse, late eighteenth to early nineteenth century

*Linen worked with silk in tent, cross and long and short stitch with some couching stitches.*

The large pictorial element and its curving frame of wheat ears and tendrils is reminiscent of some of the 'fancy' samplers produced in the ladies seminaries and Quaker schools on the east coast of America. They were always meant to be kept for their decorative as well as instructional value and were occasionally sent as presents to relatives in England.[1] The use in the picture of long and short silk work bears some similarities to the type of silk embroidery believed to be distinctive of the Stivour School (*c.* 1778–86).[2] There is, however, no direct evidence to suggest that LL5334 is American and the purchase invoice refers to it as a 'Fine Old English' sampler. Contrary to the suggestion in the Macquoid catalogue there is no date visible on LL5334, though the date proposed of 1790 is an appropriate one for this piece.

39.5 × 27 cm

Provenance: purchased through M. Harris and Sons, 22 April 1919, £25 and displayed at The Hill, Hampstead.

References: **1** Anne Sebba, *Samplers*, 1979, pp. 83–105. **2** As above pp. 89, 94–5.

1928 Catalogue no. 132.

LL5334

LL5326 (WHL3191)

## Crucifixion with Angels, Religious Verse and Biblical Quotation

Worked by Deborah Jones, 1801

*Woollen canvas worked with silk in satin, long and short, running, stem, thorn and split stitch and knots.*

Crucifixion scenes on English samplers are very rare, though they appear slightly more often in Germany and Denmark in the latter part of the eighteenth century.[1] A Welsh example dated 1823,[2] shows an adult Christ on the cross, as do the European examples, not a child on the branches of a fruiting tree, as here. Francis Payne stated that the verse on the Welsh example commemorated Good Friday, but it is now believed that it belongs to a general group of biblical motifs rather than specifically commemorating Easter.[3] The symbolism of the verse on LL5326 is similar to that used by Isaac Watts (1674–1748) in some of his hymns.[4] Within a tetragram at the top of the sampler the words, Word, Father, Spirit and God have been embroidered.

55.5 × 28 cm

Provenance: purchased through M. Harris and Sons, 31 May 1917, £5 for display at The Hill, Hampstead.

References: **1** Leigh Ashton, *Samplers*, 1926, fig. 65b, 68; Averil Colby, *Samplers; Yesterday and Today*, 1964, p. 67. **2** Worked by Hannah Kemp, F.G. Payne, *Guide to the Collections of Samplers and Embroideries in the National Museum of Wales*, 1939, p. 38, pl. XIII. **3** F.G. Payne, as above, p. 38; Letter 29 November 1988. **4** See his 'Tree of Life', Book III, no. VIII, Selma Bishop, *Hymns and Spiritual Songs by Isaac Watts*, 1962, pp. 354–5.

1928 Catalogue no. 129.

LL5326

LL5324 (LT5)

## Adam and Eve and Verse on Virtue

Worked by Elizabeth Hesketh, 1804

*Canvas worked with silk in cross stitch.*

42.5 × 35 cm.

Provenance: presented by Miss Lydia Sherwood Brown, great grand-daughter of Elizabeth Hesketh, 1952.

References: **1** For other family embroideries see LL5323 and LL5322 (pp. 168, 236). **2** T.172–1928 and T.51–1938 Fitzwilliam Museum, Cambridge, *English Samplers at the Fitzwilliam*, July–October 1984, nos. 69, 74, 84.

Not previously catalogued.

LL5324 may have been worked by Lever's grandmother at the age of fourteen.[1] The verse at the top reads:

Virtues the chie[f]est Beauty of the Mind
The Noblest ornament of Human kind
Virtues our safeguard
And our Guiding Star
That stirs up Reason when our senses err

In the centre Adam and Eve stand beside a tree. The borders below and around them are formed of geometrical plant pots, flowers and dogs.

The verse appears to be a common one. It can be found on three samplers in the Fitzwilliam Museum, Cambridge, dated 1795, 1824 and 1800.[2] On the latter the verse is included among others on advice, virtue and death.

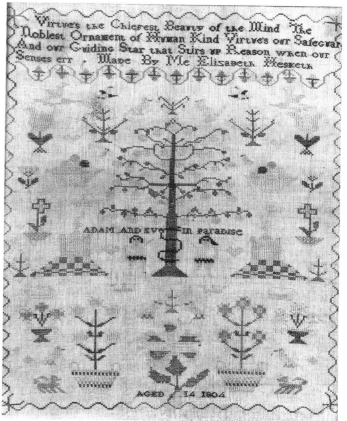

LL5324

235

LL5322 (LT2)

## Genealogy of the Hulme Family, Verse and Motifs

Worked by Ann Hulme, 18 September 1827

*Linen worked with silk in cross stitch.*

30.5 × 25.5 cm.

Ann Hulme was the grandmother of Elizabeth Ellen Hulme, later Lady Lever. William Hesketh Lever added his wife's maiden name to his own to create his new title on becoming a viscount. The verse has not been identified and is either incomplete or inaccurately set down.

Provenance: presumably the Hulme family. First inventoried after Lord Leverhulme's death and so is not listed in the Macquoid catalogue.

Not previously catalogued.

LL5322

LL5336 (WHL4306)

## Stylized Motifs of Vases of Flowers, Birds and Stags with Verse

Worked by Margaret Pearson, aged nine, 1836

*Linen worked with silk in cross stitch.*

43 × 41.5 cm

Provenance: found in the Chairman's Room, Port Sunlight, June 1919.

Reference: **1** Roszika Parker, *The Subversive Stitch*, 1984, p. 89.

1928 Catalogue no. 131.

The first verse of the rhyme (which takes up most of the sampler) appears to be traditional. It bears a very strong similarity to the verse found on an undated and unsigned sampler of a late seventeenth-century date,[1] which reads:

When I was young I little thought,
That wit must be so dearly bought
But now experience tells me how
If I would thrive then I must bow
And bend unto another's will
That I might learn both art and skill
To get my living with my hands
That I might be free from band
And my owne dame that I may be
And free from all such slavery.
Avoid vaine pastime the youthful pleasure
Let moderation allways be thy measure
And so unto the heavenly treasure

The sentiments expressed after the first few lines, however, differ significantly from one another, demonstrating the use of samplers in the nineteenth century as much for a child's moral indoctrination, as for her embroidery education. The embroidery's moralizing must have appealed to Lever, as he kept the work in his factory office.

LL5336

LL5335 (WHL3799)

## Triple-towered House Flying Union Jack, Vases of Flowers, Bowls of Fruit, Animal Motifs and Verse

Worked by Naomi Harrison, aged ten, first quarter of the nineteenth century

*Woollen canvas worked with silk in tent stitch, long and short, cross and satin stitch.*

When LL5335 was purchased it was dated to *c*. 1810. The ebulliently naturalistic vase of flowers in the centre is particularly finely worked in a variety of flat stitches.

41.3 × 31 cm

Provenance: purchased through Frank F. £8.10.0; displayed at The Hill, Hampstead.

1928 Catalogue no. 133.

LL5335 (see also colour plate 21)

LL5330 (WHL3587)

## Seven-gabled Country House and Coat of Arms with Verse within Floral Sprig Border

Worked by Elizabeth Harris, aged ten, 4 March 1847

*Woollen canvas worked with silk in very fine cross, satin, chain and a form of thorn stitch edged with a beige silk satin stitch border.*

The large schematized house may represent a real country house but the coat of arms with its two supporters of a pegasus? and a crowned lion may be a motif taken from a pattern book.[1]

44.5 × 31 cm

Provenance: purchased through M. Harris and Sons, 13 June 1918, for £5 and displayed at The Hill, Hampstead.

References: **1** The design of LL5330 was adapted and printed in *Stitchcraft*, August 1936, vol. IV, no. 11, which led to a reader's letter suggesting that the design was very close to, or the same as, one disposed of at the sale of Miss Catherine Brown, Victoria Cottage, Touch End, Bray. But no further research was done at the time and the provenance would seem unlikely.

1928 Catalogue no. 136.

LL5330

LL5337 (WHL4307)

## Alphabet, Numbers, Religious Text with Animal and Floral Motifs

Worked by Ellen Bleckley, aged nine, late nineteenth century

*Coarse linen canvas worked with silk in cross stitch.*

The text is from Psalm 37:4. The sampler hung in Lever's office at work like LL5336 (p. 236), which has a similarly moralistic verse.

24 × 23 cm

Provenance: found in the Chairman's Room, Port Sunlight, June 1919.

1928 Catalogue no. 127.

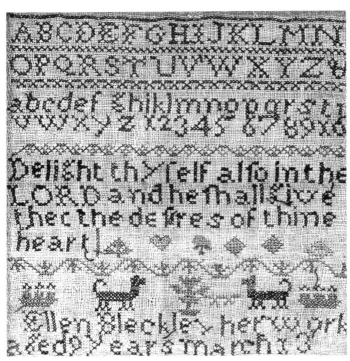

LL5337

LL5328 (WHL3336)

## Adam and Eve in the Garden of Paradise with Verse

Nineteenth century

*Canvas worked with silk in cross stitch.*

66 × 57.5 cm

Provenance: purchased through M. Harris and Sons, 21 August 1917, £23.2.0 as a piece of Queen Anne embroidery.

1928 Catalogue no. 134.

LL5328

LL5423 (TM184)

**Embroidered map**

## Map of Europe

Worked by 'E Smith', 1797

*Linen worked with silk in cross, stem and long and short stitch.*

23 × 32 cm

Embroidered maps are commonly found in the last three decades of the eighteenth century, when they were a particularly favoured method of children's schooling. The Victoria and Albert Museum also has an oval map of Europe dated 1796 and signed 'F. Smith'.[1] This is, however, much more decorative than LL5423 (which is worked simply and predominantly in brown) with a floral border surrounding the map, a greater range of colours and a scroll depicted between Iceland and Norway.

Collectors' interest in embroidered maps had already developed by 1900[2] and LL5423 was probably part of a set owned by Lever, which also included LL5424, *Map of Asia*.[3]

Provenance: unknown. A note in the Gallery files states it was acquired before 1911 and its old inventory number shows that it was at Thornton Manor before 1913.

References: **1** T.17–1948. **2** M.B. Huish, *Sampler and Tapestry Embroideries*, 1900, pl. XXVI, XXIX illustrate a map sampler of England dated 1777 by Ann Hope in the collection of the late Mr A. Tuer, and another of Africa dated 1784, possibly embroidered in a school owned by Mrs Seton Christopher. **3** Lever also owned a further two or three maps. See Appendix KFR1, lots 251–2; AG1, lot 448; C1, lot 28.

1928 Catalogue no. 185a.

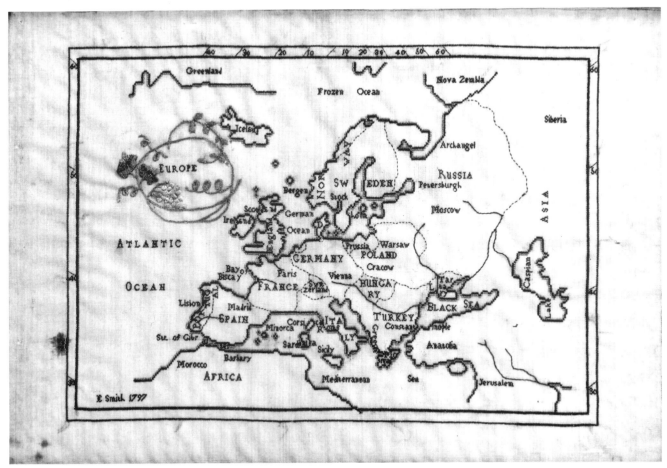

LL5423

LL5424 (TM184)

**Embroidered map**

## *Map of Asia*

Worked by 'E Smith', *c.* 1797

*Linen worked with silk in cross, stem, running and long and short stitch.*

A companion piece to LL5423 *Map of Europe*. The *Map of Asia* could be a rather squashed up version of a map of Asia engraved for the *Lady's Magazine* and reprinted in the *Political Magazine* for 1786 (fig. 35)[1] Both printed map and embroidery have a large number of the same names in common, such as Samoledi and Kalmucks, and the fine dotted lines used to show borders and rivers on the needlework are similar to the lines used to denote borders on the map.

23 × 32 cm

Provenance: unknown. See LL5423 for possible acquisition date.

References: **1** The *Political Magazine* vol. 10, May 1786.

1928 Catalogue no. 185a.

Figure 35   A map of Asia engraved for the *Lady's Magazine* and reprinted in the *Political Magazine* for 1786

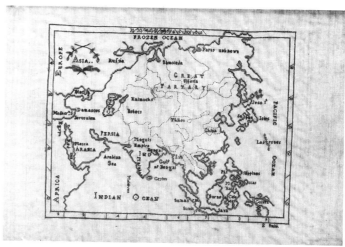

LL5424

# COSTUME, DRESS ACCESSORIES AND MISCELLANEOUS NEEDLEWORK

Detail from an early seventeenth-century glove (LL5416, p. 251)

The majority of the more elaborately worked Stuart and Georgian costume accessories were produced by specialists in professional workshops. This is certainly the case with the small group of items that Lever acquired, and particularly so of the gloves and shoes in the collection. The highly decorated gloves of the period of James I and VI (1603–25) (such as LL5416, p. 251) were not intended for daily wear – their cream satin cuffs or gauntlets, sometimes trimmed with gold thread lace and embellished with metal thread raised-work, seed pearls and spangles, and the unnaturally long and slender cut of the fingers, ensured that they were impractical for anything but ceremonial use, by either gentlemen or ladies. As both sexes were lavish in their dress it is often difficult to know for whom they were made, although the shorter and narrower gloves were more likely to be for women. As well as being the ultimate in conspicuous status symbols – visible, portable – gloves also had specific and symbolic social uses. Perfumed and decorated gloves were presented as expressions of loyalty to monarchs and members of the nobility or as gifts to visiting dignitaries. They could also be used to seal a contract and in this context were often exchanged by couples at the betrothal ceremony and given to wedding guests, sometimes accompanied by beadwork baskets, such as LL5343 (p. 91), in which the gloves might be displayed before the wedding. The preciousness and symbolic nature of the gloves probably ensured their preservation. The floral and animal motifs chosen to decorate the gloves, such as flaming hearts, roses and peacocks, were often also symbols of love, marriage and fertility or bereavement.

Some purses (see LL5399, p. 254) played a similar role in the marriage ceremony, and like gloves and other clothes accessories, the more luxurious were commissioned from professionals, made and sold by embroiderers and seamstresses. The less complex were probably sewn by female relatives, or in aristocratic households, by specially employed sewing women. In comparison to gloves, elaborately worked purses were more likely to have been in daily use in wealthy households, although the ones that now survive probably do so through lack of use. An exception to this appears to be LL5407 (p. 255) whose condition suggests that purses were sometimes passed on to or bought by a second owner and reused. The small fashion accessories popular at the end of the eighteenth century were mostly worked by professionals and adults but might also be embroidered by children. The delicate pocket-book (LL5401, p. 262) was worked between 1780 and 1790 by someone 'when a girl'. Pocket-books such as LL5401 were intended as a general 'holdall', with divisions for letters as well as squares of felted fabric for pins and needles.

As not even London had an effective paving act until the last decades of the eighteenth century embroidered and delicate silk shoes were not suitable for outdoor wear, unless accompanied by leather-covered clogs and pattens (LL5420, p. 269), which could be slipped underneath the shoe to keep it from the dirt and mud of the streets. In the eighteenth century, as in the previous century, professional workshops concentrated on elaborately worked costume: court suits, dresses, shoes and accessories such as the fine-beaded purses (LL5397–8, pp. 257–9) and trinkets produced by the huge French workshops in Lyons (which in 1778 employed 6,000 embroideresses) and Paris and the smaller London ones.

The French eighteenth-century beadwork technique differed from that in use in Stuart Britain. The beads were about half the size and strung in parallel rows along fine silk, which was stretched on a frame. Once the design had been worked and the rows interlocked with simple looped stitches, the finished piece was taken from its frame and attached to the purse, wallet or letter-case as required. This way of working beads was much quicker than the more painstaking methods used on the pictures and baskets created by amateurs in the previous century. The resulting beadwork costume accessories produced by professional workshops were impractical for continuous use and it is likely that they were treated as adult 'playthings' for the rich.

# Gloves

LL5412 (X3383)

Second quarter of the seventeenth century

Length 34 cm × width across gauntlet 13 cm, width across knuckles 9 cm

*Buff leather gloves with angled side opening to the gauntlet, which is cut in one with the glove. Embroidered with silk in satin stitch, couched silver thread and cord, green and red purl and spangles. Trimmed with silk and metal-thread braid and fringe. Decorative*

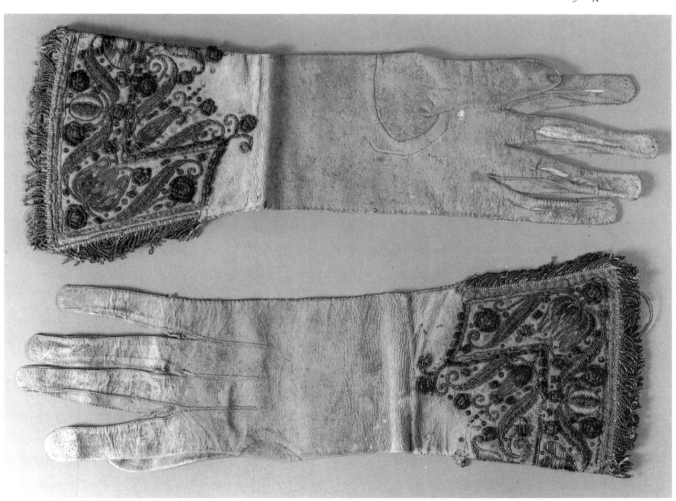

LL5412

'slashes' have been cut around the thumb joint and slits have been made on the palm side of all the fingers. The gauntlet is lined with bright green silk.

The gloves, along with other items bought by Lever from Kilbryde Castle in Perthshire (LL5244, LL5413–14, pp. 274–6), were traditionally said to have been worked by Mary Queen of Scots. Although Mary was a noted embroideress,[1] the style of all four items is that of a much later date. The design embroidered on the gauntlet, in red, green and silver thread, incorporating stylized coiling tendrils, tulips and roses(?) is, however, similar to that on a pair of gloves whose provenance is said to go back to one of the queen's attendants at her execution.[2] Like other clothes accessories of the period these gloves were almost certainly produced by a specialist craftsman.

Provenance: Sir James A.C. Campbell, Bt., Kilbryde Castle, Perthshire; sold Christie's, 3 June 1919, as part of lot 86; purchased £220.10.0 for four items.

Exhibited: Edinburgh Museum [sic], 1856.

References: 1 Margaret Swain, The Needlework of Mary Queen of Scots, 1973. 2 Saffron Walden Museum; William Beck, Gloves their Annals and Associations, 1883, p. 44–5, illus; W.B. Redfern, Royal and Historic Gloves and Shoes, 1904, p. 25, pl. XVII.

1928 Catalogue no. 68(9).

## LL5415 (X3803)

c. 1610–30

Buff leather gloves with long, square-tabbed cream satin gauntlets embroidered in blue purl and couched metal and vellum strips and metal thread in raised detached buttonhole(?) stitch and knots trimmed with gold bobbin lace and spangles. The gauntlets are lined with salmon pink silk.

Length 36 cm × width across gauntlet 16 cm, width across knuckles 9.5 cm

Provenance: purchased through F. Partridge, 4 March 1920, £44.

References: 1 Guy de Tervarent, Attributs et Symboles dans l'art Profane, 1958–9, vol. II, p. 334. 2 Gift of Marian Hague, 1959. Adolph S. Cavallo, Needlework, 1979, p. 35 illus. fig. 33. 3 No. 23348 on loan to the Museum of Costume, Bath; Connoisseur, vol. IV, September–December 1919, p. 92, no. 17.

1928 Catalogue no. 68(10).

LL5415 (see also colour plate 22)

Gloves with long square-tabbed gauntlets were particularly popular in the early decades of the seventeenth century, when the tabs allowed the gauntlet to pass more easily over the cuffs of long sleeves. The embroidered design incorporates stylized motifs on each of the six tabs, alternately depicting fruit (a strawberry?) and a heavily padded salamander(?) or snail-like(?) reptile. The embroidery is of a high professional standard and is still in a good condition. The motifs may have symbolic references. The salamander was a religious and secular symbol of eternal constancy.[1] The animal is featured along with other reptilian and snail-like animals, similar to those found on LL5415, on a raised-work casket or book cover worked in metal thread, now in the Cooper Hewitt Museum.[2] It is thought to be French and dated 1575–1625. The symbolic meaning of a snail (sloth and touch) would not seem appropriate as a decorative motif, except that snails do appear on a pair of gloves in the Spence collection of the Worshipful Company of Glovers, whose design is traditionally given to a French playing-card manufacturer.[3]

Length 35 cm × width across gauntlet 18 cm, width across knuckles 9 cm

Provenance: Mrs Shipwith Parker, Easter Rise, Ealing; sold Christie's, 2 March 1920, lot 57; purchased through M. Harris and Sons for £75.12.

References: **1** Bianca M. du Mortier, 'De Handschoen in de Huwelijksymboliek van de Zeventiende Eeuw', *Bulletin van het Rijksmuseum,* 1984, vol. 32, no. 4, pp. 232–3; Ann Monsarrat, *And the Bride wore . . . The Story of the White Wedding,* 1973, p. 23. **2** G. De Tervarent, *Attributs et Symboles dans l'art Profane,* 1958–9, vol. II, p. 303. **3** Jane Ashelford, *Dress in the Age of Elizabeth I,* 1988.

1928 Catalogue no. 68(10).

## LL5416 (X3809)

*c.* 1610–30

*Buff leather with separately worked cream satin square-tabbed gauntlets worked in metal thread, purl, spangles and silks in satin stitch trimmed with gold lace and spangles. The gauntlets are lined with salmon pink silk.*

Such splendidly decorated gloves would have been worn rarely if at all. In England it was common to give gloves to wedding guests and officiating clerics as tokens of fidelity rather than for wearing.[1] This elaborate pair is more likely to have been made for a specific individual as a love token or *memento mori*. The motifs of flaming hearts, a winged crown(?), an eye weeping tears, and pansies would have been symbolically appropriate to both emotions, or perhaps were intended to refer to love unrequited or lost through death. The pansy symbolized sad thoughts, as suggested by its other names, love-in-idleness and heart's-ease.[2] Yet in Shakespeare's *A Midsummer's Night Dream* Oberon orders Puck to pick pansies for his love potion. A weeping eye similar to, but not the same as, that on LL5416 is found on a glove in the Metropolitan Museum, New York. Its motif is derived from an emblem of sorrow in Henry Peacham's, *Minerva Britannia,* published in 1612.[3]

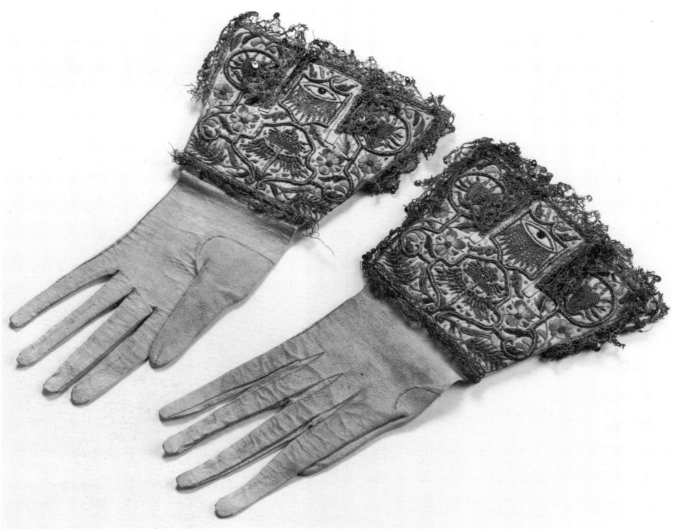

LL5416 (see also colour plate 23)

## LL5417 (X3810)

### Mid-seventeenth century

*Dark grey leather with stepped, angled gauntlets cut in one piece with the glove worked with couched silver thread, lace and strips raised over a silk cord. There are slits on the palm side of some of the fingers.*

Shorter length gloves, such as LL5417, were fashionable for men after the restoration of Charles II.[1] The combination of dark leather with richly embroidered silver slips suggests that the gloves could have been meant to be worn at a funeral or during a period of mourning. Pepys ordered gloves, hoods

Length 26 cm × width at gauntlet 13.3 cm, width across knuckles 9.5 cm

Provenance: Mrs Percival Griffiths, Sandringbury, St Albans;[3] sold Christie's, 2 March 1920, lot 84; purchased through M. Harris and Sons along with LL5418, a leather pocket-book (p. 265), for £22.1.0.

References: 1 Valerie Cumming, *Gloves: the Costume Accessories Series*, 1982, pp. 32, 36–7. 2 As quoted by Valerie Cumming, see above, p. 33; Ann Monsarrat, *And the Bride Wore . . . The Story of the White Wedding*, 1973, p. 49. 3 The wife of Percival

LL5417

Griffiths, who created a large embroidery collection similar to Lever's at the beginning of the twentieth century.

1928 Catalogue no. 68(8).

and scarves for himself, his wife and servants to be worn during the mourning period for his father who had died in 1667.[2]

# Purses and Wallets

LL5399 (H46)

**Drawstring woven purse**

## *Floral Bouquets and Tassels*

Second half of the seventeenth century[1]

*Woven in gold thread with brocaded design in coloured silk with gold thread and yellow and red silk plaited drawstrings and tassels with elaborate Turk's head knots.[2] Originally lined with cream satin.*

The purse, with its four woven, shield-shaped sides and finely plaited drawstrings is similar to the type of purse known to have been used in France during the marriage ceremony, where it played a very specific role, holding the symbolic number of coins given by the groom to the bride.[3] There is evidence that a similar custom existed in pre-Reformation England and that 'endowing purses' continued in use until at least the end of the seventeenth century.[4] Although LL5399 does not have any of the motifs specifically symbolic of marriage, such as cupids, lovers knots, hearts, or coats of

10 × 7.5 cm

Provenance: unknown. Acquired by January 1907, possibly lot 167, acquired by Harris as 'Property of a gentleman' from Puttick and Simpson sale, 12 July 1906. Kept at The Hill, Hampstead in a recess off the Stuart Room.

References: **1** Theresa Macquoid dated it to *c.* 1700. **2** A more detailed description of the weaving technique can be found in Sylvia Hogarth's article, 'The Stapleton-Wyvill Marriage Purse', *Textile History*, vol. 20(1), 1989, p. 28. **3** H.R. D'Allemagne, *Les Accessoires du Costume et du Mobilier*, 1928, vol. 1, p. 111, pl. XCIX. **4** Sylvia Hogarth, as above, p. 24–5. **5** Sylvia Hogarth has identified six other such purses dating from the late sixteenth to the early seventeenth century: the 'Stapleton-Wyvill' purse in Castle Museum, York (164/71); three purses in the Royal Scottish Museum (1925.128, 1925.129, 1958.572); one in the Fitzwilliam Museum, Cambridge (T.4 1922); and one in the V&A Museum (T.4666–1858). **6** G.S. Seligman and T. Hughes, *Domestic Embroidery*, 1926, p. 49, pl. XII. The dating in Seligman and Hughes is, however, sometimes unreliable.

1928 Catalogue no. 187.

LL5399

arms which are to be found on a group of similar drawstring bags in British public collections, it may have been intended as a love token.[5] A similarly constructed four-sided tapestry purse with knotted tassels, considered to be French and dated 1640–80, was in the collection of G.S. Seligman in 1926.[6]

## LL5407 (X3223)

### Shield-shaped purse

## *Bouquet of Flowers; Flowers Overlying a Previous Design in a Shield-like Cartouche*

Seventeenth century

*Silk fragments supported with linen worked with wool, silk and metal thread in satin, long and short, stem, split and couching stitches with French knots. Trimmed with a border of metal-thread braid and originally lined with blue silk satin and relined in cream silk satin.*

Underlying the partly floral and confused design on one side of the purse, there appears to be a previous design set within a

11.5 × 11.5 cm

Provenance: Mrs Nigel Heathcote Cohen, Burnham Norton; sold Christie's, 11 April 1919, lot 189 along with LL5246 (p. 134); purchased through M. Harris and Sons, 20 April 1919, for 1 guinea.

References: **1** Valerie Cumming, *Costume History: 1500–1900*, 1981, p. 28.

Not previously catalogued.

LL5407

cartouche worked in silver thread, in the shape of a coat of arms with quarters of white and yellow thread and a coronet above. A large cross stitch in red thread has been put over three swords and a three-leafed plant lies over what appears to be a crowned double-headed bird(?). The purse's poor condition shows that it was a much used, indeed, reused item of daily wear. The removal of the previous owner's coat of arms even suggests that it could have been bought from one of the second-hand shops near London Bridge, to which seventeenth-century courtiers sold their cast-off clothing.[1] Although Theresa Macquoid did not catalogue LL5407 she thought it could be early eighteenth century in date.

LL5407

LL5404 (X558)

### Shield-shaped purse

Late eighteenth century(?)

*Silk worked with silk and metal thread in satin, long and short, chain, and cross stitch with couched threads and French knots*

11.5 × 11.5 cm

Provenance: Jeffrey Whitehead, East Grinstead; sold Christie's, 11 June 1915, lot 780 along with seven other items; purchased through F. Partridge for £5.3.11 for items LL5400–6, LL5408 (pp. 260–5, 267–8) and kept at The Hill, Hampstead.

Literature: Virginia Glenn Pow, 'A New Look in Traditional Textiles', *Discovering Antiques*, 1970, no. 19, pp. 446–7 fig. 7 colour illus.

References: **1** Vanda Foster, *Bags and Purses*, 1982, col. pl. 2–3.

Not previously catalogued.

*trimmed with looped gold thread and pink ribbon. Lined with salmon pink silk.*

The purse's central motif of a strapwork heart-shaped cartouche is vaguely seventeenth-century in style but its shape and materials are definitely closer to those of eighteenth-century purses[1] and when it was first purchased it was thought to have been work of that century.

LL5404

## LL5397 (H48)

### Beadwork wallet

### *Cupids at Archery Practice* and *Aurora Pulled through the Sky by Cupids·*

Second quarter of the eighteenth century

*Very finely strung glass beads stitched on silk(?) and trimmed with silver lace with green brocaded silk lining.*

The designs on both flaps of this letter-case, showing Aurora (back) and cupids using a heart-shaped target for practice (front), and the metal lace trimming are exactly the same as those found on a pocket-book in the Museum of Fine Arts, Boston.[1] As the design, trimmings and sablé beads are the same it is very likely that they were made by the same workshop. Clothes accessories or trinkets such as LL5397, covered in very fine glass beads, sometimes a thousand to the square inch, were commonly produced by French, particularly Parisian, workshops during the later eighteenth century

14 × 23 cm

Provenance: Viscountess Wolseley; sold through Puttick and Simpson, 12 July 1906, lot 104; bought M. Harris for £6.16.6. Kept at The Hill, Hampstead.

References: **1** Elizabeth Day McCormick Collection #43.2371; the same cupids at archery practice scene also appears as the top fold of a Louis XV period sablé 'necessaire' illustrated in *Connoisseur* 1910, p. 262. **2** Larry Salmon, 'Eighteenth-century French Beadwork Accessories in the Boston Museum', *Dress*, 1976, vol. 2/1, pp. 1ff.; Vanda Foster, *Bags and Purses*, 1982, p. 21.

1928 Catalogue no. 185(6).

as luxury items.[2] Such beaded accessories were impractical for continuous use and were probably used as decorative playthings. The wallet's many references to love, including the flaming torch of Hymen, the god of marriage, held by one of the cupids, suggest that it might have been meant as a betrothal gift.

LL5397 (see also colour plate 24)

LL5398 (H47)

**Beadwork lettercase**

*Landscape with Hunting Dog and Stag and Phoenix Rising from a Fire with French Motto*

Mid-eighteenth century

*Fine sablé beads strung on silk trimmed with yellow silk border and lined with blue watered silk.*

12 × 17 cm

Provenance: Viscountess Wolseley; sold through Puttick and Simpson, 12 July 1906, lot 103; bought M. Harris for £6. Kept at The Hill, Hampstead.

References: **1** Elizabeth Day McCormick Collection #43.2365. **2** Larry Salmon, see LL5397, in *Dress*, 1976, vol. 2/1, p. 3. **3** James Hall, *Dictionary of Subjects and Symbols in Art*, 1974.

1928 Catalogue no. 185(7).

Another wallet almost identical in size, design and trim, apart from the colour of its silk lining, is in the Museum of Fine Arts, Boston, USA, and almost certainly came from the same Parisian source.[1] It is likely that there were only a few Parisian workshops producing such accessories as less than four hundred items using the sablé technique are known to have survived.[2] The motto on the scroll above the phoenix, '*SI JE MEURE CE N'EST QUE POUR REVIVRE*' ('If I die it is only to be

LL5398

reborn'), obviously relates to the phoenix as a symbol of rebirth and Christ's resurrection.[3] Envelope-shaped letter-cases such as LL5398 were used to protect papers, letters and banknotes.

LL5398

LL5400 (X554)

**Notebook with embroidered case**

*Design of Border Trellis Pattern and Sprays of Flowers with Central Oval*

Last quarter of the eighteenth century

*Three-fold wallet with a satin cover, worked with green, red, yellow, and purple and pink silk and spangles in fine chain stitch and cross stitch with metal clasp.*

This sort of folding case enclosing a notebook was intended to be carried on the person and was often referred to as a

7 × 11.5 cm when closed, 25.5 × 11.5 cm when open

Provenance: Jeffrey Whitehead, East Grinstead; sold Christie's, 11 August 1915, as part of lot 780 with seven other items; purchased through F. Partridge for £5.3.11, LL5401–6 and LL5408 and kept at The Hill, Hampstead.

References: **1** Vanda Foster, *Bags and Purses*, 1982, p. 25.

Not previously catalogued.

'pocket-book'.[1] LL5400 not only contains a five-sheet notebook and a calendar but places for keeping scissors, a pincushion and a small mirror. Another satin 'pocket-book' case in the collection (LL5401), similarly stitched in fine chain stitch and spangles, is datable to 1780–90. Both these wallets, along with seven other items from the late eighteenth to the early nineteenth century, were owned by Jeffrey Whitehead, a noted late nineteenth-century collector/dealer of small *objets d'art*, from whom Lever purchased much of his collection of painted miniatures.

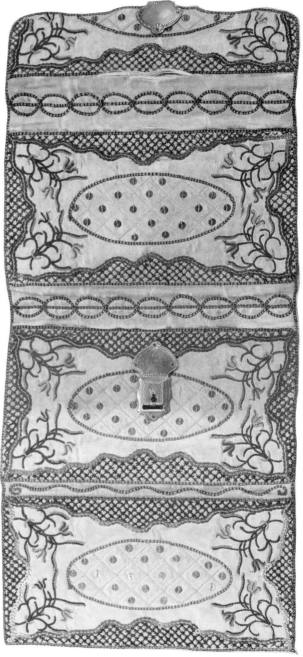

LL5400

LL5401 (X555)

**Wallet**

## *Design of Interlaced Green Circles with Trailing Floral Border*

*c.* 1780–90

*A one-fold wallet with a satin cover worked with silk, spangles, purl and cord in chain stitch and double running stitch, lined with rose-coloured silk.*

According to a card found inside the wallet, the embroidery was by O. Morgan's mother 'when a girl, between 1780 & 1790'.

9 × 15.2 cm when closed

Provenance: as LL5400.

Not previously catalogued.

LL5401

LL5402 (X556)

**Wallet**

Late eighteenth century

*Silk worked with gold thread, spangles and cord in chain stitch with a small amount of watercolour. The inner flap has a silver gilt catch and both compartments are lined with pale rose silk.*

8 × 14.6 cm when closed

Provenance: as LL5400.

Not previously catalogued.

The designs on each of the four surfaces differ, but mostly consist of flower baskets, floral sprigs and intertwined ribbons. The design on the front outer panel with a central trophy of a pair of doves(?), a flaming torch and a quiver tied together with bows and flowers suggests that this purse was a love token.

LL5402 (closed)

LL5405 (X559)

**Shield-shaped purse**

## Vase or Basket of Flowers

Last quarter of the eighteenth century or early nineteenth century

*The front and back panels are of satin worked with silk and spangles and cord in slightly padded, shaded China ribbon, split and chain stitch and couched threads with salmon-pink edge trimming. The two side panels are woven(?) in alternating pink and yellow stripes and embroidered with pale blue and black diagonal rods in satin stitch. Lined with pale blue silk.*

The mixture of spangles with small amounts of slightly raised work is similar to that found on the late eighteenth-century drawstring purse, LL5406.

10.8 × 8.3 cm

Provenance: as LL5400.

Not previously catalogued.

 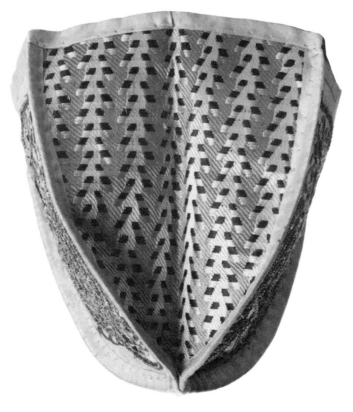

LL5405 (front and side)

LL5406 (X560)

**Semicircular drawstring purse**

*Sprays of Flowers within a Curved Interlace Design*

Last quarter of the eighteenth century or early nineteenth century

*Satin(?) with pale green and thin red stripes, and embroidered with silk, metal cord, purl, red foil and spangles in stem stitch and slightly padded, shaded China ribbon, trimmed with a crimped ruffled edge. Lined with salmon-pink linen canvas.*

12.7 × 14 cm

Provenance: as LL5400.

1928 Catalogue no. 186?

LL5406

LL5418 (X3811)

**Leather wallet**

Dated 1761

11 × 17 cm when closed

Provenance: same as the pair of gloves LL5417 (p. 252).

References: **1** Information from Simon Davies, Museum of Leathercraft, Northampton Museums. Illustrated in Vanda Foster, *Bags and Purses*, 1982, fig. 16.

Not previously catalogued.

*Red leather worked in metal thread in satin stitch(?) with an internal yellow leather pocket. Lined with fragments of deep blue cotton.*

The inner flap of the wallet is embroidered with the name John Graham and the date 1761. It was presumably a present to, or purchased by, Graham in Morocco as the reverse of the wallet is worked with the name of the Moroccan town Tetuan. Two similar souvenir embroidered leather pocket books (one of which was owned by Samuel Pepys) were made in Constantinople in the last decades of the seventeenth century and the start of the eighteenth century.[1]

LL5418

LL5403 (X557)

**Pocket book**

## *Hearts within a Floral Wreath*

Late eighteenth century

*Silk painted in pink, blue, orange, yellow and green pigments.*

The inside covers have trophies symbolizing gardening and music painted on them.

9.3 × 14 cm

Provenance: as LL5400 (p. 260).

Not previously catalogued.

LL5403

LL5408 (X561)

**Album cover**

*Design of Bow and Quiver, Branches and
Ribbon Bows*

Early nineteenth century

*Satin worked with green silks in stem stitch, and applied, shaded
China ribbon, circular and lozenge-shaped gold and green spangles
and trimmed with gold thread, cord and white, silk ribbon. Lined
with pastel-green silk.*

LL5408 might have been a cover for an autograph or keepsake
album popular from the late eighteenth century and through
the nineteenth century.

24 × 19.5 cm

Provenance: as LL5400 (p. 260).

Not previously catalogued

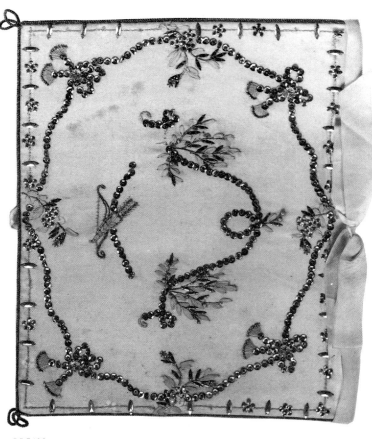

LL5408

# Shoes

LL5420 (H50)

**Pair of ladies shoes with pattens**

Early eighteenth century

24.5 cm × 9.5 cm × heel 6.5 cm

*Broad silk ribbons embroidered with stripes and geometrical pattern in pale green, in fine satin stitch with narrow latchet straps. One shoe has a broad band of metal-thread braid with a lozenge pattern*

LL5420

*running from toe to tongue attached, to cover over the central join. The shoe is lined with hessian, its heel is of white leather and the patten is of brown leather, stitched with a design in white thread, and fabric latchet straps with lace holes.*

The pattens may not originally have been intended to be worn with this pair of shoes as their latchets are of a pale blue fabric which is different from the overall pale green colour of the embroidery on the shoe. Pattens were essential wear for anybody venturing out in seventeenth- and eighteenth-century England. As protective footwear, keeping shoes above the muck of the streets, they were favoured by townspeople over the much taller and more cumbersome iron pattens used in the country. The pattens, like the shoes themselves, would have been tied with the silk ribbons and laces, which women preferred to the metal and jewelled buckles worn by men. Laces no longer exist for this pair of shoes. The broad band of braid which still remains on one of the shoes had become fashionable by 1690.[1]

Provenance: Viscountess Wolseley; sold through Puttick and Simpson, 12 July 1906, lot 107; bought M. Harris for £9.19.6. Kept at The Hill, Hampstead.

References: **1** June Swann, *Shoes*, 1982, p. 15, col. pl. 1.

1928 Catalogue no. 185(2) and (3).

## LL5419 (H49)

**Pair of ladies strap shoes**

Mid–eighteenth century

*White silk, embroidered in silk with floral sprays in satin, long and short and stem stitch. The shoes have blunted, pointed toes, covered*

10 cm × 23 cm, heel 5 cm

LL5419

Provenance: Viscountess Wolseley; sold through Puttick and Simpson, 12 July 1906, lot 105 'a pair of Stuart shoes'; bought M. Harris for £6. Kept at The Hill, Hampstead.

References: **1** June Swann, *Shoes*, 1982, p. 29, pl. 24b.

1928 Catalogue no. 185(4).

24 cm × 8 cm × heel 7 cm

Provenance: unknown. Acquired by sometime between 1912 and 27 March 1913. Displayed at Thornton Manor.

Exhibited: Gemeentemuseum, The Hague, *The Age of Shakespeare*, 22 January–1 April 1958, cat. no. 328.

References: **1** June Swann, *Shoes*, 1982, p. 7.

1928 Catalogue no. 185(5).

*heels, and wide straps, now stitched together in place of a buckle(?). The leather insole and straps are lined with white leather.*

The slightly rounded, pointed toes suggests a date towards the middle of the eighteenth century, as earlier toes were brought to a sharp point and upturned.[1] However, the embroidered design appears to be slightly earlier in date and does not fit the shape of the shoe. It would seem that the shoe was re-covered with embroidery from some other source such as an apron or dress.

## LL5421 (TM190)

Early eighteenth century(?)

*Silk embroidered with floral motifs in silks and metal thread with narrow latchet straps, one of which still retains its lace ties. The shoes are lined with soft white leather and the heels are a glossy light brown leather.*

The Macquoid catalogue dated this pair of shoes to *c.* 1600, presumably because of the shoes' high, narrow heels and pointed toes which may have suggested the style fashionable in the early seventeenth century.[1] However, the slightly upturned toes suggest a date from the opposite end of the seventeenth or the early eighteenth century.

LL5421

# Miscellaneous Accessories

LL5293 (X2565)

**Bible and cover**

Bible published by Robert Barker 1632

*Satin worked with couched and padded silver thread and cord, braid, spangles and red and blue silks in long and short stitch.*

The design on both the front and back cover is the same, although in different states of preservation. It shows in the centre an apple(?) tree, with a snake coiled around its trunk, placed beneath an arch which rests on two grotesque animal-like heads. In the upper corners are two stylized blooms. In its use of a rounded arch as a frame to the central motif, it bears some similarities to another metal-thread embroidered cover for a 1632–3 London Bible now in the Bible Society's collection in Cambridge University Library.[1] Like many bible-covers of the 1630s LL5293 was at one time attributed to the nuns' workshop at Little Gidding, Huntingdonshire. In fact the design and materials used on LL5293 bears no resemblance to those thought to be favoured by the Huntingdon workshop.[2] At one time the Bible belonged to Samuel Ward of Yarmouth, Norfolk who inscribed on a flyleaf, the Lord's Prayer in minute writing, within a circle, on 13 June 1768.

15.4 × 9 cm

Provenance: Samuel Ward, Yarmouth, 1768; for sale at unknown date £18; purchased through Arthur Edwards, 8 May 1918, £38.10.0 and first sent to The Hill, Hampstead.

Exhibited: Manchester, Whitworth Art Gallery, *Exhibition of Ecclesiastical Art*, 1958, no. 10.

References: **1** Cyril Davenport, 'Embroidered Bindings of Bibles in the possession of the British and Foreign Bible Society', *Burlington Magazine*, 1904, vol. IV, p. 275. **2** Cyril Davenport, ibid p. 270; M. Jourdain, *English Secular Embroidery*, 1910, pp. 76–7.

1928 Catalogue no. 68(5).

LL5338 (X3690)

**Psalmbook and Cover**

Psalms collected by Sternhold and Hopkin and published in 1636

*Satin worked with silks and spangles in satin and running stitch, and couched silk cord.*

The front and back of the cover have the same simple design of a tulip-like flower, streaked in yellow, orange and cream,

10.7 × 5.3 cm

Provenance: purchased through F. Partridge, 21 October 1919, £12 and taken personally by Lever to The Hill, Hampstead.

References: **1** See Cyril Davenport, *English Embroidered Book-*

*bindings*, 1899, pp. 103–5 illus. 48 for 1641 psalmbook with tulip; *Burlington Magazine*, vol. IV, 1904, p. 279, illus. p. 273, for 1633 combined New Testament and psalmbook now in the Bible Society collection, Cambridge University Library; V&A 1636 psalmbook T.101–1964; British Library 1646 Bible illustrated in S.T. Prideaux, 'Embroidered Book-Covers', *The Magazine of Art*, 1891, p. 65.

1928 Catalogue no. 68(6).

in an oval cartouche. The spine is decorated with a row of four-petalled flowers. This is perhaps the most common type of design on early seventeenth-century satin embroidered books. Several other books with a similar design style, one with a finely shaded tulip, are all datable to the 1630s and 1640s.[1] The satin ground of LL5338 is worn and has lost many of the spangles, which would originally have given a sparkling and richer effect to the cover.

LL5293

LL5338

LL5244 (X3386)

**Brush**

## *Allegorical Female Figure and Flowers*

First third of the seventeenth century

*Satin worked with silks, gold-thread cord and spangles in long and short stitch and French knots. Trimmed with a gold-thread tassel. The satin is now very worn.*

The female figure placed within an oval pomegranate shape is holding what may be an olive branch and appears to be dancing or swaying. On either side of her are schematic representations of what could be oak leaves and at the top there is a cornflower. A similar figure, standing up on her toes holding a palm leaf and representing Peace, can be seen on the embroidered binding of a book published in 1610 once belonging to Queen Henrietta Maria.[1] When LL5244 was purchased along with three other items from the Kilbryde

12 × 5.5 × height 7.5 cm

Provenance: Sir James A. Campbell, Bt., Kilbryde Castle, Perthshire; sold Christie's, 3 June 1919, as part of lot 86, for £220.10.0 along with LL5412 (a pair of gloves, p. 249) and LL5413–14.

References: **1** British Library Henry Davis Gift P. 404 for which see Mirjam M. Foot, *A Collection of Bookbindings: Catalogue of North-European Bindings*, 1983, vol. II, p. 111. The library has several more bindings of this type some datable to the first couple of decades of the seventeenth century. Another similar figure dated to about 1630–40 also thought to represent Peace was illustrated in Mrs Head, 'English Secular embroidery of the sixteenth and seventeenth centuries', *Burlington Magazine*, 1904, p. 172.

1928 Catalogue no. 68(4).

LL5244

Castle collection it was said to have been worked by Mary Queen of Scots. This romantic tradition probably ensured the high price paid at sale.

LL5413 (X3384)

**Embroidered panel**

*Central Motif of a Twelve-petalled Flower Surrounded by a Circular Band of Flowers with Tendrils and Flowers Coiling from Two Vases*

Early seventeenth century

22.5 × 32 cm

*Silk worked with coloured silks and metal thread in satin stitch, long and short stitch and couching stitches.*

LL5413

LL5413 was probably intended as a pillow or sachet cover. When it was bought by Lever it was said to be a muff-cover, but a similarly shaped, though smaller panel in the Shuttleworth collection at Gawthorpe Hall, worked with a comparable design, is described as a herbal or perfumed pillow.[1] The silks are badly faded on the design side, but the reverse shows its original strong greens, yellows, salmon pinks and purple-blues.

Provenance: as LL5244.

Exhibited: Edinburgh Museum [sic] 1856 No. 354(?); Great Stanhope Street, London, *Royal Treasures Exhibition*, 12 April–15 May 1937, no. 22; Gemeentemuseum, The Hague, *The Age of Shakespeare*, 22 January–1 April 1958, no. 326.

References: **1** F/6/54. Pauline Gittins, *A Brief Survey of the Shuttleworth Collections*, Museums Diploma thesis 1984, pl. 9, 10.

1928 Catalogue no. 68(3).

## LL5414 (X3385)

### Pincushion

## *Standing Lady Holding an Olive(?) Branch*

Early seventeenth century

*Linen cushion covered with silk and worked in silks and metal thread with the remains of satin and long and short stitch.*

The standing figure appears to be wearing a coif or a widow's veil. She is surrounded by various flowers including a carnation, an iris, a rose, a thistle and a tulip, all flowers commonly embroidered on accessories and pictures of the sixteenth and seventeenth centuries. The pincushion is very threadbare, revealing the under-drawing, and has lost much of its silk-work and all of the spangles which once adorned the whole surface, and the seed pearls, which formed an edging.

13 × 14.5 cm

Provenance: as LL5244.

Exhibited: Edinburgh Museum [sic], July 1856 No. 355(?); Stanhope Street, Grosvenor Square, London, *Royal Treasures Exhibition*, 1937, no. 27; Gemeentemuseum, The Hague, 22 January–1 April 1958, no. 327.

1928 Catalogue no. 68(1).

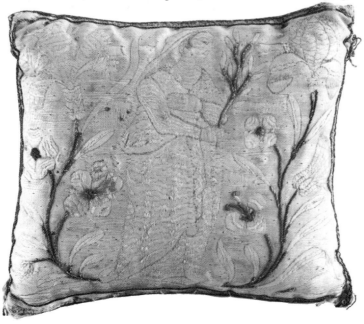

LL5414

14.7 × 11.5 cm

Provenance: purchased through F. Partridge, 18 August 1915, for £5 (possibly one of two seventeenth-century embroidered caps at the Whitehead sale, Christie's, 11 August 1915, lot 785) and kept at The Hill, Hampstead.

References: **1** See for example V&A T.286–1899. **2** C. Willet and P. Cunnington, *Handbook of English Costume in the Seventeenth Century*, 3rd. ed. 197_, p. 198; J.L. Nevinson, 'English Embroidered Costume Elizabeth and James I, Part II', *Connoisseur*, vol. 97, 1936, p. 142. **3** Aileen Ribeiro, ' "A Paradice of Flowers"; Flowers in English Dress in the Late Sixteenth and Early Seventeenth Centuries', *Connoisseur*, June 1979, p. 113.

Not previously catalogued.

LL5411 (X602)

## Child's cap

Early eighteenth century

*Padded silk worked with silk and gold-thread lace in long and short stitch and chain stitch. Trimmed with lace and pink ribbons, lined with green silk.*

The cap is embroidered on top with stylized palm fronds(?) and star-shaped flowers, and on the side with a damask rose(?). Indoor caps embroidered with coloured or white silks were worn by women and girls from the sixteenth through to the eighteenth century. This type of cap, shaped like a baby's bonnet, was particularly popular in the eighteenth century.[1] The size of LL5411 indicates that it was meant for a child[2] and whitework caps of this size and shape are sometimes referred to as 'christening caps'. Like most informal household wear it was probably embroidered at home by one of the women of the family. The embroidering of flowers on clothing began to fall out of fashion in about the mid-1620s but reappeared in the eighteenth century.[3]

LL5411

LL5411 (top)

LL5449

LL5449 (WHL4718)

**Large printed handkerchief**

*Events in the Reign of George III*

Rymer and Son, *c.* 1811–12

*Pale yellow silk printed in black inks.*                    86 × 86.5 cm

278

Provenance: purchased through M. Harris and Sons, 18 September 1923, £5.

References: **1** Mary Schoeser, *Printed Handkerchiefs*, Museum of London, 1988, pp. 1, 3. **2** V&A T.197–1957; York Castle Museum, printed by Rymer and Son of 53 Great Windmill Street, Haymarket and 3 Ossulstone Street, Somers Town. A further one passed through the Christie's salerooms in 1988. **3** See Mary Schoeser as above.

Not previously catalogued.

39 × 39 cm

Provenance: unknown. Perhaps acquired by sometime between 1912 and 27 March 1913, or it might be the 'Cambric lace edged Handkerchief' kept in the drawing-room specimen cabinet mentioned in a pre-1902 inventory of Thornton Manor.

Not previously catalogued.

Large, often headscarf-sized, printed handkerchiefs, referred to as 'mouchoirs', were produced in the eighteenth and nineteenth centuries to commemorate notable and royal events or make political statements, rather like T-shirts are nowadays.[1] At least three other identical handkerchiefs, printed by Rymer and Son of Haymarket, are known to survive including one in the Victoria and Albert Museum and one in York Castle Museum.[2] In 1809 George III had celebrated his golden jubilee and at least one design, totally different from that of LL5499, was printed to commemorate it.[3] The spiralling format derived from educational games and jigsaws popular from the 1790s onwards.

## LL5422 (TM188)

### Handkerchief

Late nineteenth century

*Fine cotton worked in drawn-thread work in chequer pattern, trimmed with a narrow edge of lace and embroidered in white silk with initials.*

According to an old inventory description, the handkerchief came from the Cheshire family of Lord Combermere. It was suggested that the initials read FAMC and represented those of Frances, eldest sister of the 1st Viscount, who married in 1792 and died in 1818. However, if the initials are read as

LL5422

FAWC, the handkerchief might have belonged to the daughter of the second son to the 5th Baronet's brother, Florence Champagne who married Augustus William Craven in 1880 and died without children in 1899. The dating of the handkerchief makes the latter identification more likely.

LL5409 (X567)

**Pincushion**

*Commemorating the Births and Christenings of Victoria, the Princess Royal and Edward, Prince of Wales*

Embroidered in 1842

*Satin worked with silk in minute cross and tent stitch with silk cord and tassel trim.*

As well as the children's names, titles and dates of birth, and Prince Edward's christening date, an inscription and pictogram runs around the side of the cushion, reading: May They Live in The [hearts] of The People.

9.5 × 9.5 cm

Provenance: Jeffrey Whitehead, East Grinstead; sold Christie's, 11 August 1915, as part of lot 782; purchased through F. Partridge for 1 guinea.

Not previously catalogued.

LL5409

38 × 18.5 cm each

Provenance: found in the gallery 13.3.1989, but described as on settee in furniture valuation of Thornton Manor, November 1904 and later moved to The Hill, Hampstead.

References: **1** Letter Mrs S.K. Hopkins, National Army Museum, 30.1.1990.

Not previously catalogued.

LL5450–51

## Pair of army badges

*c.* 1860

*Raised silver thread, purl and metal strips couched on to black cloth and attached to faded red silk brocade.*

The army badges both display a scroll inscribed PENINSULA: WATERLOO, which separates a crown from the intertwined initials LG and the badge of the Order of the Garter. The badges come from the cavalry saddle-cloth (shabraque) of the 1st Life Guards.[1] They appear to have been used to decorate the crimson damask loose cover to a settee (LL4084) which Lever purchased.

LL5450

LL5425 (TM183)

## Beaded spectacle case

Nineteenth century

*Leather covered with dark brown knitted wool and white beads. The case opening is semi-hexagonal in shape.*

12.5 × 4 cm

Provenance: unknown. Its old inventory number shows that it was at Thornton Manor before 1913.

Not previously catalogued.

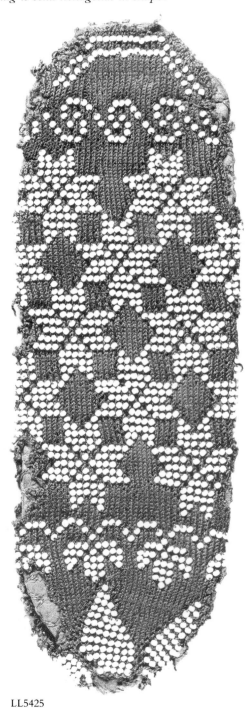

LL5425

# Appendix

The Appendix is taken from the sale catalogues at which the works were sold. It consists of summarized descriptions of all the embroideries sold from Lever's collection after his death, including sale date, lot number, former Lever collection number where known (the numbers prefixed by WHL or X) and whether the item was illustrated in the sales catalogues, and its present location where known.

**Knight, Frank and Rutley. House sale at The Bungalow and Rivington Hall, Horwich, Lancashire, 9–13 and 16–17 November 1925.** (Abbreviated to KFR 1.)

OVAL *PETIT-POINT* PANEL, dated 1736. 18½ × 16½ in. Two men in landscape with archway. WHL 2786 (lot 193).

SILKWORK PICTURE, eighteenth century. 21¼ × 34½ in. Pastoral scene. Two women and two boys seated, three men and animals. WHL 3339 (lot 194).

BEADWORK, Stag Hunt. 21 × 32 in. Two huntsmen, one on horseback with hounds. WHL 2741 (lot 195).

GEORGIAN OVAL SILKWORK PANEL. 6 × 3½ in. Lady guitarist and partner with flowers. WHL 2655, 2866B (lot 196).

GEORGIAN SILKWORK PANEL. 9 × 6¼ in. A classic female seated playing a lyre. WHL 1352 (lot 197).

OVAL STUMP- AND SILKWORK PICTURE. 11¼ × 2¼ in. Blue-coated boy in landscape. WHL 2865 (lot 198).

NEEDLEWORK PANEL, early nineteenth century. 28 × 23 in. Parrots in shrubs in arched window frame. WHL 3355 (lot 199).

OVAL SILK PICTURE. 8 × 6½ in. Seated female in crimson with flowers and monument. WHL 2279 (lot 200).

GEORGIAN SILKWORK PANEL. 16 × 13½ in. A lady harvesting within floral border. WHL 2211 (lot 201).

COMPANION PICTURE. 16 × 13½ in. Woman and child in landscape. WHL 2212 (lot 202).

OVAL SILKWORK PANEL, eighteenth century. 17½ × 15½ in. Pastoral subject, girl with lamb seated and shepherd with dog. WHL 2864 (lot 203).

GEORGIAN OVAL SILKWORK PANEL. 4½ × 3½ in. Standing boy with hat. WHL 3798 (lot 204).

ELIZABETHAN *GROS* AND *PETIT-POINT* PANEL. 11 ft 4 in × 6 ft 6 in. Centre oblong – hunting scene, six male and female figures, fruit trees, animals and birds; extreme border fauns, classical figures, etc. In coloured wools, mainly blues and yellows. WHL 1203 (lot 205).

GEORGIAN SILKWORK PICTURE. *Joseph and his Brethren*: Jacob and his wife instructing the youthful Joseph, while four of his brothers watch. WHL 2273 (lot 207).

ITALIAN SILKWORK PICTURE. 18 × 28 in. Europa reclining in wooded landscape with two riders, reclining attendants, hounds, and dead deer. WHL 2706 (lot 208).

STUMPWORK PANEL. 11½ × 16½ in. *Story of Esther*: king seated in centre receives queen, with Haman hanging on gallows. WHL 514 (lot 209).

STUART STUMPWORK PANEL. 13¼ × 19 in. Centre – seated cavalier and lady, with chateau, fountain, various animals, birds, insects. WHL 515 (lot 210).

STUART *PETIT-POINT* AND SILKWORK PANEL. Seated lady centre, castle and fish pool. Corners have floral symbols, lion and leopard at sides. WHL 212 (lot 211).

STUART *PETIT-POINT* PANEL. 17½ × 20½ in. Centre–seated, lady guitarist, courtier at tree, in corners floral emblems, lion and leopard at sides, birds, insects, etc. WHL 493 (lot 212).

STUART SILKWORK PANEL. Signed and dated, Elizabeth Ema, 1680. 18 × 26 in. Twelve figures in two rows. WHL 2815 (lot 213).

STUART *PETIT-POINT* PANEL. 10¼ × 15 in. *Lot and his daughters* with, left, lot's wife turning to pillar of salt. At base, leopard, pool and bird. WHL 2722 (lot 214).

STUART STUMPWORK PANEL. 15½ × 12½ in. Queen Henrietta under arched bower. A fountain and lion in corners of base. WHL 1370 (lot 215).

*PETIT-POINT* SQUARE PANEL. 9 in square. Worked in floral sprays, insects, birds, etc. WHL 2767 (lot 216).

GEORGIAN SILKWORK OVAL PANEL. 18 × 12 in. Bouquet of flowers. WHL 2276 (lot 217).

QUEEN ANNE *PETIT-POINT* PANEL. 21 × 23½ in. Pastoral subject: woman, man and child in landscape with parrot, squirrel, etc., church and houses in background. WHL 1199 (lot 218).

QUEEN ANNE *PETIT-POINT* PANEL. 11½ × 10 in. Lady standing near tomb on black and white tesselated paving. WHL 3589 (lot 220).

*PETIT-POINT* PANEL, early eighteenth century. 8¼ × 10 in. Pastoral subject: man playing flute, seated lady in landscape, sheep and dogs, etc. WHL 2721 (lot 221).

STUART *PETIT-POINT* PANEL. 11¾ × 14¾ in. King Charles I, Queen Henrietta, child in archway, amidst pool, lion and chateau, flowers and insects. WHL 3424 (lot 222).

SAMPLER. Dated 1723. 15½ × 8 in. Sun rays in centre, alphabet and inscriptions with a floral banding at the base. WHL 3359 (lot 223).

STUART SAMPLER. 18¾ × 7¾ in. With flowers, etc. geometric designs on canvas. WHL 3357 (lot 224).

CHARLES II *PETIT-POINT* APPLIQUE WORK PANEL. 20 × 21 in. Standing cavalier and lady in centre, with animals, flowers, birds, etc. WHL 2723 (lot 225).

EIGHTEENTH-CENTURY PANEL OF LONG SILK STITCHERY. 13 × 11 in. A sportsman shooting game, with dog, trees, insects, etc. WHL 2652 (lot 226).

SILKWORK PICTURE, eighteenth century. 8 × 8½ in. Man, woman and children in landscape, with trees each side. Another picture. 7½ × 6 in. Pastoral figures in landscape. WHL 1387/8? (lot 227).

STUART PANEL IN SILK NEEDLEWORK. 21½ × 24½ in. Large variegated flowers in applique work. WHL 2816 (lot 228).

SIMILAR PANEL OF SAME PERIOD. 22 × 25 in. WHL 2817 (lot 229).

COMPANION PANEL. 22 × 25 in. WHL 2818 (lot 230.)

GEORGIAN OVAL PANEL IN SILK STITCHERY. 15 × 19 in. Basket of flowers on table. By Margaret Tomlin. WHL 2630 (lot 231).

GEORGIAN OVAL SILKWORK PANEL. 14¾ × 10 in. Seated lady in garden with two sheep, in floral border. WHL 2865D (lot 232).

COMPANION PANEL. WHL 2865C (lot 233).

GEORGIAN OVAL SILKWORK PANEL. 8¾ × 6½ in. Lady feeding lamb in landscape, with gate and tree. WHL 1353 (lot 234).

GEORGIAN OVAL SILKWORK PICTURE. 12¼ × 14¾ in. Various flowers tied with ribbon. WHL 1357 (lot 235).

COMPANION PANEL. (lot 236).

OLD GEORGIAN SILKWORK OVAL PICTURE. 14¼ × 10 in. Allegorical female figure and grey obelisk, in floral border. WHL 1365 (lot 237).

COMPANION PANEL. WHL 1349 (lot 238).

GEORGIAN OVAL SILK AND PAINTED PANEL. 9½ × 7 in. Mother, boy and girl in landscape. WHL 1358 (lot 239).

PAIR OF OVAL SILK PICTURES. 5¾ × 4¾ in. Boy and girl (faces and hands painted), at play in gardens. WHL 1361 (lot 240).

GEORGIAN OVAL. 7¾ × 5½ in. Woman and sexton, trees above right. WHL 2278 (lot 243).

QUEEN ANNE *GROS* AND *PETIT-POINT* PANEL. 36 × 55½ in. Standing lady with mandolin, tulip centre, dog at foot, floral and foliated border, in wools. WHL 2262 (lot 244).

GEORGIAN OVAL SILKWORK PANEL. 14 × 16½ in. *Rebecca at the Well* WHL 1348? (lot 245).

SET OF 18 GOLD-RIMMED SATIN BUTTONS. Female allegorical figures, etc. in sepia needlework on white ground. WHL 2651 (lot 246).

GEORGIAN SILKWORK PICTURE, IN BLACK AND SEPIA. 16 × 13¼ in. Caernarvon Castle and shipping. WHL 2632 (lot 247).

GEORGIAN SILK- AND WOOLWORK OVAL PICTURE. 12 × 9½ in. Pastoral. Shepherd piping under tree, Peace places flowers on altar, with houses and trees right. WHL 1374 (lot 248).

GEORGIAN OVAL SILKWORK PICTURE. 8¾ × 6¾ in. Shepherd and sheep. WHL 2182 (lot 249).

COMPANION PANEL. 8¾ × 6¾ in. Shepherdess. WHL 2183 (lot 250).

NEEDLEWORK MAP, early nineteenth century. 18½ × 26½ in. The two hemispheres, printed and large letters in black within border of large coloured flowers. WHL 3348 (lot 251).

SIMILAR SUBJECT. 16 × 23½ in. WHL 2623 (lot 252).

PAIR OF GEORGIAN SILKWORK PANELS. 12½ × 10 in. Shepherd and dog beneath tree and shepherdess plaiting a chaplet of flowers. WHL 2567/8 (lot 253).

GEORGIAN PANEL OF SILKWORK. 10½ × 14 in. A lawn, tree and bridge to left, partially visible to right, a house. WHL 2631 (lot 254).

GEORGIAN OVAL PANEL IN LONG SILK STITCHERY. 9¾ × 8 in. A lady in white dress inscribing 'Emma' on tree. WHL 2865B (lot 255).

COMPANION PICTURE. 9¾ × 8 in. Lady playing lyre. WHL 2865A (lot 256).

GEORGIAN SILK AND WOOL WORK PICTURE. 12 × 9½ in. *Charity,* with two babes in arms and one ragged child in front. WHL 1376 (lot 257).

GEORGIAN OVAL SILKWORK PICTURE. 9 × 6½ in. Girl in blue skirt and pink bodice trimming her hat. WHL 1359 (lot 260).

COMPANION PANEL. 9 × 6½ in. Young girl in blue skirt and pink jacket seated on a bank, with sheep. WHL 1360 (lot 261).

QUEEN ANNE *PETIT-* AND *GROS-POINT* PANEL. 34 × 26 in. Centre, dancing cavalier and lady, piper in tree, floral border and strapwork on dark ground. WHL 529 (lot 262).

PAIR OF GEORGIAN OVAL SILK PANELS. 2 × 10 in. Sprays of flowers tied by ribbons. WHL 1343/4 (lot 263).

GEORGIAN OVAL SILKWORK PICTURE. 15½ × 12 in. Seated woman beneath tree with spaniel. WHL 2277 (lot 264).

GEORGIAN OVAL SILKWORK PANEL. 10½ × 8½ in. A young boy in white frock standing by a stream. WHL 1355 (lot 265).

GEORGIAN OVAL SILK PANEL. 7½ × 26 in. A youth presenting fruit to maiden. WHL 2280? (lot 266).

GEORGIAN OVAL SILKWORK PICTURE. 13 × 12 in. A female figure holding a cornucopia. WHL 1350 (lot 267).

GEORGIAN CIRCULAR SILKWORK PICTURE. 10½ in diameter. A basket of flowers. WHL 1342 (lot 268).

GEORGIAN PAINTED SILKWORK PICTURE. 11 × 17 in. Figures, cattle and cottages in landscape, with mountains. WHL 1354 (lot 269).

ITALIAN SILKWORK PICTURE. 20½ × 32 in. A Roman landscape, with buildings, ruins, equestrian and other figures. WHL 1371 (lot 270).

SIMILAR SUBJECT. 12½ × 17½ in. WHL 1372 (lot 271).

COMPANION PICTURE. 12½ × 17½ in. WHL 1373 (lot 272).

GEORGIAN CIRCULAR SILKWORK PANEL. 16 in diameter. Bouquet of flowers. WHL 3554 (lot 273).

GEORGIAN SILKWORK PANEL. 16¼ × 14½ in. Black ground, with bouquet of flowers. WHL 3555 (lot 274).

GEORGIAN OVAL SILKWORK PANEL. 23½ × 21½ in. Flowers, on black ground, leaf border. WHL 3553 (lot 275).

OLD GEORGIAN TRUMPET BANNERETTE, *c.* 1800. 22 × 24 in. The royal arms of England, raised needlework on red silk ground. WHL 3340 (lot 276).

COMPANION BANNERETTE. WHL 3341 (lot 277).

TUFFED WORK, first part nineteenth century. 42 × 34½ in. A vase of raised flowers, standing under arch. WHL 4437 (lot 278).

## *DINING-ROOM*

STUART SAMPLER. 26 × 6¾ in. Twenty-three bands worked in alphabet and coloured designs. WHL 3362 (lot 280).

GEORGIAN *PETIT-POINT* PANEL. 25 × 21 in. *The Woman of Samaria and Jesus at the Well.* WHL 1200 (lot 282).

SILKWORK PANEL, early eighteenth century. 26 × 23½ in. Trees and stag in hilly landscape, within a floral border. WHL 1386 (lot 283).

PANEL OF OLD PERSIAN NEEDLEWORK, WITH DIAGONAL BANDS. 25 × 19 in. Flowers worked in various bright colours. (lot 284).

QUEEN ANNE NEEDLEWORK CURTAIN. 97 × 37½ in. Tree foliage design with fruit, flowers and birds, in green, red and blue, on cream ground. WHL 530 (lot 285).

SIMILAR HANGING. 96½ × 36 in. WHL 530A (lot 286).

A SET OF FOUR JAPANESE SILK PANELS. Each 64 × 23 in.

1. A cage with cock on top, brown and white hens, chicks, marguerites and honeysuckle.
2. A large white cock, canes, marguerites and honeysuckle.
3. Brown hen and two chicks.
4. Golden brown and black cock, white and grey hen, four chicks, flowers, etc. WHL 1377–80 (lot 287).

JACOBEAN NEEDLEWORK CURTAIN, PERSIAN TYPE DESIGN. 106 × 62 in. One tall tree with crimson trunk and another with golden scales, with foliage, leopard, pavilion, tiger, bamboos, birds, etc. WHL 2773 (lot 288).

COMPANION CURTAIN. WHL 2774 (lot 289).

JACOBEAN NEEDLEWORK PANEL. 72 × 76 in. Rococo design in wools on linen worked with trees. WHL 4539? (lot 290).

## *CORRIDOR*

STUART SAMPLER, dated and initialled R.H. 1697. 30½ × 7¾ in. WHL 3364 (lot 291).

STUART SAMPLER, WITH FIFTEEN BANDS. 36 × 6¾ in. Conventional flowers, trees and alphabet. WHL 3361 (lot 292).

GEORGIAN SILKWORK PANEL, WITH OVAL MEDALLION. 17 × 14 in. Print of girl enclosed within a shield-shaped floral border. WHL 3552 (lot 293).

GEORGIAN WOOL AND SILKWORK PICTURE. 8¾ × 10¾ in. Two children with dog in landscape. Faces painted. WHL 3738 (lot 294).

GEORGIAN SILKWORK PANEL. 20 × 22 in. Battlescene with five horsemen, one wounded. WHL 4053 (lot 295).

GEORGIAN NEEDLEWORK PANEL. 7½ × 11¼ in. Pastoral. Seated boy and girl with trumpet. WHL 3192 (lot 296).

STUART PANEL. 12¾ × 15½ in. *Abraham sacrificing Isaac* WHL 3409 (lot 297).

STUART SAMPLER, dated and initialled SMM 1694. 33 × 9¾ in. WHL 3365 (lot 298).

SAMPLER, dated 1743. 36 × 8½ in. Eleven alphabets, Lord's Prayer, Commandments, numerals. WHL 3363 (lot 299).

GEORGIAN SILKWORK PANEL. Mary Anne Carter, aged 9. 15 × 13 in. Pastoral subject. Seated shepherdess, sheep and dog under a tree, within a floral border. WHL 3672 (lot 300).

GEORGIAN PICTURE IN RAISED WOOLWORK. 11½ × 9½ in. A shepherdess, lambs and dog, man resting against tree, fountain with lion surmount. WHL 1375 (lot 301).

GEORGIAN PANEL. 13 × 9½ in. Tippoo Sahib's children bidding farewell to their mother. WHL 3518 (lot 302).

COMPANION PANEL. 13 × 9½ in. The above children being delivered to Lord Cornwallis. WHL 3519 (lot 303).

GEORGIAN WOOLWORK PANEL. 12½ × 11 in. Seated woman spinning on a lawn path, house in background. WHL 1367 (lot 304).

GEORGIAN SILKWORK PANEL. 16½ × 18¾ in. *Christ and the Woman of Samaria.* WHL 1347 (lot 305).

STUART NEEDLEWORK MIRROR. 31 × 21¼ in. The border depicts the king under canopy facing the queen, below a female in ovals, above animals in corner circles, with flowers and insects. WHL 4344 (lot 306).

EIGHTEENTH-CENTURY SILK PICTURE. 12 × 8¾ in. Vase of flowers on white satin. WHL 3704 (lot 307).

GEORGIAN SILKWORK PICTURE. 13 × 10½ in. *The Gleaner.* Young girl carrying sheaf of corn, with cottage and coppice. WHL 1341 (lot 308).

COMPANION PANEL. Shepherdess with sheep. WHL 1340 (lot 309).

GEORGIAN WOOLWORK PANEL. 13½ × 18 in. *The Annunciation.* WHL 3776 (lot 310).

QUEEN ANNE PANEL. A lacework centre with flowers, with standing woman and bird, initials A.B., floral border in silks. WHL 3407 (lot 311).

GEORGIAN SILKWORK PANEL. 16½ × 13 in. An oval with parrot on tree within a floral border. WHL 3777 (lot 313).

GEORGIAN *PETIT-POINT* PANEL, dated 1736. 15½ × 9¾ in. A bouquet of flowers on reddish-brown ground, signed Eleanor Nicholsand. WHL 3516 (lot 314).

GEORGIAN OVAL SILKWORK PANEL. 15¾ × 14½ in. A woman holding flowers, among sheep, trees, etc. within a floral border. WHL 3187 (lot 315).

STUART SAMPLER WORKED IN ELEVEN BANDS. 29¾ × 6 in. Alphabet with flower and leaf designs. WHL 3366 (lot 317).

STUART SAMPLER. 32 × 6½ in. Rows of fancy work in flowers, etc. WHL 3360 (lot 318).

GEORGIAN SILKWORK PANEL. 16½ × 21¾ in. *The Apotheosis of a Hero.* A Roman soldier in a golden chariot driven by a flying female figure of 'Fame', and green dragons. WHL 2629 (lot 319).

GEORGIAN PANEL. 10¼ × 10½ in. Floral bouquet in silks and wools on cream satin ground. WHL 4183 (lot 320).

GEORGIAN SILKWORK OVAL PANEL. 13 × 11¼ in. A lady and a gentleman either side of a tree. WHL 3611A (lot 321).

GEORGIAN SILKWORK PANEL. 12½ × 12½ in. Basket of flowers, with butterflies, etc. WHL 1351 (lot 322).

## BALLROOM

JACOBEAN VALANCE. 17 × 146 in. With spiral branches of flowers and fruit on cream ground. WHL 2775 (lot 323).

SIMILAR SMALLER VALANCE. 16 × 82 in. WHL 2776 (lot 324).

JACOBEAN NEEDLEWORK PANEL. 72 × 76 in. Reddish-brown waving tree branches, bearing raised flowers of a rococo design and figures, etc. in coloured wools on linen. WHL 2780 (lot 325).

PANEL OF SAME WORK. 84 × 48 in. With raised flowering trees. WHL 2781? (lot 326).

SIMILAR PANEL. 77 × 35 in. WHL 2778 (lot 327).

JACOBEAN PANEL. 66 × 76 in. Flowering trees, birds, figures and animals in various coloured wools. WHL 2777 (lot 328).

SIMILAR PANEL. 80 × 54 in. With raised flowering trees in coloured wools. WHL 2779 (lot 329).

JACOBEAN PANEL. 76 × 50 in. Worked with trees, with waving branches, flowers, foliage, birds and figures. WHL 4358? (lot 330).

ITALIAN FIFTEENTH CENTURY ECCLESIASTICAL EMBROIDERY. 40 × 8 in. Figures of a bishop, saint, and evangelist in separate borders. WHL 3580 (lot 331).

SIMILAR PANEL. 40 × 5 in. WHL 3581 (lot 332).

PAIR OF CRIMSON VELVET CURTAINS. 91 × 48 in. Decorated with applied ornament of scrolls and foliage, in buff and blue (lot 335).

COMPANION PAIR OF CURTAINS. (lot 336)

LONG VALANCE EN SUITE. (lot 337)

SILKWORK PANEL. 62 × 70 in. Trees, deer and birds in a hilly landscape, the base with a scroll of ribbonwork inscribed with a motto (lot 338).

STUART SCREEN PANEL. 26 in. square. Flowering tree. Also A SIMILAR OBLONG PANEL. 30 × 17½ in. With deer. WHL 2626A (lot 339).

ITALIAN SILKWORKED PANEL. 40 × 23½ in. Floral centre medallion and serpentine border in crimson and blue (lot 340).

ITALIAN COVER OF CRIMSON AND BLUE VELVET. 48 × 37 in. Embroidered in Persian style in elaborate floral and bird designs in gold and silver threads and silks (lot 341).

CHINESE SILK COVERLET. 11ft 1 in. × 9ft 6 in. Yellow ground, embroidered birds, flowers, etc., within a green and red border (lot 342).

ITALIAN OBLONG COVERLET, CRIMSON SILK. 46 × 31 in. Persian design with floral medallions and border in the centre, a bird occupies each corner worked in silks and gold and silver threads (lot 343).

## CORRIDOR

GEORGIAN SILKWORK PANEL. Farm scene, with farmer, wife and child, and numerous animals. WHL 2634 (lot 344).

EIGHTEENTH-CENTURY GROS-POINT PANEL. 19 × 24 in. Seven Chinese figures, and birds, in trellis panels within border of floral sprays. WHL 3708 (lot 345).

CHINESE SILK EMBROIDERED PANEL. 40 in. square. Worked in close stitchery, a medallion of flowers centre, amid numerous vases of flowers, on green ground. WHL 2283 (lot 346).

JAPANESE SILKWORK PANEL. 44 × 28 in. Peacocks and other birds of fine plumage, flowering trees and rockwork. WHL 1345 (lot 347).

## LIBRARY

SILKWORK PICTURE. 19 × 25¾ in. Three horses galloping along a beach. WHL 1194 (lot 348).

SILKWORK PICTURE. 16½ × 22 in. Japanese pagodas and figures. WHL 1195 (lot 349).

SILKWORK PICTURE. 16½ × 24 in. Sheep in snowstorm. WHL 1193 (lot 350).

SILK PICTURE. 17 × 11¾ in. Two dead birds. WHL 1198 (lot 351).

SILK PICTURE. 16½ × 24½ in. An interior, with woman sewing by candlelight. WHL 1196 (lot 352).

SILK PICTURE. 16¼ × 24 in. An old English market house. WHL 1197 (lot 353).

PAIR OF CUT VELVET PICTURES. 12½ × 15¾ in. Japanese landscape (lot 354).

COMPANION PAIR. (lot 355)

SIMILAR LOT. (lot 356)

DITTO. (lot 357)

DITTO. (lot 358)

## BEDROOM CORRIDOR

JACOBEAN HANGING. 114 × 84 in. Tree with crimson trunk and waving branches of flowers and foliage, bamboos, birds, and pavilion, etc. WHL 2771 (lot 359).

COMPANION DRAPERY. WHL 2772 (lot 360).

## Anderson Galleries Sale, New York, 9–13 February 1926. (Abbreviated to AG1.)

LANDSCAPE IN GROS POINT, c. 1740. 9 ft 6 in × 13 ft 2 in. Exotic birds amid landscape with distant view of a mansion with round towers. Yellow to light chocolate border, enclosed by bands of pink mouldings. The angles hold oval panels with two repeated coats of arms, the Arms of Kirkcaldy, and the Sheldon Family. Illus. p. 16. WHL 4731 (lot 25).

PANEL OF GROS AND PETIT-POINT, c. 1570. 13 in × 8 ft 1½ in. Seven divisions containing a leopard, lion, unicorn, etc. under fruit trees, vine with strawberry, tiger-lily and other plants on a yellow ground, within a border of fruit and foliage. WHL 4486 (lot 26).

STUART PANEL c. 1635. 11 × 15½ in. Petit point, open canvas stitch, lace stitches, long and short stitch, basketwork, with portions in painting, with oval medallion in foliated frame, with the Judgement of Paris. WHL 3477 (lot 27).

PORTRAIT OF QUEEN ANNE IN ROBES OF STATE, c. 1710. 26 × 19 in. Silk embroidery decorated with pearls on white satin ground. Illus. p. 19. WHL 4765 (lot 28). Now in Metropolitan Museum, New York. Hackenbroch, fig. 154.

SILKWORK PICTURE, c. 1680. 14 × 20½ in. Figure of a lady surrounded by floral emblems, insects, etc., in applique work. WHL 497 (lot 29). (Resold 24 February 1926 for the account of Mr H. Glemby.)

SILKWORK POCKET-BOOK COVER, *c.* 1640. 5½ × 8 in. Standing male and female figures, divided by a vertical floral banding. With initials M.B. WHL 516 (lot 30).

ENGLISH *PETIT-POINT* PANEL, *c.* 1660. 8½ × 11½ in. King Charles II and queen, with lion and tiger, and basket of flowers. WHL 3730 (lot 31). Now in Metropolitan Museum, New York. Hackenbroch, fig. 49.

CHARLES II PICTURE, *c.* 1670. 12½ × 18 in. *The Story of Esther* in long and short stitch, basketwork and knots. Illus. p. 20. WHL 3205 (lot 32).

SIX OLD ITALIAN SILKWORK PICTURES, *c.* 1760. 10¼ × 8 in. Allegorical subjects, including *Leda and the Swan, Diana Surprised,* etc. WHL 3448–53 (lot 63).

SMALL COVERLET IN *PETIT* AND *GROS POINT, c.* 1710. 32 in. square. In design of playing cards, utensils, a bowl with suspended tassels in centre, within scrolled border, with floral groups at each corner, finished with fringe. WHL 4349 (lot 64).

ENGLISH PANEL, *c.* 1710. 60 in. square. Cream ground; embroidered floral and bird designs. WHL 3622 (lot 65).

STUMPWORK PICTURE inscribed. '16 C.M. 66' 11½ × 16 in. *Charles II and Court at Pontefract Castle.* The king seated to left under a rich canopy, with decorated curtains. To right the queen accompanied by two ladies. Above right Pontefract Castle. WHL 513 (lot 66).

ENGLISH SEVENTEENTH-CENTURY PICTURE. 17¼ × 20½ in. In *petit point,* openwork, long and short stitch and knots, a nobleman and lady extending hands centre, with animals and insects, including dragonfly, peacock, tortoise, grasshopper and elephant. WHL 520 (lot 68).

STUART EMBROIDERY, *c.* 1670. 12½ × 19¼ in. *Story of Susanna and the Elders* in long and short, brick, laid and chain stitches. Standing on her bath, and on either side of her an Elder, two ladies and a man with sword and lance. WHL 4190 (lot 69).

ENGLISH WORK BOX, *c.* 1670. 6 × 11¼ × 9 in. With divisions inside and drawer below, lined and padded with old yellow silk. Mirror panel inside top. Top and four sides with fine *petit-point* panels and applied on old cream satin. Illus. p. 43. (lot 72)

PANEL, *c.* 1670. 11½ × 16½ in. Centre, a queen appearing from her tent, approaching attendant, boy and girl stand either side between floral emblems. Worked in silks and silver threads. WHL 2695 (lot 73).

*PETIT-POINT* PANEL, *c.* 1670. 11 × 14¼ in. In silks and silver threads. Group of fruit-bearing trees, with birds in branches, within a brocaded border. WHL 522 (lot 74).

STUMPWORK PICTURE, *c.* 1670. 12½ × 17 in. *King Solomon Receiving the Queen of Sheba.* WHL 501 (lot 75).

ENGLISH STUART PICTURE, *c.* 1670. 16¾ × 15 in. In silk, with *petit-point* appliques. Two court ladies stand either side of a fountain surmounted by a cupid, symbolic floral sprays occupy the sides. WHL 523 (lot 76).

*PETIT-POINT* PANEL, *c.* 1675. 16¾ × 21 in. The Queen of Sheba and two train-bearers, offering floral tributes to King Solomon, guarded by a pikeman. WHL 3412 (lot 77).

SILKWORK PICTURE, *c.* 1640. 16¾ × 21 in. In long-stitch, *petit point* and stumpwork. Charles I at Pontefract Castle receiving tributes from a court lady with attendants. WHL 508 (lot 78).

SILKWORK PANEL, *c.* 1640. 18 × 23 in. Centre, a medallion showing a landscape with man, woman and child in a garden, in the corners are Minerva with sword and buckler, Jael with hammer and nail, a queen and Judith holding Holofernes' head. Illus. p. 45. WHL 506 (lot 79).

SPANISH SILKWORK PANEL, *c.* 1590. 11½ × 10¾ in. An embarkation, in canvas and other stitches. The border, bounded by curled bands shows, below, Neptune. Illus. p. 46. WHL 511 (lot 80).

SILKWORK PICTURE, *c.* 1640. 16 × 21 in. Floral design surrounding Queen Henrietta, base with a lion and tiger in *petit-point* appliques. WHL 3427 (lot 104).

CHARLES II PANEL, *c.* 1680. 15 × 18 in., unfinished. *Salome before Herod with John the Baptist's Head.* The border of floral emblems, lion, tiger, and birds. WHL 2836 (lot 105).

*PETIT-POINT* PICTURE, *c.* 1640. 15½ × 20 in. *Rebecca and Jacob at the Well,* with warrior and two female attendants. WHL 3474 (lot 106).

STUMPWORK PICTURE, *c.* 1640. 21½ × 17 in. In the centre the king and queen. Bust portraits of Charles I and Henrietta Maria are at the top. WHL 4056 (lot 107).

PANEL OF SILKWORK, *c.* 1640. 10 × 15¼ in. Centre, two male figures standing either side of a rock; left, man holding glass of wine, with other figures; right, spangled groundwork with insects and flowers; WHL 3134 (lot 108).

STUMPWORK PANEL, *c.* 1680. 11 × 16 in. *Abraham's Sacrifice.* WHL 3722 (lot 109).

*PETIT-POINT* PANEL, *c.* 1710. 13½ × 10½ in. Landscape, with goat, swan and two stags. WHL 3338 (lot 110).

*PETIT-POINT* PANEL, *c.* 1630. 11½ × 15½ in. Henrietta Maria offering Charles I a rose. Illus. p. 62. WHL 512 (lot 111). Now in the Metropolitan Museum, New York. Hackenbroch, fig. 48.

STUMPWORK PANEL, *c.* 1660. 10½ × 16¼ in. Centre – a seated lady under a tree; bottom corners show a youthful piper and angler. WHL 527 (lot 112).

*PETIT-POINT* PANEL, *c.* 1660. 17¼ × 22 in. Oval centre with three figures in landscape, flying bird with crown; top corner, figures of *Peace* and *Plenty.* WHL 2837 (lot 113).

STUART PANEL, *c.* 1660. 16 × 19¼ in. Raised figures of cavalier, lady and child standing beneath a flowering tree. WHL 494 (lot 114).

SILKWORK PICTURE, *c.* 1730. 16½ × 25 in. Landscape with shepherd, shepherdess and sheep. Left, a boy on a gate, and another figure, with windmill above. WHL 3594A (lot 115).

*PETIT-* AND *GROS-POINT* PANEL, *c.* 1760. 13½ × 16 in. Landscape with red cottage, lion, trees, etc. WHL 3784 (lot 116).

STUART PANEL, *c.* 1640. 13½ × 17 in. Centre, cavalier and lady, each with attendant in landscape with castle, and fish pond, at corners floral emblems. WHL 3723 (lot 117).

NEEDLEWORK PICTURE, *c.* 1820. 21 × 25 in. A courtyard with sportsman, black and white horses, etc. WHL 4439 (lot 118).

TWO *PETIT-POINT* CUSHION COVERS, early eighteenth-century. 17 × 32 in. (incl. fringe). Pastoral scene with, in distance, shepherd and sheep; to left, sportsman and dog by stream; above, a figure near trees. Border with coloured lozenges, with a tasselled fringe and a crimson velvet lining. WHL 4340 (lot 121).

*PETIT-POINT* AND CROSS-STITCH PANEL, *c.* 1725. 8¾ × 9½ in. Landscape with seated shepherdess, crook in left hand, basket of flowers on right arm, with sheep, lamb and dog. WHL 3478 (lot 122).

CHAIR SEAT COVER, *c*. 1740. 18 × 21 in. Large flowers springing from a mound, and stag below, in colours on a chocolate ground. WHL 4361 (lot 123).

EIGHTEENTH CENTURY PANEL, *c*. 1770. 6ft 8 in × 3ft 7 in. Groups of flowers in compartments, on crimson ground (lot 124).

THREE *GROS-POINT* PANELS, *c*. 1770. 32 × 25 in. Worked in flowers on a black ground (lot 125).

STUMPWORK PANEL, *c*. 1668. 13 × 18¼ in. *Solomon receiving Sheba*. WHL 3429 (lot 126).

SCOTTISH SILKWORK PICTURE, *c*. 1630. 14¾ × 18¼ in. Seated figure of a sportsman beside a stream accompanied by a dog. Illus. p. 69. WHL 4118 (lot 127). (In fact probably *c*. 1730?)

TENT-STITCH PANEL, *c*. 1625. 7 × 11¼ in. *Solomon Receiving Sheba*, who kneels before him, two ladies holding her train and a balcony with two courtiers. WHL 4058 (lot 128).

EMBROIDERED PANEL, nineteenth century. 26 × 19 in. The birth of a prince of Wales, with the queen in a four-poster bed. With female attendants and court officers watching and kneeling. WHL 4493 (lot 129).

ELIZABETHAN PANEL, dated 1569. 16½ × 23½ in. *The Saviour appearing to Mary Magdalen*. Illus. p. 79. WHL 4637 (lot 145). Now in Metropolitan Museum, New York. Hackenbroch, fig. 223.

BEADWORK PICTURE, *c*. 1640. 11¾ × 15½ in. Charles I and his Court at Pontefract Castle. In the lower angles a lion and camel. WHL 517 (lot 146).

CHARLES II PANEL. 12 × 15½ in. Silk applique work in short stitchery. A lyre-playing Orpheus seated amid floral emblems, birds and wild animals. WHL 521 (lot 147). (Resold 24 February 1926 for the account of Mr J.R. Shields.)

CHARLES II *PETIT-POINT* PANEL. 9 × 12½ in. *The Repudiation of Hagar*. In silks and gold threads. WHL 3468 (lot 148).

PANEL OF ZIGZAG NEEDLEWORK, *c*. 1740. 9 × 9¾ in.: WHL 4209 (lot 149).

STUART PANEL, *c*. 1640. 16 × 21 in. Oval medallion with *Susanna and the Elders*. Illus. p. 85. WHL 505 (lot 157).

SPANISH PANEL IN HIGH RELIEF, *c*. 1670. 13½ × 15½ in. *The Last Supper*. WHL 1206 (lot 159).

*PETIT-POINT* PANEL, *c*. 1670. 11 × 14 in. Landscape with lady presenting a cavalier with flower. WHL 512 (lot 160).

STUMP- AND NEEDLEWORK PANEL. 17 × 20½ in. Various figures, lady with serpent, another with flowers; below a house, stag and unicorn. From collection of the late Sir Edward Hopkinson Holden, Bt. WHL 4185 (lot 161).

OVAL SILK PANEL, *c*. 1640. 4¾ × 3¾ in. Queen Henrietta Maria and castle. WHL 518 (lot 162).

STUART PANEL, *c*. 1670. 32 × 26 in. Seated Virgin and Child praying, against distant hillside, within a draped, floral border. WHL 4753 (lot 173). (Resold 24 February 1926 for the account of Mrs F.J. Matchette.)

MID-EIGHTEENTH-CENTURY PANEL. 62½ × 34½ in. Three groups of figures in landscapes, dark blue ground, within each section a flying bird. Chinese taste in manner of Soho tapestry. WHL 4286 (lot 174). (Resold 24 February 1926 for the account of Mrs F.J. Matchette.)

SET OF FOUR GEORGIAN CHAIR SEATS, *c*. 1740. Average size,

17 × 17 in. Worked in wools in large flowers on brown ground. X.3663/66 (lot 175).

*PETIT-POINT* PANEL, first half of eighteenth century. 21 × 26½ in. *Farm Scene*. Illus. p. 101. WHL 3174 (lot 197). Now in Metropolitan Museum, New York. Hackenbroch, fig. 136.

STUMPWORK PANEL, *c*. 1670. 17 × 22 in. Charles I and Henrietta Maria seated in centre with pageboy and horse. Left, a lady holding flowers. Right, a fountain with lions, floral emblems, etc. WHL 3206 (lot 200).

*PETIT-POINT* PANEL, *c*. 1689. 17 × 21 in. William and Mary standing under tree, a lion, leopard and large flowers in corners. WHL 3426 (lot 201).

STUART PANEL, *c*. 1680. 10 × 11½ in. King and queen in centre with tree, floral emblems, corners with a dragon, unicorn, etc. in silk on cream ground. WHL 3475 (lot 202).

STUART PANEL, *c*. 1640. 9 × 9¾ in. Bust portrait of Queen Henrietta Maria with flower sprays, butterflies and thistles in border. WHL 3724 (lot 203).

NEEDLEWORK PANEL, early eighteenth-century. 11 × 10¼ in. A group of four floral sprays in coloured silks, bordering an eight-pointed star medallion in gold thread. From the collection of the late Sir E.H. Holden, Bt. WHL 4184 (lot 204).

OVAL *PETIT-POINT* PANEL, *c*. 1715. 31 × 24 in. *Diana at the Bath*. Illus. p. 115. WHL 2176 (lot 231).

STUMPWORK PICTURE, *c*. 1660. 16½ × 18 in. *Abraham Sacrificing Isaac*. WHL 3327 (lot 240). Now in Metropolitan Museum, New York. Hackenbroch, fig. 88.

TWO ITALIAN WALL HANGINGS, *c*. 1590. 7ft 6 in × 3ft 3 in Applique on crimson velvet ground, with large conventional, semi-natural flowers and birds including parrots, hoopoes, and peacocks, in metal thread and silk. X 4343/4. Illus. p. 123 (lot 245). Companions to the following hangings.

TWO ITALIAN WALL HANGINGS, *c*. 1590. X 4345/6 (lot 246).

TWO ITALIAN WALL HANGINGS, *c*. 1590. X 4347/8 (lot 247).

TWO ITALIAN WALL HANGINGS, *c*. 1590. X 4349/50 (lot 248).

TWO ITALIAN WALL HANGINGS, *c*. 1590. X 4351/2 (lot 249).

TWO ITALIAN WALL HANGINGS, *c*. 1590. X 4353/4 (lot 250).

TWO ITALIAN WALL HANGINGS, *c*. 1590. X 4355/6 (lot 251).

CHAIR BACK COVER, *c*. 1725. 24 × 18 in. *Gros-point* border with strapwork, formal ornament and conventional flowers on yellow ground. *Petit-point*, shaped, top panel with four figures playing cards. WHL 3596. Illus. p. 136 (lot 274). Companion to the following covers (nos. 275–9).

ENGLISH CHAIR BACK COVER, *c*. 1725. 24 × 18 in. Panel with two men and women card players in fancy dress. WHL 3597 (lot 275).

ENGLISH CHAIR BACK COVER, *c*. 1725. 24 × 18 in. Panel with figures as above. WHL 3598 (lot 276).

ENGLISH CHAIR BACK COVER, *c*. 1725. 23½ × 18½ in. Panel with four card players. WHL 3599 (lot 277).

ENGLISH NEEDLEWORK SETTEE BACK COVER, *c*. 1725. 36 × 24 in. *Petit-point* panels, first the fox and stork fable; second with landscape and lion with bridge and landing stage. WHL 3600/1 (lot 278).

ENGLISH SETTEE BACK COVER, *c*. 1725. 35 × 24 in. Similar

border to above. First panel – two dogs attacking bull in meadow; second has plant, bird and insect motifs. WHL 3602/3 (lot 279).

SILKWORK PICTURE, *c.* 1680. 13 × 19 in. *Salome, with the head of John the Baptist.* WHL 4068 (lot 280).

*PETIT-POINT* SCREEN PANEL, *c.* 1780. 31¾ × 23 in. A vase of various flowers. WHL 3703 (lot 281).

*PETIT-POINT* SCREEN PANEL, *c.* 1710. 26 × 21 in. *Judith and Holofernes.* WHL 3733 (lot 282).

*PETIT-POINT* AND STUMPWORK PANEL, *c.* 1670. 16 × 20½ in. Charles I, Queen Henrietta, with lion and leopard. WHL 4065 (lot 283).

NEEDLEWORK PICTURE, dated and inscribed Sarah Saunders 1795. *Jacob and Ishmael.* WHL 3135 (lot 284).

ENGLISH *PETIT-POINT* AND *GROS-POINT* CHAIR SEAT COVER, *c.* 1700. 20 × 24 in. Indo-Chinese design. Interior with person of high rank seated on carpet with kneeling servant and courtiers. X 3647. Illus. p. 139 (lot 285).

*PETIT-POINT* AND STUMPWORK PANEL, *c.* 1670. 16½ × 21 in. Oval central medallion with king receiving queen with her page; motif repeated in bottom left corner. Top right, king reclines in canopied bed with kneeling figure; right corner, king on charger approaches castle. (Probably Esther and Ahasuerus?) WHL 4064 (lot 286).

STUMPWORK PANEL, *c.* 1680. 16 × 21 in. *Susanna and the Elders,* in central oval panel, with Deborah, Jael, Esther, Judith in corners. WHL 3428 (lot 287).

PANEL, *c.* 1680. 9 × 16½ in. Justice, with castle, tree, rabbit and squirrel. WHL 3515 (lot 311).

STUMPWORK PANEL, *c.* 1680. 12 × 17 in. Centre – seated woman, infant, attendant and nymph each side, pool and fountain below, palace, lion and leopard above. WHL 3431 (lot 313).

PANEL, *c.* 1630. 12¾ × 16 in. Silkwork and *petit point.* Central oval medallion, landscape with seated shepherd and shepherdess. WHL 3138 (lot 314).

*PETIT-POINT* PANEL, *c.* 1640. 13½ × 17½ in. Seated lady holding nosegay surrounded by floral emblems. Top, a stag, below, a lion. WHL 524 (lot 315).

*PETIT-POINT* PANEL, *c.* 1710. 28 × 24 in. Lady in yellow, floral decorations, with garland. WHL 2728. Illus. p. 160 (lot 347).

STUMPWORK PANEL, *c.* 1670. 11½ × 18 in. *The Repudiation of Hagar.* WHL 3347 (lot 348).

*PETIT-POINT* PANEL, dated 1649. 15½ × 19¼ in. *Esther and Ahasuerus.* WHL 509 (lot 349).

STUMPWORK PICTURE, *c.* 1660. 10½ × 15¾ in. Cavalier and lady in centre, with castle, pool and animals etc. WHL 3681 (lot 350).

STUMPWORK PANEL, *c.* 1640. 14½ × 21 in. Centre – king and queen beneath canopy; seated – female figures, dog, bridge and mermaid. WHL 2692 (lot 351).

UNFINISHED JACOBEAN PANEL, *c.* 1615. 10 × 39 in. Two angels, saint, animals and trees in palace garden. WHL 4367 (lot 352).

*PETIT-POINT* OBLONG TABLE SCREEN, *c.* 1730. 8½ × 13½ in. Central vase of flowers, with squirrel and bird in foliage. X 3762. Illus. p. 164 (lot 360).

CHINESE EMBROIDERED WALL HANGING OR COVERLET,

eighteenth century. 10ft × 7ft 7 in. Wine ground, yellow and blue silk embroidery, panel with oval floral garland, shells and roses at ends, four birds on mound, background leaves and flowers with fringe and tassels. WHL 3618. Illus. p. 170 (lot 370).

NEEDLEWORK SAMPLER, 1789. (No size given.) A poem and conventional flowers. WHL 3345 (lot 373).

TWO SCOTTISH SAMPLERS. 23 × 6¼ in. Alphabet and floral designs. One dated 1669. The other 1702, inscribed 'My daughters have done vertuously but thou excellest them all.' WHL 3356 (lot 374).

STUMPWORK PANEL, *c.* 1680. 13 × 16¾ in. *The Rape of Europa.* WHL 2466 (lot 375).

TWO BEADWORK AND *PETIT-POINT* PANELS FOR HAND SCREENS, *c.* 1750. 9 × 6 in, and 8¼ × 6 in. Shield-shape. A page on one, a girl standing amid flowers on the other. WHL 3140 (lot 376).

PAIR OF HEPPLEWHITE HAND SCREENS, *c.* 1790. Stumpwork and needlework panels, floral bouquets. WHL 2306–7 (lot 377).

PERSIAN EMBROIDERED HANGING, eighteenth century. 9 ft 3 in × 6 ft 6 in. Centre – large flower with five rows of petals in two bands of pomegranates and scallop-edged floral forms, oblong pointed panels above and below, set in close embroidered floral panel. With border filled with flowers in green, white, yellow, red and black, with fringe and tassels all around. WHL 3619 (lot 379).

*GROS-* AND *PETIT-POINT* PANEL, *c.* 1570. 13 in × 5 ft 10 in. Woodland with various animals including ostrich, elephant, unicorn, swan and stork. Border of fruit and flowers on red ground. WHL 3144. Illus. p. 197 (lot 423).

PANEL, *c.* 1640. 8 × 8¾ in. Lady and Death in two panels, with seed pearls. WHL 4049 (lot 426).

SILK PICTURE, *c.* 1780. 5½ × 11 in. Lady in white dress with book in garden, monumental vase in background. From collection of G. Harland Peck, Belgrave Square, London, 1920. WHL 4264 (lot 427).

*PETIT-POINT* PANEL, *c.* 1640. 10¾ × 13½ in. *Joseph and Potiphar's Wife.* WHL 3731 (lot 428).

*PETIT-POINT* PANEL, *c.* 1660. 10¾ × 16¾ in. *Abraham's Sacrifice.* WHL 3136 (lot 429).

*PETIT-POINT* PANEL, *c.* 1770. 10¼ × 15¾ in. Landscape with seated shepherd and shepherdess, sheep and dog. WHL 3705 (lot 430).

PAINTED SILK PICTURE, *c.* 1780: 17½ in. square. Lady and gentleman seated in garden, left a temple and pool. From collection of Colonel H.H. Mulliner. WHL 4762 (lot 447).

EMBROIDERED MAP IN CHIPPENDALE CARVED AND GILT FRAME, *c.* 1770. 18 × 26 in. The western hemisphere and the eastern hemisphere in black silk with figures representing the continents in the corners (lot 448).

STUMPWORK PANEL initialled M.H., *c.* 1680. 12½ × 17½ in. *The Judgment of Solomon.* From collection of Sir Edward Hopkinson Holden, Bt., 1920. WHL 4189 (lot 449).

PANEL, *c.* 1670. 17¾ in. × 5 ft. *Story of David and Bathsheba.* WHL 3435. Illus. p. 207 (lot 450). (Resold 24 February 1926 for the account of Mrs F.J. Matchette.)

STUMPWORK SATCHEL COVER, *c.* 1670. 9 × 13 in. *The Fall of Man.* Borders with animals, birds, etc., and knots of ribbon. WHL 496 (lot 451). (Resold 24 February 1926 for the account of Miss Edith Wetmore.)

PETIT-POINT PANEL, c. 1710. 10 × 15¼ in. *The Finding of Moses* with gold-threaded border. WHL 4057 (lot 452).

SILKWORK PANEL, c. 1680. 7¾ × 12½ in. *Rebecca and Eliezer*. WHL 3680 (lot 453).

STUMPWORK PANEL, c. 1670. 10 × 13 in. *The Fall of Man*. Floral border and six-pointed rosettes. WHL 347 (lot 454).

SILKWORK PICTURE, c. 1670. 10¼ × 12¼ in. *The Flight of Lot and His Family*. WHL 499 (lot 455).

STUMPWORK PANEL, c. 1630. 16½ × 21½ in. Time and Justice appear against castles in relief. WHL 3614. Illus. p. 220 (lot 480).

SILKWORK PANEL, c. 1660. 6½ × 10¼ in. Equestrian lady, attendant, two cavaliers and tents in landscape. WHL 498 (lot 481).

STUART PANEL, c. 1640. 11½ × 15½ in. Female figures of Justice and Peace, within border. WHL 3721 (lot 482).

STUMPWORK PANEL, c. 1660. 11½ × 14¾ in. Cavalier, two ladies, attendant and camels. WHL 4150 (lot 483).

PANEL, c. 1660. 12 × 15½ in. Six figures, one on a goat, flowers, etc. on drab ground. WHL 4090 (lot 484).

SILKWORK PANEL, c. 1640, initialled B.M.C. 12 × 12½ in. Charles I, Queen Henrietta Maria and a dog, with floral motifs in *petit point*. WHL 526 (lot 485).

PETIT-POINT PANEL, c. 1710. 11½ × 12¾ in. Lady standing with large formal flowers at sides. WHL 3421 (lot 486).

SILK PANEL, c. 1740. 20 × 18½ in. White silk, with balanced design in gold thread, with flowers. Formerly the property of a lady in Cornwall. WHL 4472 (lot 490).

PAIR OF CHINESE CRIMSON SILK CURTAINS, c. 1800. 10 ft × 3 ft. Embroidered with pagodas, clouds, balustrades, figures, etc. Green silk lining (lot 492).

PETIT-POINT PANEL, c. 1690. 19 × 22 in. Rural occupations of the twelve months. WHL 4269. Illus. p. 239 (lot 511). (Now in Metropolitan Museum, New York. Hackenbroch, fig. 91).

SILKWORK PICTURE, c. 1670. 11½ × 13 in. Various subjects and initials – I.L., L.E., M.I., D.O., J.E, E.W., M.D., A.N., M.B. WHL 4149 (lot 512).

SILKWORK PICTURE, eighteenth century. 14½ × 11 in. A girl in white dress teaching dog to beg; an overhanging tree and a temple. From collection of Col. H. H. Mulliner. WHL 4763 (lot 513).

SILKWORK PICTURE, c. 1630. 12¾ × 19½ in. *Peter Denying Christ.*

With raised oval framing. From collection of Sir Edward Hopkinson Holden, Bt. WHL 4186 (lot 514).

SHAPED CUSHION, c. 1740. 19 × 18 in. Trellis design. Cream ground and crimson borders. WHL 4726 (lot 515). En suite with following cushions.

SHAPED CUSHION, c. 1740. WHL 4727 (lot 516).

SHAPED CUSHION, c. 1740. WHL 4728 (lot 517).

SEVENTEENTH-CENTURY SPANISH PANEL, c. 1610. 16½ × 16½ in. Grandee and lady standing under three-arched arcade in silk and gold thread. WHL 4145. Illus. p. 252 (lot 547).

PANEL, c. 1640. 16¾ × 20¾ in. Charles I and Queen Henrietta Maria seated beneath canopy, with court ladies, and a boy. WHL 510 (lot 548).

STUMPWORK PANEL, c. 1680. 17¾ × 16 in. *Solomon Receiving Sheba*; frieze of *The Judgment of Paris*. WHL 3207 (lot 549).

PETIT-POINT PANEL, c. 1680 10½ × 13½ in. *David Slaying Goliath*. WHL 3188 (lot 550).

PETIT-POINT PANEL, c. 1630. 7 × 10¼ in. River scene with figures, chateaux and trees. WHL 495 (lot 551).

PANEL, c. 1710. 10 × 11 in. Shepherd, huntsman and dog in landscape. WHL 4205 (lot 552). Now in Metropolitan Museum, New York. Hackenbroch, fig. 166.

THREE PETIT-POINT PANELS, c. 1580. 18½ in × 7ft 3 in, 19 in × 5ft 7 in, 18½ in × 6ft 11½ in. *The Creation of Eve, Temptation, Fall and Expulsion of Man from the Garden of Eden*, with borders of fruit, flowers, animals, boys with grapes or riding beasts, figures in fancy dress in silk and gold and silver thread on a dark ground. From the collection of the Earl of Kinnoull, Balhousie Castle, Perthshire, Scotland. WHL 4709/11. Illus. p. 265 (lot 579).

STUMPWORK PANEL, c. 1660. 13¼ × 20¾ in. Peace with olive branch with tall-spired buildings. WHL 2693 (lot 580).

PETIT-POINT PANEL. Signed Mary Williamson. c. 1670. 9¾ × 14¾ in. *The Story of Jephtha*. WHL 3337 (lot 581).

SAMPLER, c. 1710. 19 × 21½ in. Centre – the Exodus in crimson silk print in two arcaded panels with the Lord's Prayer and the Creed in the corners and archiepiscopal saints each side. WHL 4385 (lot 582).

STUMPWORK PICTURE, c. 1640. 13 × 17½ in. *Rebecca and Eleazar*. In central oval panel with large flowers in corners. WHL 4067 (lot 583).

## Anderson Galleries Sale, 24–27 February 1926. (Abbreviated to AG2)

PETIT-POINT PANEL, c. 1600. 14 × 18 in. *Susanna and the Elders*. WHL 3514. Illus. p. 8 (lot 25).

MINIATURE NEEDLEWORK FRAME, c. 1640. 9 × 8½ in. Floral emblems with tasselled fringe border. WHL 3373 (lot 26).

SILKWORK PANEL, initialled H.E., c. 1680. 10½ × 14½ in. Charles I enthroned in pavilion, with a pair of lovers and a scandalized couple to right. WHL 3430 (lot 27).

STUMPWORK PANEL, dated 1658, initialled M.S. 17½ × 24¾ in. Central oval medallion with lady and cavalier standing beneath a draped canopy. WHL 526 (lot 28).

PANEL, c. 1665. 12 × 20 in. *Jacob and Rachel at the Well*. WHL 528. Illus. p. 15 (lot 53).

FOUR CHAIR SEAT COVERS, c. 1730. Two 25 × 23 in; others 24 in square. Central red rose radiates sprays of tulip, tiger-lily, anemone, etc. X 2112/5 (lot 54).

ITALIAN SILKWORK PANEL, c. 1650. 6 ft 8 in × 6 ft. Feather pattern in red, blue and green tints, gold stitches outlined with black, and a gold and black chequer band between panel and border, with tasselled gold fringe (lot 55).

PANEL, c. 1670. 11 × 12½ in. *Lot and his Wife*. WHL 3190 (lot 56).

SAMPLER, dated 1689. 19½ × 6½ in. Flowers, arabesques and at base the alphabet. WHL 3677 (lot 57).

EMBROIDERED COAT OF GREEN SILK, c. 1760. Embroidered with flowers of various colours. X.4236 (lot 87).

ALMS BAG, *c.* 1640. 21 × 17½ in. Floral sprays, birds and butterflies in applique *petit-point* with silver and gold thread border and corner silk tassels. WHL 4348 (lot 88).

SAMPLER by Mary Swift, *c.* 1666. 36 × 7 in. Inscribed 'She was born the 14 of April 1657.' WHL 3674. Illus. p. 24 (lot 89).

PANEL, *c.* 1670. 10½ × 15 in. *The Finding of Moses.* WHL 3593A. Illus. p. 29 (lot 107).

SILKWORK PANEL, *c.* 1670. 17½ × 22 in. *The story of Esther.* WHL 3563. Illus. p. 41 (lot 142).

CROSS-STITCH PANEL FOR A FIRESCREEN, *c.* 1705. 25 × 22 in. Vase with voluted handles and knopped stem, with large bunch of flowers on a black background. WHL 3142 (lot 143).

EMBROIDERED WAISTCOAT, *c.* 1760. Cream silk, embroidered with brown sprigs, borders with coloured silk flowers and foliage. X.4243 (lot 146).

NEEDLEWORK PICTURE, *c.* 1710. 19 × 25 in. A sportsman shooting ducks, with dog. WHL 3367. Illus. p. 49 (lot 162). (Sold 21/4/1926?)

CHINESE VALANCE, eighteenth or nineteenth century. 32 × 57 in. Embossed work with gold threads, beads and feathers on cream ground. On a frieze are boat-shaped animals, crown and cross in middle, and oval panels with symbols. Jewels and ornaments constructed of blue, green, white, purple and yellow beads, and pendants of knotted fringe. WHL 4501 (lot 163).

CHINESE VALANCE, eighteenth or nineteenth century. 33 × 51 in. Companion to the preceding. WHL 4502 (lot 164).

FAN CASE, *c.* 1710. In *petit-point* with trees, buildings, etc. in the Chinese style. X 2742 (lot 165).

*PETIT-POINT* FLORAL PANEL, *c.* 1705. 25 × 21 in. A blue and white vase of sprays of flowers on a marble slab; red and brown background. WHL 3575. Illus. p. 55 (lot 179).

PANEL, *c.* 1640. 21 × 25 in. *The Five Senses.* WHL 3349. Illus. p. 83. (lot 261). Now in Metropolitan Museum, New York. Hackenbroch, fig. 114.

EIGHTEEN PIECES OF CROSS AND TENT STITCH EMBROIDERY, chiefly eighteenth-century in various floral patterns on dark grounds. WHL 4310/29 (lot 262).

TWO CHINESE IMPERIAL-YELLOW SILK PANELS, *c.* 1760. 20 × 18½ in. and 28 × 9½ in. One with four circular medallions of blue, crimson and white floral groups; the other with three panels of exotic birds and flowers. WHL 2235/36? (lot 263).

CHINESE SILK FAN CASE, *c.* 1740. Floral emblems and arabesques on each side. H.580 (lot 264).

PERSIAN PRAYER CARPET, eighteenth century. 5 ft 10 in × 4 ft. Applique embroidery on blue ground. X 973. Illus. p. 89 (lot 284).

SILKWORK PANEL, *c.* 1640. 19 × 21 in. Central medallion, flanked by man and woman, of a landscape with man and dog. Bottom – fountain, black boy, camel and leopard. Corners filled by large flowers. WHL 500 (lot 301).

CHINESE CRIMSON OBLONG PANEL, *c.* 1760. 30 × 10 in. Three circular medallions of dragons and flames in blue, pink and green embroidery. WHL 2237? (lot 302).

CHINESE FAN CASE AND PAIR OF SMALL OVAL MATS, *c.* 1760. Fan case embroidered in silver thread and coloured silks, and dragon on blue ground. H 580 & WHL 2236? (lot 303).

DOUBLE LENGTH OF CHINESE SILK EMBROIDERY, *c.* 1770. 49 × 7 in. Peacocks and other birds and flowers on imperial-yellow ground. WHL 2233/4? (lot 304).

ITALIAN COMPRESSED SILK PANEL, seventeenth century. 14 × 11 in. *Mater Dolorosa.* WHL 4657. Illus. p. 95 (lot 305).

MAHOGANY POLE SCREEN, eighteenth century. 27 × 25 in. *Boar Hunt.* (Damaged) H 308 (lot 336).

PANEL, *c.* 1710. 32 in × 5 ft. Blue vase with gadroon decoration. Illus. p. 120 (lot 393).

PAIR OF LADY'S OVER-SLEEVES, *c.* 1620. In gold and silver thread, with crimson and black silk, cream satin groundwork. From collection of the Hon. R. Stuart-Wortley, Highcliffe Castle, Christchurch, Hampshire. X 4237/8 (lot 394).

PAIR OF LEATHER GAUNTLET GLOVES, *c.* 1600. Cream-coloured leather, embroidered with vine leaves and bunches of grapes, edged with gold-spangled lace. X 4239/40 (lot 396).

CHINESE HANGING OR COVERLET, eighteenth century. 7 ft 10 in × 6 ft. Sage-green ground, two peacocks in central star medallion of floral outline. Panel ends with waves and shaped floral mounds, with tree, leaves and partly crimson flowers, fringed and tassels at corners. WHL 3620 (lot 397).

CHINESE EMBROIDERED PALE BLUE SILK FRONTAL, ENGLISH, *c.* 1800. 6 ft × 15 in. Vases of flowers, utensils, ribbon work, with a three-sided border of blue and white flowers and butterflies on black ground. WHL 2235? (lot 398).

CHINESE PALE YELLOW SATIN PANEL, *c.* 1770. 24 × 15 in. Three medallions with vases of peonies and other flowers. WHL 2260? (lot 399).

CHINESE PALE YELLOW SATIN PANEL, *c.* 1770. 30 × 18 in. Similar to preceding, but with six circular medallions with nine-claw dragons in blue, green and crimson. WHL 2261? (lot 400). (Sold 21 April 1926?)

SAMPLER, worked by Elizabeth Searles, 1701. 26 × 6¾ in. WHL 3675. Illus. p. 130 (lot 422).

SAMPLER, dated 1720. Floral designs, alphabet, names, numerals, and two poems. WHL 3676 (lot 423).

SAMPLER, dated 1742. 13½ × 8½ in. Floral sprays, birds, arabesques, the alphabet and the Lord's Prayer. WHL 3678 (lot 424).

SAMPLER, worked by Sarah Watson, dated 14 May 1730. WHL 3679 (lot 425).

SAMPLER, worked by Matilda Peel, aged 13, dated 1843. WHL 3454 (lot 426).

PAIR OF *GROS-POINT* CHAIR SEAT COVERS, *c.* 1688. 2 ft square. Mound design with tree ending in a central rose on white ground with crimson border of undulating stems of flowers. Corner pattern indicated, not worked. WHL 4340 (lot 427).

STUMPWORK PANEL, *c.* 1670. 14 × 18 in. King and queen holding hands under a blue pavilion with maid and page attending. WHL 3371 (lot 428).

*GROS-POINT* CARPET, *c.* 1710. 9 ft 6 in × 8 ft. Deep grey ground, centre and border in a floral design. X4772 (lot 462).

PANEL, *c.* 1635. 10 × 13 in. *The Finding of Moses.* WHL 4780. Illus. p. 144 (lot 474).

SAMPLER, dated 1802. 25 × 26 in. Emblems, inscriptions and floral sprays in pale colours (lot 476).

ITALIAN EMBROIDERED STOLE, *c.* 1690. Flowers and arabesques in silks and gold and silver thread. X 4235? (lot 477).

27 FEBRUARY (ADDENDA CATALOGUE).

## Knight, Frank and Rutley Sale, Hanover Square Galleries, London, 3–4 June 1926. (Abbreviated to KFR2)

EARLY EIGHTEENTH-CENTURY KNITTED SILK PURSE. Blue, with fleurs-de-lis, within miniature gilt beaded trellis work. Said to have belonged to Queen Charlotte. From the Whitehead collection. X 541 (lot 49).

EARLY EIGHTEENTH-CENTURY SILK STOMACHER. Cream, with embroidered elaborate flowers in gold thread. From the Whitehead collection. X 547 (lot 50).

EARLY EIGHTEENTH-CENTURY PERSIAN BED COVERLET. 116 × 81 in. Cream ground with warriors, animals, etc. in faded brown silk. WHL 2782 (lot 51). (Sold 8 July, lot 1?)

EARLY EIGHTEENTH-CENTURY *GROS-* AND *PETIT-POINT* PANEL. 16 × 64 in. Horizontal, Chinese figures, symbolizing the elements, flowers on black ground, buff-coloured border to three sides, the lower part escalloped. WHL 2258 (lot 52).

COMPANION PANEL. WHL 2259 (lot 53).

EARLY EIGHTEENTH-CENTURY LONG COAT AND KNEE BREECHES. Brown ribbed silk, embroidered borders in floral design also embroidered buttons. HH 216 (lot 54).

SPANISH SEVENTEENTH-CENTURY PATEN CASE. 11 in square. Square, of silver tissue, both sides embroidered with elaborate designs in gold thread and coral beads. X 551 (lot 55).

EARLY EIGHTEENTH-CENTURY SMALL PARASOL. Embroidered with beadwork, with broad blue banding in floral design. From the Whitehead collection. X 570 (lot 56).

EARLY EIGHTEENTH-CENTURY BEADWORK PURSE BAG. With floral medallions and border, cut-steel mount and chain. From the Whitehead collection. X 562 (lot 57).

EARLY EIGHTEENTH-CENTURY BEADWORK AND BLUE SATIN PURSE. With white, gold and silver beads and gilt charm pendants. From the Whitehead collection. X 564 (lot 58).

EARLY EIGHTEENTH-CENTURY PEAR-SHAPE ESCARCELLE. Grey velvet, with gold-thread needlework and silver clasp. From the Whitehead collection. X 565 (lot 59).

EARLY EIGHTEENTH-CENTURY BEADWORK PURSE. Oblong, cream ground, with rose colour flowers and green foliage. From the Whitehead collection. X 566 (lot 60).

EARLY EIGHTEENTH-CENTURY ALMS PURSE. Crimson velvet embroidered with gold, circular cushion shape, base with small circular shield of arms and coronet. From the Whitehead collection. X 545 (lot 61).

TWO EARLY EIGHTEENTH-CENTURY NEEDLEWORK PURSES. Crimson and silver tinsel, another of gold thread. X 542/3 and X 544 (lot 62).

SEVENTEENTH-CENTURY GENOA CRIMSON VELVET COVERLET. 58 × 38 in. Embroidered flowers and birds in silver and gold thread and silks, within border of Persian taste foliage. X 913 (lot 63).

EARLY EIGHTEENTH-CENTURY APRON. Cream satin with embroidered flowers in gold thread. From the Whitehead collection. X 549 (lot 64).

GEORGE IV PERIOD WAISTCOAT. Cream satin, wide border, flowers in coloured silk embroidery. From the Whitehead collection. X 550 (lot 65).

LATE SEVENTEENTH-CENTURY STOMACHER. White silk, embroidered formal flowers. X 548 (lot 66). Unsold?

EIGHTEENTH-CENTURY HERALD'S TABARD. Back and front panels embroidered with Royal Arms of George III, raised in gold threads and coloured silks, crimson and blue satin quarterings. WHL 4341/42 (lot 67).

EARLY EIGHTEENTH-CENTURY FLORAL PANEL in gold thread, unfinished. X 546 (lot 68).

EARLY EIGHTEENTH-CENTURY LENGTH OF EMBROIDERY. 7¼ × 38 in. Strapwork, vases and scrolls in gold thread and silks, on crimson ground. From the Whitehead collection. X 553 (lot 69).

EARLY EIGHTEENTH-CENTURY *PETIT-POINT* SHIELD-SHAPE PANEL. 9¾ × 8½ in. Crowned queen with sword, amorini and floral emblems in surround, with gold thread embroidery. From the Whitehead collection. X 552 (lot 70).

QUEEN ANNE VERTICAL HANGING. 99 × 15 in. With three escalloped ovals, each with allegorical female figure, in landscape panels, flowers and foliage, on black ground. WHL 2244 (lot 71).

EARLY EIGHTEENTH-CENTURY *GROS-POINT* VALANCE. 16 × 78 in. Persian foliage, various coloured flowers, three-sided narrow border and escalloped base. WHL 2251 (lot 72).

COMPANION VALANCE. WHL 2252 (lot 73).

SIMILAR VALANCE. WHL 2253 (lot 74).

COMPANION VALANCE. WHL 2254 (lot 75).

VALANCE, EN SUITE. WHL 2255 (lot 76).

EARLY EIGHTEENTH-CENTURY HORIZONTAL HANGING. 13½ × 51½ in. Centre – two phoenix and lion in *petit-point*, conventional foliage on black ground with floriate lower banding. WHL 2242 (lot 77).

EARLY EIGHTEENTH-CENTURY *PETIT-POINT* CHAIR COVER. Large coloured flowers on maroon ground. X 214 (lot 78).

EARLY EIGHTEENTH-CENTURY *GROS-POINT* HORIZONTAL PANEL. 13½ × 54 in. Conventional flowers in various colours on black ground, of four fragments. WHL 2241 (lot 79).

EARLY EIGHTEENTH-CENTURY *GROS-POINT* HORIZONTAL PANEL. 66 × 17 in. Crimson, green, drab and blue foliage, on black ground, ½ in blue border, a 4½ in strip on lower edge. WHL 2239 (lot 80).

EARLY EIGHTEENTH-CENTURY *GROS-POINT* VALANCE. 17 × 79 in. Chinese style figures and conventional foliage, escalloped base. WHL 2247 (lot 81).

EARLY EIGHTEENTH-CENTURY *GROS-POINT* VALANCE. 17 × 79½ in. Enthroned king and attendant in Chinese dress, floral, bird and animal surround in coloured wools, on black ground. WHL 2248 (lot 82).

COMPANION VALANCE. WHL 2240 (lot 83).

EARLY EIGHTEENTH-CENTURY HANGING. 14½ × 55 in. Foliage and flowers in various colours, on black ground. WHL 2240 (lot 84).

STUMPWORK PICTURE, *c.* 1660. 25¾ × 19½ in. Juno, Jupiter and symbolic figures of Plenty with a courtier and lady. WHL 3342 (lot 493B).

## Knight, Frank & Rutley, Hanover Square Galleries, London, 24 and 25 June 1926.
(Abbreviated to KFR3.)

PANEL. 48 × 61 in. *Douglas's death at the Battle of Langside.* Illus. pl. XXVI (lot 131).

STUART PANEL. 16½ × 20 in. The History of King Saul, and David slaying Goliath; flowers, animals, etc. (lot 132).

## Christie's, London, 2 December 1926, 'Property of a Nobleman'. (Abbreviated to C1.)

SATIN PANEL, late eighteenth century. 22 × 28 in. *Farmyard Scene* in wools. WHL 2634 (lot 4).

PAINTED SILK ITALIAN PICTURE, eighteenth-century. 20½ × 32 in. *Classical Ruins.* WHL 1371 (lot 5).

TWO SIMILAR PANELS. 12 × 18 in. *Classical Ruins.* WHL 1372/3 (lot 6).

ITALIAN VESTMENT PANEL, fifteenth-century. 40 × 5 in. Bishop and Saints. WHL 3581 (lot 7).

CHARLES II SATIN PANEL. 17½ × 20½ in. Courtier and lady with animals, birds and flowers. WHL 493 (lot 8).

SIMILAR PANEL. 20 × 21 in. WHL 2723 (lot 9).

CHARLES II PANEL. 15½ × 12½ in. Queen seated in an arbour, castle and flowers. WHL 1370 (lot 10).

CHARLES II SATIN PANEL. 13¼ × 17½ in. Lady, animals, birds and flowers. WHL 1216 (lot 11).

CHARLES II MIRROR. 31 × 21½ in. King and queen, courtiers, animals, etc. WHL 4344 (lot 12).

CHARLES II *PETIT POINT.* 11¾ × 14¾ in. Courtier and lady with background of branches of flowers and fruit. WHL 3424 (lot 13).

QUEEN ANNE *PETIT POINT.* 11½ × 10 in. Lady on a terrace. WHL 3589 (lot 14).

PANEL, late seventeenth century. 12¾ × 15½ in. *Abraham's Sacrifice.* WHL 3409 (lot 15).

PANELS, seventeenth century. 10¼ × 13¾ in. *Susannah and the Elders* and PANEL, eighteenth-century. 7½ × 11¼ in. Shepherdess and shepherd in a landscape. WHL 3773 and 3192 (lot 16).

TWO JACOBEAN PANELS. 17½ × 30 in and 27 in square. One with stag and hounds in wool on green background, other with birds and foliage on linen ground. WHL 2626A and 4365 (lot 17).

BROWN LINEN PANEL worked by ELEZERBETH SMART, 1680. 18 × 26 in. Twelve Figures. WHL 2815 (lot 18).

SAMPLER dated 1697. Alphabets and flowers, and two others similar. WHL 3364, 3361 and 3357 (lot 19).

*PETIT-POINT* PANEL. 9 × 9½ in. Birds and flower-sprays in fretwork frame. SILK PANEL. 11½ × 8½ in. Vase of flowers. WHL 2767 and 3704 (lot 20).

OVAL PANEL. 23½ × 21½ in. Sprays of flowers and foliage on black silk. SIMILAR PANEL. 15½ × 14 in. WHL 3553 and 3555 (lot 21).

*PETIT POINT* worked by ELEANOR NICHOLLS, 1736. 16½ × 10 in. Bouquet of flowers on red ground. OVAL PANEL. 19 × 14½ in. Basket of flowers in wools. WHL 3516 and 2630 (lot 22).

FOUR OVAL SATIN PANELS, late eighteenth century. 15½ × 13½ in and 15 × 10½ in. Ladies and children with flower wreaths around borders. WHL 2211/12 and 2865C and D? (lot 23).

QUEEN ANNE NET EMBROIDERY. 14 × 12½ in. Lady on a lacework ground with border of flowers. OVAL PANEL. 14 × 11½ in. Lady and gentleman. WHL 3407 and 3611A (lot 24).

OVAL SATIN PANEL, eighteenth century. 18 × 12 in. Bouquet of flowers. CIRCULAR SATIN PANEL. 16 in diam. SIMILAR SQUARE PANEL. 10½ in square. WHL 2276, 3554 and 4183 (lot 25).

TWO OVAL PANELS, eighteenth century. 12 × 10 in. Bouquets of flowers. CIRCULAR PANEL. 11 in diam. Basket of flowers. From Holland House, Kingsgate, Broadstairs. WHL 1342–4 (lot 26).

TWO PANELS, eighteenth century. 16 × 24 in and 19 × 26 in. The hemispheres with flower borders. WHL 2613 and 3348 (lot 27).

OVAL PANEL worked by Elizabeth Winterflood, 1797. 22½ in × 19½ in. Map of the British Isles within a floral border. WHL 2729 (lot 28). Previously on sale as Map of England and Wales KFR1 (lot 219.)

GEORGIAN PAINTED SILKWORK PICTURE. 24¼ × 19¼ in. National mourning at Nelson's death, with Britannia, Fame and lion, left, the fleet, above, angel adorns his bust with laurel wreath. BATTLE SCENE. 20 × 22 in. WHL 1369 and 4053 (lot 29).

TWO PANELS, late eighteenth century. 17 × 14 in. Printed portrait of girl surrounded by flower-sprays and ribands and shepherdess with border of strawberries on net by Mary Anne Carter. WHL 3552 and 3672 (lot 30).

THREE PAINTED SILK OVALS, late eighteenth century. 10½ × 8 in. Nymphs and a boy. WHL 2865 (lot 31).

TWO SATIN OVALS. 14 × 10 in. Emblematic figures with floral border. TWO PANELS. 12½ × 10 in. Shepherd and shepherdess in floral border. WHL 1365–6 and 2657–8 (lot 32).

SILKWORK PICTURES, late eighteenth century. 20 × 16 in. *Britannia* with lion, deer and sheep. BOAZ AND RUTH in wools. 17½ × 14 in. WHL 2274 and 1368 (lot 33). Previously on sale KFR1 (lots 279 and 281).

THREE SATIN PANELS, eighteenth century. 16 × 14½ in. Shepherdess and wreath of flowers. 16 × 13 in. Parrot with flower wreath. 12½ in square. Basket of flowers. WHL 3187, 3777 and 1351 (lot 34).

TWO PANELS, late eighteenth century. 12 × 9½ in. *Peace and Charity* in wools. TWO OVAL PANELS. *Christ and the Woman of Samaria* and girl with spinning wheel. WHL 1374 (lot 35).

FOUR PANELS. 10½ × 14½ in. A landscape, children in a landscape, two panels with the children of Tipoo Sahib. WHL 2631, 3738, 3518–19 (lot 36).

THREE PANELS, late eighteenth century. 16¾ × 21 in. Mythological subject on painted silk. 13½ × 18 in. *Annunciation* in wools. 20 × 25 in. Woolwork panel with figures on trellis ground. WHL 2629, 3776 and 3708 (lot 37).

FOUR SILKWORK OVALS, late eighteenth century. 9 × 6¼ in. Two with *Elijah and the Ravens* and *Moses and the Burning Bush* : two with a boy in kneebreeches and blue mantle, blowing a pipe, dog at feet and a young woman in blue skirt and brown cloak with basket of flowers. WHL 1363–4 and 1336–7 (lot 38). Previously on sale KFR1 (lots 241–2, 258–9).

OVAL PANEL. 13 × 11½ in. Girl with cornucopia : and two other panels with children, one with a shepherdess. WHL 1353, 1350, 1360, 1355 (lot 39).

TWO SMALL PANELS with children, and six other small panels with various subjects. WHL 1361 the pair, 3798, 2655, 2866, 1352, 2273 and 2279 (lot 40).

JACOBEAN LINEN PANEL. 6 ft 8 in × 4 ft 6 in. Formal flowers, foliage and scrollwork. WHL 2779 (lot 41).

PAIR OF JACOBEAN LINEN PANELS. 8 ft × 3 ft. Birds, stags and flowering trees. WHL 530 and 530A (lot 42).

JACOBEAN LINEN PANEL. 6 ft 5 in × 2 ft 11 in. Birds and flowering trees. WHL 2778 (lot 43).

JACOBEAN LINEN PANEL. 5 ft 6 in × 6 ft 4 in. Flowering trees and birds with, in the foreground, small figures, stags and hounds. WHL 2777 (lot 44).

SILK PANEL, late seventeenth century. 8 ft 10 in × 5 ft 2 in. Flowering trees and birds in Chinese taste. WHL 2773 (lot 45).

COMPANION PANEL. 8 ft 11 in × 6 ft 5 in. WHL 2774 (lot 46).

SATIN PANEL. 5 ft × 6 ft. Stags and trees and an inscription in wools. WHL 2768 (lot 47).

TWO PAIRS RED VELVET CURTAINS. 7 ft 4 in × 4 ft. Appliqué embroidery of scrollwork in green and white silk. VALANCE en suite. 15 ft 8 in × 11 in. X 4924–6 (lot 48).

# Glossary

There is no standard way of describing all stitches. The names used to describe the most common stitches, for example satin, long and short, tent or buttonhole stitch, are found in Mary Thomas's *Dictionary of Embroidery Stitches* (1934). Listed below are the more specialized stitches or types of embroidery referred to with their commonly agreed descriptions.

**Berlin woolwork**: Embroidery in wool on canvas, worked from patterns drawn on squared paper, each square of which corresponds to a square of the canvas. Patterns and wool were introduced in the early decades of the nineteenth century from Germany. The technique remained popular until the 1880s.

**Brocade**: a type of woven patterned cloth in which the coloured weft threads are not carried the whole width of the woven piece but only across the width of the area in which they are needed.

**Bullion**: a type of metal wire larger and heavier than purl.

**Bullion knots**: a long, caterpillar-like knot made by twisting the thread around the needle as the stitch is worked. Bullion knots are often used to provide texture to a design and are often worked on, or on top of, other stitches such as tent stitch.

**Chenille**: a fluffy, round thread. Its name derives from the French for caterpillar. It was often used in embroidered pictures from the late eighteenth century and particularly in rural scenes where it was appropriate for sheep and trees.

**Couched stitches**: a stitch used to secure threads which have been laid in parallel lines on the surface of a ground material. The stitch was often used in conjunction with metal thread, which cannot be pulled through the backing material without damaging it.

**Florentine or Flame Stitch**: Straight upright stitches worked on canvas in an undulating pattern, in different shades, to produce a flame-like or zig-zag effect, similar to that produced on seventeenth-century marbled paper. It was also known as Irish stitch, as well as Hungarian, or more recently Bargello work.

**Mica**: a glistening mineral often found in granite. It can be separated into thin, transparent and usually flexible slices which were often used in seventeenth-century raised-work to simulate window-panes and water.

**Patten**: wooden wedge covered in strong leather, fitted under the arch of a shoe and attached to the shoe with a tie over the toe and a socket at the heel. The wedge was underlain by a flat sole which kept the shoe away from muddy ground. Pattens were often of different height or robustness according to whether they were intended for indoor or outdoor, town or country wear.

**Purl**: tightly coiled copper wire made by gold and silver wire-makers in the seventeenth century, which can be attached like a bead or uncurled slightly and couched down. Its corkscrew-like rings were very effective at catching the light in a sparkling way and it was sometimes used to reproduce hair ringlets. It was also often dyed green to reproduce grass or trees or closely bound round with shades of coloured silk. It was mostly used in short lengths and fastened down like a bead.

**Raised-work or stumpwork**: embroidery given a three-dimensional effect by raising it with wooden moulds or pads of wool. Stumpwork was a term invented in the nineteenth century to describe this type of needlework common in the second half of the seventeenth century, when it was referred to as embossed or raised-work.

**Sablé**: minute glass beads, so fine that when used they appeared to cover the textile backing like sand (hence the French term sablé). In the mid- to late eighteenth century they were used by Parisian workshops to cover a range of accessories including purses, shoes, trinket boxes and bookcovers. Up to one thousand of these beads might be found on one square inch. Sablé was a later term for the technique, the eighteenth-century term appears to have been 'en perle'.

**Slips**: a gardener's term for a cutting, which was applied in the sixteenth and seventeenth centuries to individual floral and animal motifs. They were embroidered separately on canvas, usually in tent or rococo stitch and then applied to the picture ground. They were quick and easy to embroider and could be worked on small, hand-held frames.

**Spangles**: small flat discs, usually of shiny metal (silver or silver-gilt) attached to the backing by stitching through a small hole in the centre. They were the equivalent of modern sequins and were in use on European needlework from at least the fifteenth century.

# Select Bibliography

Place of publication is London unless otherwise indicated.

Allemagne, Henry-René, *Les Accessoires du Costume et du Mobilier*. 2 vols. New York, 1928, reprinted 1970.

Altick, Richard, *Paintings from Books: Art and Literature in Britain, 1760–1900*. Columbus, Ohio State University Press, 1985.

Amman, Jost, *Opera Josephi*. 1580.

Ashton, Leigh, *Samplers, selected and described*. 1926.

Ayres, James, *The Art of the People in America and Britain*, exhibition catalogue. Manchester, Cornerhouse Art Centre, 1985.

Baker, Muriel, *Stumpwork: Historical and Contemporary Raised Embroidery*. 1987.

Barnard, W.A., and Wace, A.J.B., 'The Sheldon Tapestry Weavers and their Work', *Archaeologia*. Vol. LXXVIII, 1928, pp. 255–314.

Bellaigue, Geoffrey de, *Waddesdon Manor Furniture, Clocks and Gilt Bronzes*. National Trust, 1974.

Birmingham Museum and Art Gallery, *British Embroidery from the Thirteenth to the Nineteenth Century*. Exhibition catalogue, 1959.

Boler, James, *The Needle's Excellency*. 1634.

Brett, Katherine B., *English Embroidery, Sixteenth to Eighteenth Centuries*. Royal Ontario Museum, 1972.

Bridgeman, Harriet, and Drury, Elizabeth, ed., *Needlework: an Illustrated History*. 1978.

Brinton, Selwyn, *Bartolozzi and his Pupils in England*. 1903.

British Museum, *100 Examples of Engravings by Francesco Bartolozzi*. 1885.

Brooke, Xanthe, 'Tales in Thread', *Antique Collector*. Nov. 1990, pp. 118–21.

Buck, Anne, *Dress in Eighteenth-century England*. Batsford, 1979.

Cabot, Nancy Graves, 'Pattern Sources of Scriptural Subjects on Tudor and Stuart Embroideries', *Bulletin of the Needle and Bobbin Club*. New York, vol. 30, 1946, pp. 33ff.

—— 'Some Pattern Sources of Eighteenth and Nineteenth-century Printed Cottons', *Bulletin of the Needle and Bobbin Club*. New York, vol. 33, 1949, pp. 3–21.

Campbell, R., *The London Tradesman*. 1747.

Cavallo, Adolph S., *Needlework*. New York, Smithsonian Institute, 1979.

Christie's, *Sale Catalogue 23 June 1987*. South Kensington, 1987.

Clabburn, Pamela, *The National Trust Book of Textile Furnishings*. National Trust, 1988.

Colby, Averil, *Samplers, Yesterday and Today*. 1964.

Cumming, Valerie, *Costume History: 1500–1900*. 1981.

—— *Gloves: The Costume Accessories Series*. Batsford, 1982.

Davenport, Cyril, *English Embroidered Bookbindings*. 1899.

—— 'Embroidered Bindings of Bibles in the Possession of the British and Foreign Bible Society', *Burlington Magazine*. Vol. IV, 1904, pp. 267–80.

Digby, Wingfield, *The Tapestry Collection*. Victoria & Albert Museum, 1980.

Embroiderers' Guild, *Treasures from the Embroiderers' Guild Collection*. Newton Abbot, 1991.

Fitzwilliam Museum, *English Samplers at the Fitzwilliam*. Cambridge, 1984.

Foot, Mirjam M., *A Collection of Bookbindings: Catalogue of North European Bindings*. Vol. II, British Museum, 1983.

Foster, Vanda, *Bags and Purses: The Costume Accessories Series*. Batsford 1982.

Frankau, Julia, *Eighteenth-century Colour Prints*. 1900.

Garde, Georg, *Dansk Silkebroderede Laerredsduge*. Copenhagen, 1961.

—— *Silkebroderede Laerredsduge frå 16 og 17 århundrede*. National Museet, Copenhagen, 1962.

Gibson, Eugenie, 'Mr P.D. Griffiths' Collection of Old English Needlework, Parts I–IV', *Connoisseur*. Vols. LIX–LXIII, 1921–2.

—— 'Old Needlework in the Collection of Sir William Plender, Bart', *Connoisseur*. Vol. LXXVII, 1927, pp. 29–36.

Gittins, Pauline, *A Brief Survey of the Shuttleworth Collection*. Museums Diploma thesis, 1984.

Globe, Alexander, *Peter Stent, London Printseller (c. 1642–1665): Being a Catalogue Raisonné of his Engraved Prints and Books*. Vancouver, University of British Columbia Press, 1985.

Hackenbroch, Yvonne, *English and other Needlework, Tapestries and Textiles in the Irwin Untermyer Collection*, 1960.

Hague, Gemeentemuseum, *The Age of Shakespeare*. The Hague, 1958.

Hailstone, S.H. Lilla, *Catalogue of a Collection of Lace and Needlework*. Published privately, 1868.

—— *Illustrated Catalogue of the Ancient Framed Needlework Pictures in the Possession of Mrs Hailstone*. Published privately, 1897.

Head, Mrs, 'A Collection of Needlework Pictures', *Connoisseur*. Vol. I, 1901, pp. 154–61.

—— 'English Secular Embroidery of the Sixteenth and Seventeenth Centuries', *Burlington Magazine*. Vol. IV, 1904, pp. 168–74.

Heywood, T., *The Exemplary Lives and Memorable Acts of the Nine Most Worthy Women of the World*. 1640.

Hind, Arthur, *Engraving in England in the Sixteenth and Seventeenth Centuries*. Vol. III, 1964.

Hogarth, Sylvia, 'The Stapleton-Wyvill Marriage Purse', *Textile History*. Vol. 20(1), 1989.

Hollstein, F.W.H., *Dutch and Flemish Etchings and Engravers*. Vols. 1–15, 1949–64.

Holme, Randle, *The Academy of Armoury*. 1688.

Honour, Hugh, *Chinoiserie: The Vision of Cathay*. 1961.

Hughes, Therle, 'Old English Beadwork', *Country Life*. May and June 1955.

—— 'Stuart Needlework', in Anthony Howarth, *Treasures of Britain*. Drive Publications, n.d.

Huish, Marcus, *Samplers and Tapestry Embroideries*. 1900.

Jode, Gerard de, *Thesaurus Sacrarum Historiarum Veteris Testamenti*. Antwerp, 1585.

Jourdain, Margaret, *English Secular Embroidery*. 1910.

Kendrick, A.F., 'Embroideries in the Collection of Sir Frederick Richmond, Bt.' *Connoisseur*. Vol. XCV, 1935, pp. 282–9.

—— *English Needlework*. Revised 1967.

Kensington Palace, *Exhibition of Embroidered Quilts from the Museu Nacional de Arte Antiga*. 1978.

Kerrich, Thomas, *Catalogue of Marten van Heemskerk*. Cambridge, 1829.

Marks, Richard, *Burrell: a Portrait of a Collector*. Glasgow, 1983.

Mayhew, Charlotte, *The Effects of Economic and Social Developments in the Seventeenth Century, upon British Amateur Embroideries with Particular Reference to the Collections in the National Museums of Scotland*, M.Litt. thesis, University of St Andrews, 1988.

Mayorcas, M.J., *English Needlework Carpets Sixteenth to Nineteenth Centuries*. Leigh-on-Sea, 1963.

Monsarrat, Ann, *And the Bride Wore . . . the Story of the White Wedding*. 1973.

Morris, Miss A.F., 'Needlework Pictures: their Pedigree and Place in Art', *Connoisseur*. June 1906, pp. 93–100.

Mortier, Bianca M. du, 'De Handschoen in de Huwelijksymboliek van de Zeventiende Eeuw', *Bulletin van het Rijksmuseum*. Vol. 32, 1984.

National Gallery of Art, *The Age of Brueghel: Netherlandish Drawings in the Sixteenth Century*. Washington, 1986.

Nevinson, J.L., 'Peter Stent and John Overton, Publishers of Embroidery Designs', *Apollo*. Vol. XXIV, 1936, pp. 279–83.

—— 'English Embroidered Costume, Elizabeth and James I, Part II', *Connoisseur*. Vol. 97, 1936.

—— *Catalogue of English Domestic Embroidery of the Sixteenth and Seventeenth Centuries*. Victoria & Albert Museum, 1938 and 1950.

Nevinson, J.L., 'English Domestic Embroidery Patterns of the Sixteenth and Seventeenth Centuries', *Walpole Society*. Vol.XXVIII, 1939–40, pp. 1–13.

—— 'The Embroidery Patterns of Thomas Trevelyon', *Walpole Society*. Vol. 41, 1968, pp. 1–38.

Overton, John, *A New Book of all Sorts of Beasts*. 1671.

—— *A New Book of Flowers and Fishes . . . .* 1671(?).

—— *A New and Perfect Book of Beasts, Flowers, Fruits, Butterflies, etc. . . .* 1674.

Paludan, Charlotte, *Alverdens Broderier i Kunstindustrimuseet*. Copenhagen, 1983.

Passe, Crispin van de, *Hortus Floridus*. Arnhem, 1614.

Payne, F.G., *Guide to the Collection of Samplers and Embroideries*. Cardiff, National Museum of Wales, 1939.

Pow, Virginia Glenn, 'A New Look in Traditional Textiles', *Discovering Antiques*. BBC Publications, 1970.

Prideaux, S.T., 'Embroidered Book-covers', *Magazine of Art*. 1891, pp. 61–5.

Redfern, W.B., *Royal and Historic Gloves and Shoes*. 1904.

Ribeiro, Aileen, '"A Paradice of Flowers": Flowers in English Dress in the Late Sixteenth and Early Seventeenth Centuries', *Connoisseur*. June, 1979, pp. 110–18.

Salmon, Larry, 'Eighteenth-century French Beadwork Accessories in the Boston Museum', *Dress*. Vol. 2/1, 1976, pp. 1ff.

Salomon, Bernard, *Quadrins Historiques de la Bible*. Lyons, 1555.

Schama, Simon, *The Embarrassment of Riches*. Collins, 1987.

Schoeser, Mary, *The London Collection: Printed Handkerchiefs*. Museum of London, 1988.

Schuette, Marie, and Muller-Christensen, S., *The Art of Embroidery*. 1964.

Sebba, Anne, *Samplers: Five Centuries of a Gentle Craft*. 1979.

Seligman, G.S., and Hughes, Talbot, *Domestic Needlework*. Country Life, 1926.

Shorleyker, Richard, *A Schole-house for the Needle*. 1624.

Solis, Virgil, *Biblische Figuren*. Frankfurt, 1560.

Stent, Peter, *A Therd Book of Flowers*. 1661.

—— *A Book of Flowers, Beasts, Birds and Fruits*. 1662(?).

—— *A Book of Branches, Slips, Flies, etc. . . .* 1662.

—— *A New Book of Flowers, Beasts, Birds, Invented by J. Dunstall*. 1662.

Strauss, Walter L., (ed.), *The Illustrated Bartsch*. Vol. 20, New York, Abaris, 1985.

Swann, June, *Shoes: The Costume Accessories Series*. Batsford, 1982.

Swain, Margaret, *Historical Needlework: A study of influences in Scotland and Northern England*. Barrie and Jenkins, 1970.

—— *The Needlework of Mary Queen of Scots*. 1973.

—— 'Embroidered Pictures from Engraved Sources', *Apollo*. Feb. 1977, pp. 121–3.

—— 'Engravings and Needlework in the Sixteenth Century', *Burlington Magazine*. Vol. 118, May 1977, pp. 343–4.

—— *Scottish Embroidery*. Batsford, 1986.

—— *Embroidered Stuart Pictures*. Shire Album no. 246, 1990.

—— 'Covered with Care', *Country Life*. 14 March 1991, pp. 50–3.

Swain, Margaret, and Nevinson, John, 'John Nelham, Embroiderer', *Bulletin of the Needle and Bobbin Club*. New York, 1982, pp. 3–19.

Synge, Lanto, *Antique Needlework*. Blandford Press, Poole, 1982.

Tait, A. Carlyle, 'English Needleworks in the Lady Lever Art Gallery – Part I', *Apollo*. Vol. 45, 1947.

Tarrant, Naomi, *The Royal Scottish Museum Samplers*. Edinburgh, 1978.

Tervarent, Guy de, *Attributs et Symboles dans l'Art Profane*. 2 vols, Geneva, 1958–9.

Thornton, Peter, *Seventeenth-century Interior Decoration in England, France and Holland*. 1978.

Trudel, Verena, *Schweizerische Leinensticherien des Mitellalters und der Renaissance*. Berne, 1954.

Wace, A.J.B., 'An Exhibition of Old English Needlework, Hove', *Old Furniture*. Vol. II, 1927, pp. 112–22.

—— 'Sheldon Tapestry Cushions in the Collection of Sir William Burrell', *Old Furniture*. Vol. IV, 1928, pp. 78–81.

Wace, A.J.B., 'Antique Needlework in the Collection of Frank Ward', *Old Furniture*. Vol. IV, 1928, pp. 63–7.

—— 'Exhibition of Early English Needlework', *Old Furniture*. April 1928, pp. 228–39.

—— 'Embroidery in the Collection of Sir Frederick Richmond, Bart.', *Apollo*. Vol. XVII–XVIII, 1933, pp. 207–12 and pp. 23–8.

—— 'English Domestic Embroidery, Elizabeth to Anne', *Bulletin of the Needle and Bobbin Club*. New York, vol. XVII, 1935, pp. 12–37.

Wardle, Patricia, 'English Pictorial Embroidery of the Seventeenth Century', *Antiques International*. 1969.

—— *Guide to English Embroidery*. Victoria & Albert Museum, 1970.

—— 'Dutch Embroidery Design in the Metropolitan Museum of Art', *Bulletin of the Needle and Bobbin Club*. New York, 1986, pp. 19–44.

Watts, Isaac, *Divine Songs: Attempted in Easy Language for the Use of Children*. 1715.

Whitworth Art Gallery, *Exhibition of Ecclesiastical Art*. Manchester, 1958.

—— *The Subversive Stitch: Embroidery in Women's Lives 1300–1900*. Manchester, 1988.

Willet, C. and Cunnington, P., *Handbook of Seventeenth-century Costume*. 3rd. ed., 1972.

Woldbye, Vibeke, 'Scharloth's Curious Cabinet', *Furniture History Society Journal*. Vol. XXI, 1985, pp. 68–74.

Woolley, Hannah, *The Gentlewoman's Companion, or a Guide to the Female Sex*. . . . 1675.

Zweite, A., *Marten de Vos ils Maler*. 1980.

# Index